Stop
Memory Loss

William Cone, Ph.D.

MATTESON BOOKS
PACIFIC PALISADES, CALIFORNIA

Matteson Books
16707 Sunset Boulevard
Pacific Palisades, California 90272

Humanity I love you because you
are perpetually
putting the secret of life
in your pants
and forgetting it's there
and sitting down on it

– e e cummings

To Carolyn, and to Don Re, who both made this book possible, and to all of the people who have helped me, and yet tragically cannot remember doing so

A Note to the Reader

I am not a Medical Doctor nor a Nutritionist. The ideas and information presented in this book are not meant as a substitute for professional medical care or guidance. None of the supplements, herbs, vitamins, or medications herein should be taken or discontinued without first consulting a compentent professional.

Contents

Chapter One

Losing Our Minds

Age is of no importance, unless you are a cheese
Billie Burke (1886-1970)

We all complain at times about how bad our memory is, but for the most part, we take memory for granted. Aside from the pang of anxiety we feel over a forgotten name, a lost key, or a missed appointment, we pay scant attention to this truly magical quality of the mind.

But though we take little notice, memory actually begins to decline as early as our mid-30s. This decline is so gradual that it seldom becomes noticeable until our 40s, and doesn't really begin to plague us until our 50s.

In 1986 the National Institute of Mental Health defined this gradual decline in memory as Age Associated Memory Impairment (AAMI). AAMI is not a disease. And it is not caused by disease — not by strokes, dementia, nor any other medical condition. It is, however, a gradual decline in several components of memory.

It is Age Associated Memory Impairment that causes us to stop in mid-sentence to grope for a word, one well known but temporarily unavailable. We call our children by the wrong name, and find ourselves adding "thing-amajig," "whatsit," and "you know what I mean" to our daily vocabulary.

We may pause for a moment in conversation, only to lose our train of thought completely. As a rush of anxiety passes through us, we ask our companions, "What was I just telling you?"

We invite our children for dinner, and as we begin to share an exciting piece of information, someone rolls their eyes and says, "You already told me that twice, Mom."

There is a gradual decrease in the speed of the memory process itself — retrieval takes longer. We see the face of a well known celebrity on the television, but cannot remember her name. But three days later, the now unwanted name comes to mind instantaneously.

Because of these problems, we begin to rely on others to store our memories. We tell them, "Don't let me forget to pick up the laundry," and ask, "What was the name of the movie I saw last night?"

By 50 we begin to notice that younger people learn new skills more quickly than we do. New areas of knowledge, new technology, new ideas, and frequent change become overwhelming and unwelcome, and we fall back on habit and routine to compensate for our newfound sense of inadequacy. We cope with this difficulty by calling new methods "newfangled," and we tell our children, "That's the way I've always done it, and I'm not going to change now."

As we age, we sleep less, and consequently dream less, which results in a more fuzzy recollection of days gone by. The plot of the movie we saw only two days ago eludes us, while one we saw ten years ago pops into our heads without effort. We can tell someone what we did fifteen years ago, but not fifteen minutes ago. For this reason the years begin to rush by, and we increasingly ask ourselves, "Where did the time go?"

We find ourselves standing motionless in the kitchen, at a complete loss for why we are there. Frustrated, we return to the den, only to suddenly recall the lost purpose of our fruitless and embarrassing journey.

We find ourselves more easily distracted — it becomes harder to concentrate when too much is happening at once. We compensate for this by keeping stimuli at a minimum. Crowds, parties, and crowded freeways become a strain on the system. "Turn that music down!" and "Keep those kids quiet!" become the mantras of maturity.

It becomes more difficult to do several things at once, or to execute a smooth transition from one task to another. This difficulty in stopping one task and beginning another is called perseveration. This problem has been found to be a loss of function of the frontal lobes of the brain. In some cases, it is the first sign of mental decline.

And we keep losing things! We walk into the living room, intending to put our keys down on the end table, when suddenly we think of that last piece of cake in the refrigerator. With keys still in hand, we open the refrigerator door. As we reach in to pick up the cake, we finish our first task — putting the keys down — by placing them on the top shelf next to the milk. Later, when we need the keys, we look on the end table and notice they are missing. "Who took my keys?" we cry in frustration.

And so we lose our keys, our concentration, and eventually our peace of mind. These memory problems huddle in the back of our awareness; subtle but insidious — temporary, but troubling. As we feel our memory slip, we begin to worry, "Is it finally happening? Am I getting senile?"

In the vast majority of cases, the answer is a resounding NO. The problems just described are not warning signs of serious memory problems. In many cases they are the result of nutritional deficiencies, medication problems, depression, endocrine imbalances, alcohol and drug toxicity, or a general lack of mental maintenance. In addition, most of these problems are reversible. Diseases such as Alzheimer's and other dementias are rare.

It is a popular belief that the brain loses millions of cells each year. However, the scientific evidence does not support this notion. Some cells are lost, and unfortunately for us, the brain cells that are most vulnerable and easily injured are located in the amygdala and the hippocampus; two parts of the brain that are essential for memory storage and retrieval.

The hippocampus is necessary for the storage of facts, but not procedures. For this reason, people with damage to the hippocampus lose the ability to learn new information, but can still learn and remember new skills.

Some memory problems may be caused by the fact that the brain shrinks with age. Each aging cell contains less water, making metabolic functions more difficult. For this reason, as you will see throughout this book, proper nutrition and fluid intake are very important.

Other memory problems are thought to be caused by a decrease in the amount of certain brain-cell chemicals called neurotransmitters.

For example, the death or malfunction of hippocampal cells results in the decrease of an important neurotransmitter called acetylcholine, which is essential for learning and storing new material. Many treatments for memory problems center around increasing the level of this substance.

Although these changes in the brain do cause memory to slow down, in truth, normal aging does not destroy the ability to learn or to remember. An eighty-year-old is just as capable of learning new information as an eight-year-old, it just takes longer. Just knowing this can reduce anxiety and concern about your memory.

Even though brain changes may impair memory, we know that most memory problems are actually caused by the lack of effort to maintain and improve one's memory. The people with the best memories are those that use memory skills and techniques throughout their lives, and those who take proper care of the machinery of the mind.

Those who believe they will inevitably face foggy thinking, and a diminishing world of activities, as they grow older probably have been influenced by the prediction of medical authorities who say that 4.6 million Americans will become victims of Alzheimer's disease every year. The disease, they say, will increase about four-fold in the next thirty years as more people join the ranks of the elderly.

While the statistics may be unsettling, it is important that readers understand that severe memory loss is never a normal condition of aging. Making this clear is one of the objectives of *Stop Memory Loss*.

The second objective is to show you how the brain works and how you can improve your memory at any age.

The third objective is to demonstrate that the symptoms of mild cognitive impairment can be reversed. This is vitally important. If not treated, these symptoms can lead to more severe memory loss, depression and withdrawal.

Additionally, you will will learn how to:
- Absorb new material with minimum effort.
- Have more confidence in the fact that aging does not have to mean deterioration of the brain.
- Take advantage of the breakthroughs in medicine and nutrition that can significantly lower your risk of dementia.

This book is about minimizing memory loss, and reversing, eliminating, or slowing the most common causes of memory failure. Please read every page carefully, for you may discover something that will allow you to preserve the treasured traces of your past.

Chapter Two

Aging and Memory

"Retirement at 65 is ridiculous. When I was 65 I still had pimples:"

George Burns (1896-1996)

Memory loss is not a new phenomenon. It's been plaguing brains since the dawn of humanity, but since most of our predecessors died young, few lived long enough to develop dementia. Ironically, it is our better health and longer lives that have made us more susceptible to cognitive loss.

The eradication of many diseases has increased our average life span significantly. In 1900 pneumonia, tuberculosis and diarrhea were the three leading causes of death. But due to improvements in sanitation and the discovery of antibiotics, deaths from pneumonia and tuberculosis declined from 707 per 100,000 in 1900 to only 59 per 100,000 in 1996.

Today, the leading causes of death are heart disease, cancer, and stroke. But all three of these killers are being conquered rapidly, which will further push the population towards maximum life span.

The elderly have now become the fastest growing segment of the population. Life expectancy has climbed 30 years from 47.3 in 1900 to 76.1 in 1996. From 2010 to 2030, the number of baby boomers age 65 to 84 will grow by 80 percent, while the number of people 85 and older will grow 48 percent.

Without intervention now, we will soon be faced with an onslaught of memory problems for which the world must accommodate with new methods of brain health maintenance.

The Process of Aging

Senescence, the scientific term for aging, is the biological process of deterioration of the body and brain. It is inevitable, and is the replacement cycle of nature.

The study of human aging has been fraught with controversy, conflicting theories, and puzzling data. Indeed, "pure" senescence is often difficult to distinguish from diseases of old age.

Medical science has cataloged many signs of aging. It manifests itself as a progressive decrement in function in cells, tissues, and organs from young adulthood until death. (The aging process begins at about 11 years old).

Human life is sustained by an incredibly complex interplay of molecular reactions which regulate the physical state of the body and mind. Aging can be seen as changes in the rate and efficiency of these reactions. While there are many theories of aging, most fall into two categories: programmed aging and damage accumulation.

Proponents of the programmed aging hypothesis point out that we are all part of a perpetual process that has carried the germ line of egg and sperm for over a billion years. Human life is part of an unbroken chain of reproduction extending back in time to our earliest ancestors.

Scientists believe that this type of aging is a recent development in evolution, and that aging may have been an accident. Mutations that allowed certain species to multiply rapidly also propagated the genes that caused aging. Therefore, the organisms that were the most successful at reproducing also carried the genes for programmed death.

Many of the biochemical reactions we call life were established ages ago in single-celled organisms. Eons before multicellular organisms arose, these single-celled beings reproduced by dividing into two equal halves. Neither half was parent or child, and neither half died. Descendants of those original cells are still thriving today, living, dividing, and essentially immortal.

But by the time multicellular organisms such as humans developed, some of the cells (germ-line cells) had evolved to become sperm or egg for the next generations, while cells that make up the body (soma cells), exhibited limited ability to reproduce. In fact, many human soma cells never divide again after reaching maturity. These cells are known as postmitotic cells. The brain, skeletal muscles, and heart contain large numbers of postmitotic cells, and these are the cells most damaged by aging.

So while human germ-lines live on in the next generation, the bodies of the former generations are destined to age, wither, and die.

The damage theory of aging asserts that aging is caused primarily by a combination of the accumulation of garbage in the cells (called lipofuscin) and oxidative damage, both of which we will discuss later. Over the years, toxins, mistakes in DNA, and injury cause damage to accumulate until cells can no longer function. Over time, massive loss of cells causes organ failure and, eventually, death.

Evidence suggests that both of these theories are true. We seem to have a programmed maximum life span. While unhealthy lifestyles and environmental stresses can contribute to aging and disease, they are not solely responsible for our getting older. The fact is that regardless of how virtuous their lifestyle or how pristine their environment, we have no reliable reports of humans living past 123 years.

However, many of the changes we accept as aging are actually the effects of nutritional and behavioral interference with metabolic processes.

Proper nutrition, exercise, and changes in lifestyle can have profoundly beneficial effects upon human longevity. Animal research has shown significant lifespan extension and improved health in old age can be attained through dietary modification and calorie restriction, provided that good levels of micronutrients, protein, and antioxidants are maintained.

What's important here, and what is the central tenet of this book, is that although we have a finite lifespan, we can significantly increase our quality of life by reducing the accumulation of cell damage.

Brain Aging

Because we are mortal, the brain does age. Studies show that brain cells begin to die at an early age. Brain weight actually peaks at 20–25 years and steadily declines thereafter. In healthy people the brain loses 5 to 10 percent of its weight between the ages of 20 and 90. About 20 to 30 percent of central nervous system cells are lost from age 25 to 80. For some unknown reason, this cell-loss is greater in men than it is in women of the same age

After forty, the hippocampus, the part of the brain that allows us to store new memories, loses about 5 percent of its cells every ten years. As a result of this cell loss, the average, healthy eighty-year-old has about two-thirds of the hippocampal cells that they had when they were born. Although cell loss is significant, fortunately, there are so many cells in these brain areas that the normal loss of cells does not impair brain function.

As nerve cells are lost, glial cells (cells that support and nourish brain cells) increase in number, size, water content, and weight. The greatest loss of neurons occurs in the superior temporal gyrus, a part of the brain that moderates hearing, taste, and smell, and the anterior central gyrus, which controls movement. The smallest amount of loss occurs in the posterior central gyrus, which controls peripheral sensation.

Ventricles, (the hollow chambers in the brain that contain spinal fluid), increase in size. Myelin (the insulation around the brain cells), thins. Inter- and intracellular deposits of lipofuscin and heavy metals such as aluminum, cadmium, and iron increase. Microtubules (the scaffolding that supports the cell) decrease in number and the neurofibrillary tangles symptomatic of Alzheimer's, composed of deformed microtubules, proliferate.

Blood supply decreases. As vessels thicken they impair the transport of nutrients and oxygen. Because of this there is a 20 percent decrease in blood flow from 30 to 70 years of age.

Neurotransmitters decrease up to 50 percent in some areas. This occurs especially in the substantial nigra and basal ganglia, areas where dopamine is found, often resulting in Parkinsonian like symptoms. Dopamine also regulates pleasure and reward, and its loss can cause apathy and disinterest.

Some of the Causes of Aging

- Junk molecules accumulate inside and outside of cells.
- Repair and recycling mechanisms slow down.
- A minority of deteriorating cells release chemicals which harm other, healthy cells.
- Lifestyle and environment.

Causes of Living Longer

- Antibiotics.
- Clean drinking water.
- Control of infectious disease.
- Advances in genetics and medical technology.

Current Life Expectancy

- White women 79.9
- Black women 74.7
- White men 74.3
- Black men 67.2

All of this cell loss sounds devastating. But one of the surprises in brain research today is data that suggests cognitive decline is not due primarily to neuron loss. Instead, scientists now believe changes in brain function as we age have more to do with complex chemical interactions in the brain that occur over time. Inflammation and oxidation, subjects that we will discuss later, seem to be more important than cell loss.

After reading this section, you might be pleased to know, even at this early stage in this book, that despite all of these changes with advancing age, memory loss is not inevitable. In the brain, damage accumulation has a greater impact than programmed aging.

Many people over fifty dread aging because they are convinced that the mind deteriorates with age, and that the process continues until an aging mind and body rob them of the ability to make decisions, and worst of all, deletes precious memories that measure the quality of life.

For decades, neuroscientists fostered this belief by painting a discouraging picture of the aging brain: Millions of brains cells die every day, they insisted. This process goes on relentlessly year after year, decade after decade. Eventually, it culminates in an inevitable enormous cognitive deficit. Brains weaken, unable to supply the thinking and decision making upon which normal activity depends.

But in reality the brain is highly adaptive, durable, and also capable of repairing, reorganizing, and rebuilding itself — even in old age.

Better yet, the evidence strongly suggests that identifiable good habits and simple lifestyle changes can preserve and boost mental well being, insuring a healthy mind longer than people dare to hope — to the end of their lives.

These findings are encouraging because they suggest that mentally stimulating activities not only enrich our lives, but may significantly reduce the risks of dementia.

According to John C. Morris of Washington University School of Medicine; "When even very mild dementia is carefully excluded [from consideration], the cognitive abilities of healthy older adults generally remain intact well into the ninth decade of life."

Marilyn Albert of Harvard Medical School asserts that today 70 years old is relatively young, and people should prepare themselves for long, productive lives.

In a report printed in *Parade Magazine* in 2002, she added that "... half to two-thirds of people in their 70s are as intellectually agile as people in their 30s. Those who fall below average tend to be people who had not made a lifelong habit of reading, attending cultural events and being involved in their communities."

Albert went on to say: "New developments in neuroscience and psychology are confirming that *there are few age limits on how much the brain can absorb and for how long. In fact, continuing to learn keeps us mentally in shape and able to learn more, much as exercising our muscles keeps us in good physical condition.*" (Italics mine)

A study by scientists at the Rush Alzheimer's Disease Center in Chicago, published in the February 13, 2002, issue of the *Journal of the American Medical Association* described aging among older Catholic nuns, priests and monks. Those who participated most frequently in activities such as reading books, newspapers or magazines, doing crosswords, playing card games and visiting museums, reduced their risk of Alzheimer's by a remarkable 47 percent, compared to those with the lowest levels of mental activity.

Even more exciting is a study reported in 1996 by Richard Snowdon, Ph.D., a professor of neurology at the University of Kentucky Medical Center and author of *Aging with Grace.*

He too studied the mental acuity of Catholic nuns. In his study, he analyzed the use of richly composed sentences describing interesting ideas in autobiographies the nuns had penned sixty years earlier. Terry Needles wrote in a June, 2002 *Psychology Today* article, reporting Snowdon's research: "Those who lived to a vigorous old age were more apt to have used unusual and multisyllabic words in rich, idea-laden sentences. Nuns who developed Alzheimer's had kept their syntax simple."

Needles also observed that "The nun study underscores much that researchers do — and do not — know about Alzheimer's. Sophisticated cognitive activity may build neural connections that thwart the disease altogether, but it is also possible that people who are cognitively active — either thanks to genes or education — amass a brain 'reserve' that simply retards the noticeable symptoms of Alzheimer's, which can only be definitively diagnosed after death."

One nun, for example, lived to be an alert 102, yet her autopsy revealed a brain ravaged by the sticky protein plaques and tangles of nerve cells that signify Alzheimer's. The implications of that nun's marvelous brain level activity, which triumphed over, or ignored, a deadly disease, affirms the growing evidence that brains kept busy do indeed reduce and resist the symptoms of brain disease

Although scientists have no absolute proof that exercising the mind will keep it sharp, all the clues point in that direction. As researchers collect more histories of people who demonstrate the "busy brain is good" theory they become firmly convinced that there is no arbitrary limit that aging can impose on expanding mental activity.

A statement in the *Harvard Men's Health Watch* reflects the thinking on the subject of some famous men of letters: "Consider the case of Oliver Wendell Holmes. When the great jurist was asked why he was reading Plato at the age of 92, he replied simply, 'To improve my mind.' Or consider the advice of Cicero some 2,000 years earlier:

'Old men retain their mental faculties, provided their interest and application continue.'"

Contrary to dogma, the human brain *does* produce new nerve cells in adulthood. *Scientific American Magazine* observed in its special edition of June 2002, *The Hidden Mind*, that, "If investigators can learn how to induce existing stem cells to produce useful numbers of functional nerve cells in chosen parts of the brain, the advance could make it possible to ease any number of disorders involving neuronal damage and death — among them Alzheimer's disease, Parkinson's disease and disabilities that accompany stroke and trauma.

"It was shown that participation in a learning task, even in the absence of enriched living, enhances the survival of the cells generated by stem cell division, resulting in a net elevation of the number of new neurons. The stem cell division and neurogenesis are more evidence that the brain harbors potential for self-repair.

"Modulation of environmental or cognitive stimuli, alterations in physical activity, or some combination of these factors cause the growth of new brain cells. Although the new cells would not regrow whole brain parts or restore brain parts or restore lost memories, they could, for example, manufacture valuable amounts of dopamine (the neurotransmitter whose depletion is responsible for the symptoms of Parkinson's) or other substances."

The capacity of the human brain so far exceeds the uses to which we put it that it is staggering to contemplate. Gerald Edelman, Nobel Prize winner, gave an estimate of the brain's power by surmising that it would take 32 million years to add up all of the synapses (connection between one neuron and another) in the human brain by counting one synapse a second. According to Richard Restak, M. D., noted brain specialist, this number pales when compared to the neuronal circuits in the brain. This is a figure so impossibly hard to conceive (ten raised by one million zeros), that it is like counting all the stars in the sky, including those we cannot see.

With this sort of powerhouse available to each human, the idea of imposing restrictions of age on the brain's operations seems indeed absurd. It was Samuel Johnson almost 200 years ago who wrote: "It is a man's own fault, it is from want of use, if his mind grows torpid in old age."

Irritating gaps in memory, often called "senior moments," or "brain freezes" may convince you that something is wrong with your brain, but in most cases anxiety of this sort is unwarranted. It is true that some loss of short-term memory does occur in older people. However, if you didn't forget information stored in short-term memory, your mind would soon be jammed with all sorts of unnecessary clutter.

More than simply normal, that type of forgetting is adaptive and helpful. Forgetting items in your long-term memory bank is different, but even here there are important distinctions. Long-term memory can be *episodic* (remembering when you last rode a pogo stick, for example), *semantic* (remembering facts and principles, such as knowing what a pogo stick is), or *procedural* (remembering how to ride a pogo stick). It is perfectly normal to forget episodic memories, but semantic and procedural memories normally are much more deeply entrenched. (You will learn more about the types of memory in chapter four.)

Age Associated Memory Impairment

In chapter one, I described some of the signs of Age Associated Memory Impairment (AAMI). The Alzheimer's Association and the American Health Care Association are currently studying AAMI. Researchers are now carefully looking in to the minds of older men and women who suffer from mild memory loss that is greater than their peers. They want to determine whether those with age-associated memory impairment will eventually develop Alzheimer's disease.

As mentioned before, the most common manifestations of AAMI are benign but bothersome difficulties such as forgetting names, losing belongings, difficulty recalling a list of multiple items, and problems with tasks that require multiple actions. There also may be difficulty remembering telephone numbers and zip codes. If the individual is distracted in some way the problem is compounded, making it even harder to remember things — such as what he intended to buy at the store.

Researchers do not yet know the exact cause of age-associated memory impairment. However, there are things that contribute to memory change and/or loss. One of the causes is chronic lack of mental stimulation.

A survey sponsored by General Nutrition Centers revealed very low awareness of AAMI among those who may suffer from the condition. Although AAMI is a very real condition, the majority of survey respondents — 71 percent — had never heard of it. Two-thirds of the respondents insisted they did not suffer from it even though they reported such typical symptoms as forgetting names, phone numbers, day-to-day tasks and even important events.

AAMI does not necessarily lead to Alzheimer's. Its diagnosis in people suggests that if they become more mentally active and take steps to keep their brains healthy, their memories will improve.

Mild Cognitive Impairment

Because AAMI and Mild Cognitive Impairment (MCI) are relatively new concepts, researchers are still attempting to define and delineate the terms. MCI is considered to be more serious than age associated memory impairment, but not as serious as dementia.

An example of the difference would be a person with AAMI occasionally forgetting the name of an acquaintance for a few seconds, while in contrast, a person with MCI would repeatedly struggle to remember the names of close colleagues, which might begin to interfere with his everyday life.

Other signs of MCI include difficulty in forming memories of events that just happened. On a recall test, a person may be able to repeat a string of unrelated words — but then fail to remember even one of them 10 minutes later. No one knows how many people experience this condition. While an estimated five million Americans have Alzheimer's disease, studies to determine the incidence of this milder deficiency are only starting.

Unlike AAMI, mild cognitive impairment is now thought to be a condition that frequently precedes Alzheimer's disease. It's defined as a transitional phase between normal aging and dementia. One study estimates that between 30 and 50 percent of persons who develop mild cognitive impairment will contract Alzheimer's disease within five years.

Individuals confronted with this prediction may feel as though they are numbers on a roulette wheel, and if theirs comes up when the spinning stops, they are fated to lose their memories. While acknowledging the importance of new studies that give physicians a clearer picture of how many new victims of memory loss to expect, I believe that such announcements create unrealistic fears because they offer no alternatives.

The truth is that if MCI can be detected, it may be treatable. Preliminary data suggests that people with MCI should begin intervention and treatment as soon as the diagnosis is made.

Currently the government's National Institute of Aging is engaged in a multi-university study to test the effectiveness of drugs (e.g., Aricept™), and natural approaches including vitamins C and E, ginkgo biloba and others. So while the predicted statistics may be accurate, at least half of those who develop MCI can not only overcome it, but may prevent the onset of Alzheimer's by using corrective measures described in this book.

Getting Your Head Examined

How do you know if you have clinically significant memory loss? In most cases, people who are sharp enough to worry about misplacing their keys or forgetting a name have little cause for concern. So if you are worried about your memory, it's a good sign that you're okay. About 94 percent of memory-impaired adults do not complain about memory problems. They simply can't remember that they can't remember.

One of the most popular tests to assess memory function is the Mini Mental Status Exam. I've reproduced it here. You can have a friend or member of your family test and score your answers.

Figure 1: The Mini-Mental-State Examination

Question	Max. Score	Your Score
Orientation		
Give yourself 1 point for each correct answer.		
What is the (year) (season) (date) (day) (month)?	5	____
Where are you: (state) (county) (town) (hospital) (floor)?	5	____
Registration		
Name three common objects (such as an apple, table, penny).Take one second to name each one. Give yourself 1 point for each correct answer	3	____

Attention and Calculation
Count backward from 100 by sevens. Stop after five answers.
Give 1 point for each correct answer.
Alternatively, spell "world" backward; score 1 point for
each letter in the correct order.   5   ___

Recall
Now, correctly name the three objects previously stated.
Give 1 point for each correct answer.   3   ___

Language
Look at your wristwatch and say what it is.
Repeat with a pencil. (2 points).
Say out loud the following: "No ifs, ands, or buts." (1 point).
Next, perform the three-stage command: "Take a paper in
your right hand, fold it in half,
and put it on the floor." (3 points).
Now, read and obey the following sentence, which you
have written on a piece of paper:
"Close your eyes." (1 point).
Write a complete sentence. (1 point).
Copy a design out of a book or magazine. (1 point).   9   ___

Total score: 30   ___

A score of less than 25 is abnormal, but it must be interpreted in light
of your age, educational level, primary language, and socioeconomic
status.

*Source: Based on the Folstein MF, Folstein SE, McHugh PR, Mini-Mental State: A
practical method for grading the cognitive state of the patient for the clinician. J
Psych Res 1975;12: 196-98.*

While this test is widely used, it has several shortcomings. First,
we now know that people with high IQs and who hold advanced
degrees may do fine on the test even though they may have lost a significant amount of brain function. This is a problem known to test developers as a "ceiling effect".

Second, this test was developed primarily for a clinical assessment, that is, it's a screening device used for people who already show

signs of dementia. When a person scores low on this test, they already have memory problems so severe that it is too late for intervention or prevention.

Third, we find that some of the questions have a high failure rate even in people with intact memories. For example, in healthy adults, the failure rate on reverse spelling of WORLD increases from 6 percent at age 50 to 54 years to 21 percent for over age 80, while only 1 of 9 persons over age 55 can perform the serial sevens (subtracting seven from 100, and continuing to subtract by seven) without error.

Finally, the exam does not assess mood or thought disorders, both of which can mimic dementia, but are potentially treatable conditions.

If you feel you may be at risk for dementia, the best way to find out is to have your memory tested by a neuropsychologist who specializes in memory and cognition.

He or she will give you a variety of tests to assess mood, attention, thinking, and memory — the four basic domains of brain function.

Then get an assessment of other risk factors such as diet, lifestyle and general health.

A comprehensive assessment should include:
- A comprehensive battery of tests for cognitive and memory function
- An IQ test
- A mental health screening for mood, thought, or personality disorders
- A thorough examination of the cardiovascular system
- Blood testing for toxins, vitamin levels and cardiovascular risk factors (such as cholesterol, homocystine, and C reactive protein)
- A complete medical history
- A diet and lifestyle assessment.

If you have close relatives who suffer from dementia, or you have medical conditions or other lifestyle factors that put you at risk, I highly recommend that you be tested. Full blown dementia is preceded by a protracted, insidious decline in mental faculties, which takes place over a period of several decades. Early assessment and intervention can save you and your family years of suffering.

Recently, another method of detecting early warning signs has become popular. It is an assessment of a brain wave called the P300. The P300 wave is a measure of response time, and this has long been known to be a measure of brain health.

The test is noninvasive and can be administered in 10 minutes. By attaching electrodes to the head, clinicians can assess a patient's reaction time to an audio tone, via the P300 wave. The normal response is 300 milliseconds, plus the patient's age. This means that a healthy 40-year-old should react to the tone within 340 milliseconds.

A study conducted by Eric Braverman, MD, director of the PATH Medical Clinics, correlated age with P300 response rates. Based on the P300 norms, readings in excess of 400 milliseconds indicate a chronological age of 100, which is a typical rate found in people with dementia. He compared P300 values with MMSE and Wechsler Memory Scale scores in order to correlate the P300 readings with actual memory impairment. In this way, if a 50-year-old shows a P300 response time of 370 milliseconds, it would mean that his brain is functioning as a 70 year old. A score such as this would indicate a need for immediate intervention.

Screen, Inc. publishes a computer administered neuropsychological screen for Mild Cognitive Impairment (CANS-MCI). You can get information about this test at Screen, Inc, 3511 46th Avenue NE, Seattle, Washington, 98105. Phone: 206-517-508. Web: www.alzheimersscreen.com/

Chapter Three

Dementia

Although most memory problems are not caused by dementing illness, some of them are. Without intervention, some of us are destined to suffer from dementia.

To millions of Americans the word "dementia" immediately prompts fear and dread. It has come to stand for a devastating brain disease that gnaws away memories and voids one's life. Lost in a sea of fragmented and disappearing recollections, victims eventually lose their abilities and living skills, leaving them lost, confused, and helpless. It is no wonder that many people fear dementia more than they fear death.

The word *dementia* literally means to lose one's mind (*de* meaning away from, and *ment* meaning mind). It is a word used to describe a variety of brain disorders that affect memory. *Senility* — the word that usually come to mind when we feel our memory faltering — is derived from the Latin term *senex,* and literally means *old age.* The term *senile dementia* is based on the observation that many older people have memory problems.

But dementia is much more complicated than that. The fact is there are many types of dementia, each with different effects on the brain. There are actually more than sixty disorders that cause dementia.

While I cited figures earlier on the incidence of dementia in the U.S. population, the following is a more precise estimate of cognitive impairment and memory loss and its age-related effects.

An estimated 1 percent of the population between the ages of 65 and 74 suffer from some type of dementia, while about 7 percent of those from 75 to 84, and 25 percent of people over 85 are afflicted. Currently about two million people in the U.S. suffer from severe dementia, while another five million have mild to moderate dementia.

Dementia is characterized by multiple problems in cognitive abilities without the loss of alertness. (Loss of alertness is called delirium.)

Dementing illnesses are caused by *brain damage,* and the parts of the brain that are most often harmed are the association areas in the cerebral cortex. These sections of the brain integrate sensory information, thought, and purposeful behavior. When damage to this area occurs, both the outer and inner world become chaotic.

Brain tumors, infections, toxins, nutritional deficiencies, medication problems, metabolic problems, and other neurological disorders can also cause dementia-like symptoms. (We will explore these problems later).

But of all the types of dementing illnesses, Alzheimer's disease, (often referred to in the literature as AD, Dementia of the Alzheimer Type, or DAT) accounts for over half of the dementias in this country. Vascular disease, called Multi-Infarct Dementia accounts for another 20 percent.

Multi-Infarct Dementia

As mentioned above, *dementia* means losing one's mind. An *infarct* is the closure of a blood vessel. Multi-infarct or vascular dementia (MID) then, means damage to the mind as a result of multiple episodes of interrupted blood flow to the brain.

Most doctors agree that multi-infarct dementia is caused by atherosclerosis of the blood vessels outside of the brain that supply it with blood — the carotid artery and the basilar artery. The small blood vessels and capillaries in the brain itself may be fine, but the major blood vessels have blockages, or there can be abnormalities in the lining of the heart. Small clots (called *emboli*) break off from these areas and travel to the small vessels, where they get stuck, block the vessel, and cause a small stroke. These stokes result in the death of large numbers of brain cells.

Doing an ultrasound scan of the carotids and the heart can determine from where the clots originate.

Unlike Alzheimer's, where symptoms develop slowly, multi-infarct dementia symptoms come on suddenly, with a stepwise and highly unpredictable course. Symptoms of vascular dementia can change noticeably from one day to the next.

This disorder can sometimes be brought on by a traumatic event such as the death of a spouse, or may occur after serious illness or after a delayed recovery from surgery. Most people with multi infarct dementia have a history of *transient ischemic attacks* (which are discussed later in this book) and high blood pressure (which also comes up later). The symptoms of MID usually peak between the ages of 40 and 60.

According to clues discussed in the Summer 2000 edition of *Memory Loss and the Brain,* "It is less clear how often dementia traces to vascular problems. According to various estimates reported in the scientific literature, vascular dementia may account for one-tenth to one-third of all cases of dementia. Further complicating the situation, about one-fifth of people with Alzheimer's disease may also be suffering from vascular dementia. This is known as 'mixed' dementia.

"But even if you have already been diagnosed with vascular dementia, it is not too late to do anything about it. The most important thing is to minimize the likelihood of additional strokes that could cause the dementia to get worse. This involves use of medications and addressing the factors behind cardiovascular disease. These steps, according to some studies, may not just halt the progression of vascular dementia, but may also reduce the symptoms. This does not apply to all people all of the time; however, it does mean that vascular dementia, unlike Alzheimer's disease, does not always mean a permanent and unavoidable decline. And that may be the best news about dementia you will ever hear."

A common treatment of multi-infarct dementia is to use *vasodilators,* which are drugs that dilate the blood vessels. Two of these drugs, *Vasodilan* or *Arlidin,* are called *cerebral vasodilators,* which means that they dilate the blood vessels in the brain. The difficulty of using these drugs is that if the person has hardening of the arteries in the brain, the arteries are not flexible. Because these drugs are vasodilators, they dilate the arteries in parts of the body that are flexible, and can actually *decrease* blood flow to the brain. This makes the problems worse.

Hydergine, a drug manufactured by the Sandoz pharmaceutical company, is the most popular cerebral vasodilator. It has been shown to increase mental function in many patients who do not suffer solely from MID. This drug is under-utilized in the United States.

Alzheimer's Disease

Of all memory disorders, there is none so well-known as Alzheimer's Disease. Alzheimer's is a progressive, degenerative disease of the brain, and although most of the people affected are over 65, Alzheimer's sometimes develops at a much younger age. The older one gets, the higher the risk of Alzheimer's — approximately 45 percent of people over 85 show symptoms.

Alzheimer's is the fourth leading cause of death among adults in the United States. Four million Americans currently suffer from the disease. The families of the victims spend over a hundred billion dollars each year caring for their afflicted loved ones. Barring any rapid progress in combating the disease, there will be 14 million victims by the middle of the next century.

It is Alzheimer's that most concerns researchers. It is probable in the next few years that a vaccine to prevent Alzheimer's will be developed, but for now it is important that people in middle years, and younger, learn about preventive actions they can take to inhibit formation of the disease.

Before we present the symptoms of dementia, lets look at the progress of vaccine development:

In a fascinating story by Kathleen Fackelmann in *USA Today*, an Irish drug company revealed in 2002 its invention and study of a vaccine that melts away the abnormal brain deposits thought to cause Alzheimer's vaccine.

Fackelmann reports, "Researchers at Dublin-based drug company Elan Corp. believed they had developed a medical blockbuster with an Alzheimer's vaccine called AN-1792. Dale Schenk, a company researcher and his colleagues announced electrifying findings in 1999 that such a vaccine could virtually cure mice that had been bred to develop an Alzheimer's-like disease.

"In partnership with American drug company Wyeth, Elan developed a vaccine that contained a synthetic version of beta-amyloid, a protein fragment thought to play a major role in Alzheimer's.

"Researchers believe that beta-amyloid clumps together in the brain, killing brain cells and forming the abnormal deposits called Alzheimer's plaque. Unlike natural beta-amyloid, the synthetic version seems to send signals to the immune system, telling it to attack.

"Elan researchers and others believed that injections of AN-1792 would spur the body's own immune system to make antibodies; proteins that would target and help destroy the brain plaque which is widely thought to disrupt the normal functioning of the brain and thus cause the disease's symptoms.

"Those hopes were dashed in January 2002 when 15 out of 360 elderly people who had gotten the vaccine fell ill with a serious brain inflammation. The people in the study had received two injections of An-1792 when researchers abruptly stopped the trial."

"In addition to their disappointments, the company suffered some financial setbacks which delayed its resumption of the trials. However, "Roger Nitsch and his colleagues at the University of Zurich in Switzerland kept track of 28 people who had gotten the vaccine before Elan halted the trial. Of those, 19 had responded to the vaccine by making antibodies that targeted the Alzheimer's plaque.

"Other research by the same team suggested that such antibodies could destroy the abnormal plaque. But would the experimental treatment lead to a better memory? The new finding, in the May 22 *Neuron*, suggests that it does.

"The team found that 12 out of the 19 people had memory and cognitive test scores that either stayed the same or improved during the year-long study. The people in the study who did not make the key antibodies had test scores that worsened, a reflection of the progressive brain damage cause by the disease.

"Even more remarkable was this finding: Two of the recruits had test scores that shot into the near-normal range. If that finding holds true, it suggests the vaccine could reverse some of the damage done by the disease — if given early.

"'This is an extremely exciting result,' Nitsch says.

"But that result could vanish once the researchers look at the results for the entire group. Elan researcher Ivan Lieberburg says the company's preliminary testing of all 360 people in the trial suggests those findings might not be as dramatic as suggested by this study.

"Still, most patients in this study got only two doses. With a safer vaccine, patients might be able to get more injections — and perhaps a bigger benefit, he says.

"'The fact the AN-1792 hit some speed bumps hasn't slowed anyone down,' said an Elan Company spokesman."

Despite those speed bumps, Elan and Wyeth in the U.S. "are working on a slightly different approach, one in which patients would get injections of lab-made antibodies instead of a vaccine. The antibodies might work just as well as the vaccine but might be safer because they are unlikely to cause brain inflammation.

"The first autopsy of a patient in the first Elan vaccine study illustrates both the risk and the promise of research.

"The autopsy found evidence of inflammation in the brain of a 72-year-old woman who was part of the original trial, a problem that probably hastened her death. But it also found that the vaccine had all but eliminated the gummy deposits of Alzheimer's plaque.

"When the autopsy team compared this woman's brain with the brains of seven people with the disease who were not treated, they found the typical results at autopsy: a brain riddled with plaque. They reported their findings in the March 16 *Nature Medicine*.

"'These data suggest an astonishingly powerful effect of vaccination,' says Steven Greenberg, a neurologist at Massachusetts General Hospital in Boston."

In summary, the *USA Today* story reported that "Experts say futuristic plaque busting strategies like a vaccine or an antibody might stop the disease early on. Researchers now know plaque accumulates in the brain for years before symptoms emerge.

"New imaging devices now in the testing phase might soon allow doctors to peer into the human brain and identify those small but dangerous deposits.

"Doctors soon might be able to prescribe a plaque-busting drug. And if the product destroyed the early plaque, it might keep the disease at bay — for a lifetime."

JoAnne McLauren at the University of Toronto has intensified the specific regions of the vaccine that are responsible for the inflammation. The hope is that by eliminating these regions, a vaccine without inflammatory properties can be developed.

Warning Signs of Alzheimer's

Dementia is an exceptionally cruel and heartbreaking disease. The first warning signs are usually subtle changes in memory. The person may begin to have mild difficulties with short-term memory — what is experienced is almost immediately forgotten.

They may begin to have frequent problems with word finding; and new places and new social situations often become stressful and overwhelming. Because of this, the person may become more and more locked into a strict routine.

The victim may begin to have difficulty making simple decisions. Learning new information, calculating, and handling personal finances eventually become impossible. In addition, controlling emotions becomes more and more difficult, and the sufferer may have sudden, uncontrolled outbursts of anger or sadness.

Gradually confusion and memory loss increase. Even though the memory of past events may be maintained for a long time, simple tasks that have been performed for years are eventually forgotten. As memory continues to deteriorate, the treasured memories of the past are forgotten as well, and the person may no longer remember that he or she is married, or that children have been born.

Eventually the person begins to have problems understanding what is said to him. As language function deteriorates, trouble arises making himself or herself understood.

Despite these losses, the person with dementia does not lose the ability to hear, respond to emotion, and be aware of touch. Even though these things are still perceived, they may cause confusion and agitation. Because the afflicted person is constantly attempting to cope with this confusion, he may engage in behaviors that have no external link to the environment.

As the individual loses his grip on reality, he also becomes irritable, and may become verbally and physically aggressive. As the disease progresses, screaming, wandering aimlessly, and combative behaviors appear. In the later stages the individual might lose the ability to walk or stand up, and the ability to communicate in any meaningful way.

As the symptoms progress there is a loss of what health care providers call *activities of daily living* (ADL). About nine percent of 65 to 75 year olds suffering from dementia need assistance with ADL, while about 45 percent of those over 85 need help.

Another symptom is weight loss. In a study of 34 Alzheimer's patients and 60 non-demented people, 44 percent of the Alzheimer's group, showed weight loss in the past five years compared with 37 percent of the non-demented group, despite an increase in food intake. One year later 92 percent of Alzheimer patients had lost weight, whereas 57 percent of the non-demented patients had actually gained weight. The increase in reported food intake combined with significant weight loss suggests that the disease may induce an accelerated metabolic state.

Causes

No one knows for certain just what causes Alzheimer's, but the disease always includes atrophy of the outer layer of the brain (called the *cortex*), neuron loss, and knotted bundles of tissue called n*eurofibrillary tangles.* The primary neurological defect in the disease involves reduced activity of an enzyme called *choline-acetyl-transferase,* which causes lowered levels of the neurotransmitter *acetylcholine,* but there is also evidence of deficiencies in the neurotransmitters *dopamine* and *serotonin.*

Cell death is most rapid in the *amygdala* and the *hippocampus,* two parts of the brain discussed earlier. Tragically, these are the areas of the brain most important for the processing of memory. The next sections to deteriorate are cortical areas on the brain's outer surface.

Eventually the frontal lobes, the part of the brain that regulates personality, are damaged. Once this happens, the person may become agitated and impulsive, and may have to be hospitalized. The time between the first symptoms and eventual death may be as long as twenty years.

In 1991, suspicions were confirmed that a fragment of protein called beta-amyloid is responsible for early onset Alzheimer's. When researcher Bruce Yankner injected beta-amyloid into the brains of rats, he found that the protein destroyed the same areas of the brain that Alzheimer's does.

The beta-amyloid molecule is actually a broken piece of the longer protein called APP. This complex protein begins producing beta-amyloid because of an error in the genetic code. There are 770 amino acids in APP, and in early onset Alzheimer's, it appears that the 717th amino acid is the wrong type.

Dr. John Hardy and his research team found that this genetic mistake was present in members of two families afflicted with early onset Alzheimer's. Family members with the gene had the disease, while those who did not have the gene were symptom-free. Further study of 100 normal people showed that none of them carried the defective gene. Neither did fourteen patients who had late onset Alzheimer's, a different form of the disorder that doesn't appear until the mid to late seventies.

Other studies verify Hardy's findings, and since this first study, Hardy has found two other genetic errors in families with Alzheimer's.

There is some evidence that Alzheimer's may be caused by "slow viruses" that incubate in the brain for many years. Other researchers believe that people who have suffered a head injury, such as a fall or car accident, or people who have been exposed to radiation, are at an increased risk for Alzheimer's.

For many years elevated amounts of aluminum have been reported in the brain tissue of Alzheimer's victims, but there is controversy over whether the high aluminum level in the brain is the cause of Alzheimer's disease, or a consequence of it.

Even so, most clinicians agree that avoiding aluminum is a good idea. In addition, a Canadian research team claims that they can reduce mental deterioration by giving a drug that eliminates aluminum from the body. (For more information on aluminum, see chapter eighteen on Neurotoxins.)

Risk Factors

The risk for dementia doubles every five years between ages 65 and 85. Although aging is the largest risk factor for becoming demented several other risk factors have been found to be significant:

A Family History

The presence of dementia in a brother, sister, or a parent quadruples your risk of developing dementia. In those with two or more afflicted first degree relatives, the risk increases up to eight times. This is thought to be because of the higher probability of inheriting one or more of the genes which contribute to the development of the disease.

Even though hereditary factors do seem to play a role in the disease, the extent of the role is unclear. For example, studies done on identical twins, who share identical DNA, show that one twin may contract Alzheimer's while the other is spared. Why this is so remains a mystery, but it is hypothesized that environmental factors such as lifestyle, diet, exposure to toxins, and level of mental activity all play a part.

It's important to note that having a family history of dementia is not evidence you will become demented. If you do carry a genetic risk, reducing other risk factors can preserve your mind and save your life. For this reason, attending to the suggestions in this book is of paramount importance. A change in lifestyle now may avert a change in mind and memory later.

In fact, researcher Dr. Nancy L. Pedersen has found that environmental effects, rather than genetics, account for at least half of the variation in susceptibility to Alzheimer's disease (AD). In her paper published in the *Annals of Neurology,* she posits that genetic linkages associated with Alzheimer's were usually found in early-onset AD, but lifestyle factors were most important in the late onset type of the disease.

Pedersen, studied 662 pairs of twins age 50 and above documented in the Swedish Twin Registry. None was diagnosed with AD at the beginning of the study. During a 5 year follow-up, Alzheimer's was diagnosed in one or both members of 112 of the twin pairs.

Dementia developed in 26 of 265 identical twin pairs, but remarkably, only five pairs were found where both members were afflicted. Among the 397 fraternal twins one member was affected in 42 pairs and both members in only two. These results are clear evidence that lifestyle is a much more potent predictor of dementia than genes.

Among the environmental effects that led to the dementia were vitamin B12 deficiency and head trauma. Dr. Pedersen and her colleagues also believe that those who have a more intellectually engaged lifestyle earlier in their lives are those who are at reduced risk of dementia. More about all of these factors later.

A Family History of Down's Syndrome

The presence of Down's syndrome in your family may increase your risk two to three times. The majority of people with Down's syndrome develop dementia, but dementia seems not to be caused by the genetic error that causes the syndrome — triplication of chromosome 21. It has been observed that family members *without* Down's syndrome, who develop dementia, do not have this genetic error.

A study led by Dr. Nicole Schupf, associate research scientist at the Gertrude Sergievsky Center for the Study of Nervous System Disorders suggests that women under age 35 who give birth to babies with Down's syndrome are five times more likely to develop Alzheimer's disease in later life than mothers of children with other developmental disorders.

Family Size

As strange as it may seem, having lots of brothers and sisters can increase the risk of Alzheimer's disease. A study, reported in the January 2000 issue of the journal *Neurology,* included 393 people with Alzheimer's disease and 377 people who did not have the disease. All participants, who were members of a health maintenance organization, were aged 60 or older. The study found that the risk of Alzheimer's increased by 8 percent for each additional sibling in a family. People with five or more siblings were 39 percent more likely to develop the disease.

Besides family size, the area of residence during childhood was also related to the risk of Alzheimer's. People who grew up in suburbs, rather than in urban areas or on farms, were less likely to have the disease.

The authors of the study hypothesize that the brains of children in large families (which may tend to be less well-off than smaller families), may not mature completely. This poor quality childhood environment could possibly prevent the brain from reaching a complete level of maturation. The long-term effects of impaired development could produce a brain that is normal, but functions less efficiently.

Interestingly, the areas of the brain that show the earliest signs of Alzheimer's are the same areas of the brain that take the longest to mature. A poor-quality environment might prevent the brain from reaching a complete level of maturation, and the impaired brain maturation may put people at higher risk.

Marital Status

This may also seem farfetched, but memory scientists have discovered that marital status is a risk factor for Alzheimer's.

Though the personal physical, emotional and psychic values emanating from the marital state have been enumerated many times, the absence of the benefits from marriage have never been identified as a risk factor for Alzheimer's disease in both men and women.

However, a story from *Reuters Health Service* reported recently that individuals who never marry are two to three times more likely to develop Alzheimer's disease or another form of dementia compared with people who do marry, even compared with people whose spouses have died. Citing an article in *Neurology,* the news service reported, that as part of the Personnes Agees QUID study, Dr. Catherine Helmer from Bordeaux University, Bordeaux, France, and her multinational colleagues, assessed 3,777 elderly subjects for the presence of Alzheimer's disease or another form of dementia. Of the 3,675 nondemented subjects, 2,882 were reassessed one and three years later.

During follow up, 190 participants had developed dementia, 140 of whom were diagnosed with Alzheimer's disease, the team reported. Dementia developed in 4.4 percent of married or cohabitating subjects, 9.4 percent of widows and widowers, 12.9 percent of subjects who had never married and 5.1 percent of those who were separated or divorced.

Among individuals who developed Alzheimer's disease, 2.7 percent were married or cohabitating, 7.4 percent were widowed, 12.2 percent had never married, and 5.1 percent were separated or divorced, the authors found. The researchers pointed out that "The proportion of cases of dementia and [Alzheimer's disease] was higher in widows ... and never married ... as compared with married individuals." Dr. Helmer's group observed that "results remained unchanged after adjustment of several confounding factors such as education and wine consumption."

The higher incidence of dementia among people who never married could not be explained by the fact that they may have had "... less cognitive stimulation due to a small active social network and fewer leisure activities," because the variables were taken into consideration. Never married individuals could have premorbid personality and premorbid behaviors, the authors suggested, and they speculated that this premorbid state could account for both the marital status of such people and their subsequent risk for dementia.

A History of Depression

As described above, depression is a risk factor for dementia. It has been found that people who suffered from depression more than ten years prior to the onset of dementia have approximately double the risk of developing the disease. The reasons for this seem to be related to reduced activity in the frontal and temporal lobes and the cingulate gyrus, along with imbalances in several neurotransmitters. (More information about depression can be found in Chapter fifteen of this book.)

Sleep Apnea

In 1999 a British man was admitted to the hospital with hallucinations and symptoms of confusion and anxiety. A CAT scan showed atrophy of the brain, and his physicians concluded he was suffering from dementia.

But shortly before he was due to be discharged from the hospital, his wife reported that he snored heavily and seemed to stop breathing many times during the night.

This prompted further investigation. The hospital's respiratory service studied the patient's breathing during sleep. This investigation showed that his blood oxygen levels were falling dramatically while he slept. This assessment revealed that his symptoms were due in fact to a relatively common sleep disorder — obstructive sleep apnea.

When the patient was given oxygen therapy at night, his symptoms cleared up. This man was able to recover because his apnea was diagnosed and treated early. But left untreated, over time, such dramatic falls in oxygen level can damage the brain.

Other studies show that the brains of patients with obstructive sleep apnea show loss of gray matter. A report in the November 15, 2002 issue of the *American Journal of Respiratory and Critical Care Medicine* suggests that apnea may cause significant brain cell loss.

The oxygen loss from sleep apnea may damage brain structures that regulate memory and thinking. For example, the hippocampus and the anterior cingulate are important brain structures in memory and mood. These brain areas are often malfunctioning in depression.

Studies on depression suggest that poor recall of autobiographical memories is a marker for depression, and also can predict the course of depression. Researchers hypothesize that autobiographical memories also predict the course of depressive thoughts and feelings in sleep apnea patients.

Nasal continuous positive airway pressure (nCPAP) therapy relieves the symptoms of obstructive sleep apnea. And patients receiving nCPAP therapies not only improve their sleep, but are able to recall more specific autobiographical memories. This suggests that treating apnea can improve sleep, reduce brain damage, and increase memory.

There is also some evidence that brain abnormalities may actually cause sleep apnea syndrome. It is possible that some sleep apnea patients have disordered wiring in brain regions that control muscles of the airway. When examined, those with apnea show gray matter loss of 2 percent to 18 percent in specific brain sites, including the frontal and parietal cortex, temporal lobe, anterior cingulate, hippocampus, and cerebellum. The amount of gray matter loss was directly correlated to the severity of sleep apnea.

Patients with apnea often have other symptoms suggesting subtle brain damage, including problems with memory, cognition, and motor skills, and interestingly, a history of childhood stuttering. Stuttering is present in 38 percent of sleep apnea subjects but in only 7 percent of subjects without sleep apnea syndrome.

Because these sites are involved in motor regulation of the upper airway and also contribute to cognitive function, these findings may explain sleep apnea's cognitive deficits.

For more information on sleep apnea, contact the American Sleep Apnea Association, 1424 K Street NW, Suite 302, Washington, DC 20005 Phone: 202-293-3650 Web: http://www.sleepapnea.org/

Estrogen Deficiency

Estrogen deficiency in postmenopausal women has been implicated in a variety of studies as increasing the risk of Alzheimer's and other dementias. This has been found mostly in women who have had hysterectomies (including the ovaries). It is believed that the increased risk comes from estrogen's influence on nerve growth factor, which supports the neurons that contain acetylcholine.

For more on the implications of estrogen therapy, go to chapter sixteen on Hormones and Memory.

Head Trauma

Prolonged unconsciousness from head injuries, or multiple head injuries over time doubles the risk for dementia. This is thought to be caused by an increase of the protein beta-amyloid following head trauma. Beta amyloid is toxic to brain neurons and is found in the bundles of debris called *neuritic plaques* discovered in the brains of Alzheimer's victims. Doctors examining the brain tissue in people with head injuries found plaques and tangles indistinguishable from those found in Alzheimer's.

Surgery

Any major surgery in an older person is a risk factor for cognitive decline. About one in ten patients over sixty years old will suffer memory and cognitive loss for at least three months after any major surgery requiring general anesthesia and lasting more than two hours.

Dr. Joachim Gravenstein, professor emeritus of anesthesiology at the University of Florida College of Medicine, estimates that each year about 200,000 people in the United States are affected by anesthesia-induced memory loss.

Age is an imprtant factor in this loss: those over 70 are twice as likely to have long-term mental impairment than those between 60 and 70. Although hip surgery carries a significant risk, coronary bypass is by far the most risky for memory impairment.

Bypass surgery is performed on at least half a million Americans each year. This procedure is essential for relief from angina and reducing other symptoms of coronary artery disease, as well as for reducing the incidence of heart attacks.

It's been known for many years that these surgeries are often accompanied by a decline in memory and cognitive function, as well as putting patients at higher risk for stroke or seizures.

Depending on how cognitive decline is measured; rates between 35 and 80 percent of patients are reported. The older the person is at the time of surgery, the higher incidence of these adverse events.

Although cogntive decline after leaving the hospital generally improves over the next six months in most people, some will experince permanent cogntive damage. In 2000, a study conducted at Duke University assessed mental performance in 261 patients before and after they had bypass surgery. Patients were reassessed in six weeks, then six months, and five years after the procedure. The average age of the subjects was 61, and 72 percent were men.

The tests measured verbal understanding and memory, orientation in space, powers of concentration and attention, and visual memory. Of the 261 subjects recruited 172 completed all of the tests.

A deviation from their average score (called a standard deviation) was used to define a decrease in mental performance. In this study, a drop of one standard deviation below the mean was equivalent to a 20 percent decrease in performance.

After discharge from the hospital, a significant reduction in cognition was found in 53 percent of the participants, but after six weeks only 36 percent showed reduced mental performance. At the end of six months this number had dropped to 24 percent.

In the subjects who showed no signs of impairment after discharge, their five-year scores were about equal to their pre-operative scores. What is of major concern, however, was the finding that, within those who had shown impairment after the surgery, the five-year follow-up scores indicated that almost 42 percent of the subjects still had a significant decline in mental functioning.

The researchers found that age at the time of surgery, the person's level of education, and decline in performance at discharge, were all predictors of decreased mental function five years later. These factors all relate to *cognitive reserve* — the amount of brain cells a person can afford to lose before deficits become visible.

Other studies suggests that people undergoing cardiac bypass surgery may be at greater risk of dementia. Dr. Benjamin Wolozin at Boston University School of Medicine presented findings at the 9th Annual International Conference on Alzheimer's Disease and Related Disorders. His study shows that within five years after surgery, the risk for Alzheimer's disease is 70 percent higher in people who undergo bypass surgery compared to patients who undergo angioplasty (a procedure using a catheter to open up a blocked coronary artery).

Wolozin believes that the stress induced by the surgery is responsible for the cognitive decline, causing a sharp increase in stress hormones such as cortisol which triggers a cascade of events that reduce oxygen in the brain.

Damage may also occur from changes in blood pressure that occur when a patient is put on the heart-lung bypass machine. However, others point to an increased risk of cognitive decline if the patient requires a blood transfusion during surgery.

Still other researchers suggest that the damage can also be caused by tiny pieces of plaque that break off from clogged arteries in the heart and are carried to the brain where they lodge in capillaries and interrupt blood flow. These small bits of plaque, called *emboli* often dislodge and enter the bloodstream when a heart-lung bypass machine is used. As they travel throughout the circulation, the emboli may block blood flow, resulting in cognitive dysfunction. This phenomenon has recently become known as "pump head." For this reason some cardioligists are now promoting "off-pump surgery" whenever possible.

Surgeons at the Cleveland Clinic recently completed a study comparing the results of on- and off-pump surgery. The researchers matched 406 off-pump and 406 on-pump patients for comparison. There were fewer cognitive side-effects in the off-pump patients. There also was less kidney failure requiring dialysis, less red blood cell usage, and fewer infections of chest incisions in the off-pump patients.

Another problem may be connected to cooling the body during these procedures. During the surgery, while the patient is on the bypass machine, the body is cooled significantly to help preserve the heart and brain. Toward the end of the surgical procedure, the patient is re-warmed.

The Society of Cardiovascular Anesthesiologists suggest that spending an extra 10 to 15 minutes re-warming the patient after bypass surgery can make a significant difference in the incidence of pump-head. They suggest that if the patient is re-warmed too quickly, the brain's need for oxygen temporarily may outstrip the supply, leading to post-operative cognitive difficulties. Re-warming more slowly solves this problem. They also point out that re-warming is not standard procedure, and oftentimes must be requested.

Other Medical Risk Factors

Other medical factors that increase the risk for dementia include chronic alcohol consumption, a history of heart attack (especially in women), maternal age over 40, a family history of Parkinson's disease, and hypothyroidism — a deficiency in the activity of the thyroid gland.

Poor Education

An uneducated person has about twice the risk of developing dementia by age 75 when compared to someone with at least an eighth grade education. This may be because education causes a strengthening of frequently used brain regions and enhances the connections between neurons. This strengthening of brain regions may also explain why some people with special talents, like playing music, playing cards, or singing may retain these skills after the onset of dementia. Recently several studies have shown a strong link between lower intelligence and dementing disease.

Intelligence and Alzheimer's

Earlier we looked at some of the findings of the nun study. In this ground breaking study, it was found that women who scored poorly in cognitive ability as young adults were found to be at higher risk for Alzheimer's disease in late life.

The study examined the cognitive function of nearly 100 nuns. Participants were members of the School Sisters of Notre Dame religious congregation. It focused on those who joined the Milwaukee convent from 1931 through 1939 and who had written autobiographies at an average age of 22.

As mentioned before, the researchers found the the complexity of the sisters' writing as young women was a good predictor of how well they functioned mentally later in life. In the study, it was found that 90 percent of the nuns with Alzheimer's disease had low linguistic ability in early life, compared with only 13 percent in those without the disease.

The researchers stated that why this happens is not clear, but the findings suggest that the process of Alzheimer's disease may begin much earlier in life than previously thought.

In fact, these findings and other studies seem to indicate that brain cell deterioration may actually begin up to *thirty years* before any symptoms appear!

It may be that full development of the brain and cognitive abilities early in life, through education or other stimulation, may cause changes in the brain that protect people from Alzheimer's disease later in life.

Low linguistic ability in early life could actually be a very early symptom of changes in the brain that eventually lead to Alzheimer's disease. Those with higher language ability early on may be more resistant to later influences which lead to the disease while those with lower ability as young adults may be more at risk.

Other factors could explain the link between early cognitive differences and disease in old age. It may be that inherited differences in cognitive ability, factors that may have nothing to do with the disease per se, may affect the way the Alzheimer's process unfolds in an individual.

Research is now underway to detect these changes, in the hope that early intervention might prevent the devastating effects of the disease. New brain scan technology can pick up brain changes many years before symptoms appear

Diagnosing Dementia

What does your nose have to do with discovering if you are a candidate for Alzheimer's? More than you might imagine. Clinicians at

Tallahassee Memorial HealthCare's Memory Disorder Clinic are now using a "Smell Test" which may help differentiate Alzheimer's disease from depression.

The test asks patients to identify common odors, such as smoke, lemons and peanuts. The theory behind this test is that the entorhinal cortex, one of the brain's major areas for our sense of smell, is often the first affected by neurotangle fibers, a distinguishing marker for Alzheimer's disease. What's more, depression does not affect this area of the brain.

According to Larry Kubiak, Ph.D., a psychologist at TMH's Behavioral Health Center, Alzheimer's can be accurately diagnosed at death when an autopsy is performed, or through a brain biopsy, an invasive procedure. But the new Smell Test offers some hope that an impaired sense of smell might be the earliest clinical symptom of the disease.

"Studies performed by the National Institute on Aging and the National Institute of Mental Health confirm that the inability to recognize odors may serve as good criteria for an accurate diagnosis of Alzheimer's disease," Kubiak said.

In the study, 90 men and women with minor memory problems were asked to take a "scratch and sniff" test. None of the 30 individuals who scored well on the test developed Alzheimer's disease during the follow-up period. A total of 47 people had difficulty determining the smells. Of those, 19 went on to develop Alzheimer's during the 20-month follow-up period. And of those 19, 16 reported they had a good sense of smell at the time of the test.

What this study suggests is that when you combine the inability to recognize smells with the lack of awareness that there is a problem with one's sense of smell, it may serve as a predictor of impending Alzheimer's disease," Kubiak said.

Additionally, Memory Disorder Clinic Director Janice Carton says there are patients who score well on memory tests and depression screenings but fail the Smell Test.

"For a patients who shows no other signs of Alzheimer's or dementia, the Smell Test may prove to be an indicator that the patient needs to be tested again in six months or a year," Carton said. "The benefit of early diagnosis is that the patient can begin to take medications to help memory. There are three medications available to help memory at present. While these medications won't cure anyone they do seem to slow the progress of symptoms and keep the patients better longer."

The Smell Test is part of a battery of tests offered at the Memory Disorder Clinic, which is designed to help people determine the factors causing memory loss, as well as to offer case management, social service needs assessments and community referrals.

There is another smell test which was designed especially for physicians to test their patients. The Quick Smell Identification Test™ (Q-SIT™) is a three-odor version of the widely acclaimed University of Pennsylvania Smell Identification Test (UPSIT). It is manufactured by Senseonics, Inc.

If you have any doubts about the condition of your memory, call your doctor and ask about a "smell test."

While a smell test may predict that Alzheimer's is in your future, a complete medical assessment should be undertaken to help determine whether you have Alzheimer's. The fact that a person has the symptoms does not automatically mean he or she is suffering from the disease. Symptoms can also be caused by other treatable conditions, such as depression, malnutrition, dehydration, over-medication, and other medical problems such as heart disease, kidney or lung problems.

The diagnosis of Alzheimer's is difficult, and is currently made only by ruling out other conditions. As of this writing, the only accurate early indicator of Alzheimer's is the smell test.

However, researchers have developed a genetic test for early onset Alzheimer's. Work is now in progress to develop a reliable MRI profile to diagnose the disease. Another test being researched detects beta-amyloid in spinal fluid, while still another method involves checking the ability of the eye to dilate.

People who appear to be showing any signs of dementia should have a thorough physical, psychological, and neurological screening. This should consist of a complete physical, including blood work, a cardiac work up, and possibly a brain scan. Brain scans can help rule out certain disorders, and may show that the problems are from normal aging rather than dementia.

A complete personal medical history and a family medical history should be taken. This should include a survey of all medications currently being taken, and a history of medications taken previously.

A competent neuropsychologist can be very helpful in screening for memory and cognitive deficits, and can often suggest effective therapies to alleviate many memory related symptoms.

Treatment

Currently, no approved medical treatment exists that can entirely reverse the progress of Alzheimer's. Secondary symptoms, such as depression, anxiety, sleeplessness and paranoia, may be lessened with appropriate drug therapy, though such treatments must be carefully monitored. The good news is that many of the substances described in this book show promise in slowing the progression of the disease.

Cholinesterase Inhibitors

Several drugs have been approved that slow down the rate of brain deterioration through the inhibition of cholinesterase, the enzyme that breaks down acetylcholine in the body. These drugs are known as cholinesterase inhibitors. It's important to note that none of these medications prevents or cures Alzheimer's.

Cholinesterase Inhibitors

Isoflurophate (Humorsol) Used for glaucoma

Echothiophate (Phospholine Iodide) Used for glaucoma

Galanthamine (Reminyl) Some sustained improvements with this drug

Donepezil (Aricept) Currently this is the most widely prescribed treatment

Metrifonate (Promem) Bayer petitioned the FDA to approve metrifonate in 1997, however, respiratory side effects were severe enough that Bayer suspended the application.

Physostigmine (Synapton) Results have been disappointing

Rivastigmine (Exelon) Used often but has less history than donepezil

Tacrine (Cognex) not prescribed much any more due to liver side effects

---

Tacrine®

Tertra-hydro-amino-acridine, or Tacrine, marketed under the brand name *Cognex,* was the first of this type of drug to enter the market. This drug had shown some promise in slowing and even reversing the progress of the disease, by slowing the breakdown of *acetelycholine. However,* it also inhibits the breakdown of acetylcholine in the body, which causes side-effects.

In addition, the magnitude of the changes in patients receiving Tacrine is small, even in responsive patients. Although Tacrine has helped some patients, it has not been effective in all cases, and it has the potential to cause serious adverse effects.

The biggest problem with Tacrine is its potential to cause serious liver damage. More than 40 percent of patients given Tacrine showed increases in liver enzyme activity, and 51 percent of Tacrine-treated patients have adverse reactions related to treatment. Cognex is still available in the United States, but it is no longer actively marketed by the manufacturer.

A team of Canadian and American researchers have found that a genetic test may help identify Alzheimer's patients that are most likely to benefit from Tacrine. The test shows which of three possible types of the ApoE gene that a patient carries. In their study, Tacrine was most effective in patients who didn't have the type called ApoE4. At least 35 percent of Alzheimer's patients fall into this category. The finding is the first solid demonstration that a gene can predict response to a drug in the treatment of Alzheimer's.

Interestingly, in cultures which do not share our sedentary lifestyle, and where obesity is not epidemic, ApoE4 does not appear to be a risk factor for Alzheimer's. This evidence suggests that ApoE4 pathology requires a high blood fat environment to manifest itself as Alzheimer's.

Dr. Allen Roses headed the Duke University research team that first discovered an association between ApoE4 and Alzheimer's disease in 1993. Roses believes that ApoE testing could be used to assist in the diagnosis of patients with Alzheimer's symptoms, and to help determine the best treatment.

The gene test is now being used by drug companies to see which subgroups of Alzheimer's patients will benefit from their experimental drugs.

Aricept®

Pfizer/Eisai markets a medication called donepezil, brand named Aricept. Until recently it was the most popular cholinesterase inhibitor.

In 2000, two new drugs for treating Alzheimer's disease: galantamine (Reminyl) and rivastigmine (Exelon) entered the marketplace. Like their predecessors, Cognex and Aricept, the new drugs have been shown in clinical trials to slow the decline in memory and thinking caused by Alzheimer's disease, but the new drugs claim to have a better side effect profile.

Reminyl®

Galantamine is an alkaloid with cholinesterase-inhibiting activity derived from the Caucasian Snowdrop *(Galanthus woronowi)* and related species. It has been used in Bulgaria for more than 40 years

The Austrian pharmaceutical company Sanochemia Pharmazeutika AG was among the first to recognize the immense potential of this natural substance. The group attempted to breed its own Caucasian snowdrops, but cultivation of the wild plant produced a significant loss of the active ingredient. In 1995, galantamine was approved in Austria as a treatment for Alzheimer's. In February 2001, the U.S. Food and Drug Administration approved the substance in the United States.

Like the other cholinesterase inhibitors, Reminyl helps to maintain a higher level of acetylcholine in the brain for a longer period of time. Laboratory experiments suggest that Reminyl may also increase the sensitivity of neurons to acetylcholine. So not only is there more acetylcholine available, but Reminyl may boost the response of the brain to it. In this class of drugs, only Reminyl has this second mechanism of action.

Exelon®

Novartis markets rivastigmine (Exelon). This drug appears to be beneficial for people with mild to moderate Alzheimer's disease. Exelon appears to block a form of the cholinesterase enzyme that becomes more important in the brain chemistry of Alzheimer's later in the progression of the disease

In comparisons with placebo, improvements were seen in cognitive function, activities of daily living, and severity of dementia with daily doses of 6 to 12mg. Rivastigmine also is used sometimes to treat Lewy body dementia. A sustained-release formula is also being developed.

Rivastigmine has an added benefit. It is a potent dual inhibitor of both acetylcholinesterase and and butyrylcholine esterase (BuChE). Researchers now believe that BuChE may play a role in transforming benign amyloid in the brain into the 'malignant' form associated with dementia.

When eighteen Alzheimer patients were given rivastigmine (1 to 6mg twice a day) in an open-label study there was marked inhibition of both AChE and BuChE levels in their cerebrospinal fluid (CSF). In a separate study, long-term administration of rivastigmine showed that this effect could be maintained for at least 12 months.

Rivastigmine has shown to be effective both in patients with Alzheimer's disease and Lewy body dementia.

Gilatide

Phenserine (Gilatide) a third generation acetylcholinesterase inhibitor, is a drug being studied by Axonyx, Inc. On June 26, 2003, Axonyx announced the initiation of Phase III clinical trials. Data from this trial is expected to be available near the end of 2004.

The company believes that this drug could facilitate memory and cognitive health in normal people as well as improving learning and memory in age-related memory loss, attention deficit disorder and various dementias.

Results reported in an abstract on the transgenic mouse confirmed that Phenserine has the ability to reduce both amyloid precursor protein (APP) and amyloid peptide (amyloid-beta) formation in the brain which could have important potential implications for the treatment of Alzheimer's Disease. For more information contact Axonyx USA, 500 Seventh Avenue, 10th floor, New York, NY 10018. Phone: 212-645-7704, Web: http://www.axonyx.com/.

New evidence suggests that many of the cholinesterase inhibitors may not only ameliorate symptoms, but might alter the course of the disease itself. The new drugs may actually reduce the production of beta amyloid, the protein component found in neuritic plaques, the bundles of debris found in brain cells of Alzheimer's patients.

Namenda®

Memantine was approved in October 2003 by the U.S. Food and Drug Administration. Forest Laboratories Inc., memantine's U.S. developer, markets the drug under the trade name Namenda. This substance was first approved in Germany for treatment of neurological disorders in 1982, where it has been marketed since 2002. It has also been approved in the rest of Europe, where it is marketed by Lundbeck as Ebixa.

Memantine is the first medication to show effectiveness in treating people with moderate to severe symptoms of the Alzheimer's disease, according to researchers from the New York University School of Medicine, who published their findings in the April 3, 2003 issue of the *New England Journal of Medicine.*

Patients in the study were between the ages of 68 and 84 and had lost significant physical and mental skills, though all were able to speak and walk to a certain extent.

Those who took the drug for six months showed less cognitive deterioration and better ability to perform activities of daily living than study participants who took a placebo.

Unlike the other medications, this drug works by inhibiting glutamate, a chemical that causes damage to brain cells involved in memory and learning. This is a completely different method than existing Alzheimer's medications.

Excess glutamate overstimulates NMDA receptors to allow too much calcium into nerve cells, leading to death of cells. Memantine may protect cells against excess glutamate by partially blocking NMDA receptor. (More about glutamate damage in chapter twelve of this book.)

Clioquinol

Clioquinol is a drug that used to be a popular antidiarrheal medication. It was then thought to cause transient global amnesia, and was banned for that use. It was removed from the market in 1970 because of suspected neurological complications. But those problems are now attributed to vitamin B12 deficiencies.

The drug is now used as an antibiotic in many creams, lotions and ointments. However, new evidence suggests that this drug may actually help those with dementia.

A study published in *Archives of Neurology* suggests the drug may dissolve the plaques in the brains of Alzheimer's patients. Dr. Ashley Bush of Massachusetts General Hospital, Dr. Colin L. Masters of the University of Melbourne, and their colleagues, administered clioquinol to 18 Alzheimer's patients for nine months. Clioquinol dramatically slowed the progression in 18 patients with severe Alzheimer's; the disease got significantly worse in 18 other patients given a placebo

Recently, evidence has been gathered that suggests beta-amyloid accumulation in AD is caused by abnormal interactions with metal ions in the brain, especially zinc, copper and iron. Several studies suggest that trace amounts of copper in drinking water increases the production of beta amyloid.

Clioquinol has been shown to inhibit beta-amyloid in mice. The drug may not only inhibit beta-amyloid toxicity, but may actually reverse the accumulation of beta-amyloid accumulation in the brain.

The drug acts as a chelator and leaches zinc and copper out of the body. This also suggests that other chelators could reduce oxidative damage in Parkinson's, Alzheimer's, and other neurodegenerative diseases. Phase II clinical trials of Clioquinol began in March 2002.

Ampakines

Ampakines are a new class of drugs that may compensate for the decrease of glutamate by increasing the level of a specific neurotransmitter in the brain, AMPA-glutamate, and also increasing production of neurotrophins.

The ampakine drug that is furthest along in development is Cortex Pharmaceutical's CX-516, (Ampalex) which is being tested as a treatment for schizophrenia, Alzheimer's disease, autism and fragile X syndrome. Ampalex increases levels of a specific neurotransmitter in the brain, AMPA-glutamate.

Research conducted at the University of California, Irvine by developer Gary Lynch demonstrates that ampakines also increase the production of the important brain derived neurotrophic factor (BDNF) and nerve growth factor (NGF) in critical areas of the brain involved in memory. These proteins may also play a critical role in treating Huntington's disease, Parkinson's disease and patients recovering from stroke or brain trauma.

Other Medications

Two other drugs — *Idazoxan*, and Tenex *(guanfacine),* which is an antihypertensive medication, may be useful in combination with the new cholinergic drugs.

Linoprine is a drug that stimulates brain cells to release more acetylcholine. Another experimental drug, *HP749,* (besipirdine HCl) being studied by Hoechst-Roussel Pharmaceuticals, Inc., is said to amplify cholinergic and noradrenergic activities in the brain.

Nerve growth factor has shown promise in many animal studies, but has not yet been shown useful in humans. Another set of substances under study are those that stimulate *mitochondria,* the tiny energy factories within each brain cell. One promising substance is *acetyl-l-carnitine* (discussed in this book), while another potential treatment is a naturally occurring molecule called *substance P.,* which may help AIDS acquired dementia.

Dr. Lon Schneider, the Pharmacology Program Director of the Alzheimer's Disease Research Center at the University of Southern California School of Medicine believes that the low levels of acetylcholine found in Alzheimer's sufferers may also respond to drugs that target other brain receptors called *muscarinic* and *nicotinic* receptors. Schneider believes that using several drugs at once that affect these various receptors could be more effective against symptoms than any single medication. Currently, researchers are combining nicotine-like drugs to other dementia medications and finding the combination may work better than either drug alone.

Information

More information about Alzheimer's Disease and other dementias can be obtained from the Alzheimer's Association, 225 North Michigan Avenue, Suite 1700, Chicago, Illinois 60601-7633, Phone: 800-272-3900 Web: http://www.alz.org/

The Alzheimer's Disease Education and Referral Center is a clearinghouse of information which is supported by the National Institute of Aging. This organization also has information about vascular dementia. Their address is Alzheimer's Disease Education and Referral Center (ADEAR), PO Box 8250, Silver Spring, MD 20907-8250 Phone: 800-438-4380 Web: http://www.Alzheimers.org/

Chapter Four

The Many Types of Memory

---

*A memory is what is left when something happens
and does not completely unhappen.*

Edward de Bono

One problem researchers have in studying how memory works is the finding that there are actually several types of memory, and each type works differently. Knowing about the different types of memory I referred to briefly in chapter two, can help you use them more effectively. Of particular interest are the many types known as sensory memory — the memories we take in through our senses. Our eyes, ears, and other receptors take in data from the outside world and store it in ways we are just beginning to understand.

Smell Memory

*When nothing else subsists from the past, after the
people are dead, after the things are broken and
scattered ... the smell and taste of things remain
poised a long time....*

Marcel Proust (1871–1922)

The parts of the brain that process smell are two tiny tubular bits of tissue called the olfactory tubercles. These tiny bundles of cells are part of a primitive system of our brains — sometimes called the reptilian brain — which is responsible for body regulation and self-preservation. Because of this, we have almost instantaneous reactions to smells. Memory for smells is called *olfactory memory.*

The leap from smell to olfactory memory is a short one. Only three synapses separate the olfactory nerve from the hippocampus, which is where working memory and short-term memory are processed. The primary olfactory cortex, the area in the brain where higher-level processing of odors takes place, forms a direct link with the amygdala, which is involved in the storage of emotional memory. Only two synapses separate the olfactory nerve from the amygdala, and for this reason, our smell memories are closely tied to emotional responses

The primitive, emotional reactions we have to smells may be responsible for the longevity and durability of olfactory memory. For example, it's been found that patients of Korsakoff's syndrome, a severe memory disorder often caused by alcoholism, show less of an impairment for odor memory than for other kinds of memory. This suggests that there is in fact a mechanism for odor memory separate from other kinds of memory.

Most of us possess a fantastic ability to remember smells. We can recognize the smell of bacon frying, and tell the difference between that odor and the smell of ham frying, although the odors are very similar. As children, we are very sensitive to smells, and many of our earliest childhood memories are, in fact, smell memories.

Each one of us has our own unique set of olfactory memories, and once recorded, a fragrance is seldom forgotten. Even though many decades have passed, you might still remember the smell of fresh baked bread from your Grandmother's kitchen (as I do), or exactly how your favorite blanket or teddy bear used to smell. You might also recollect the way Aunt Beula's house smelled on Sunday afternoon, or how you hated the smell of steamed Brussels sprouts.

Although these memories are stored permanently, it may take a reminder to bring them into consciousness. In one of my memory seminars, a young woman told me a story about one of her olfactory memories. One day while she was doing her laundry, the drier broke. She took a load of wet T-shirts out of the washer, and hung them in the backyard to dry. Later that day, she went out to gather them. The moment she smelled the sun-dried clothing, she remembered sitting in her father's lap as a little girl, and smelling his fresh, sun-dried shirt. This was an event she had not thought about in thirty years.

Environment has a measurable effect on early smell memories. When researchers asked people to recall early olfactory memories, they found that people born between 1900 and 1929 remembered the childhood smells of nature. Those memories included the smell of horses, hay, sea air, pine, and meadows. Those born between the years 1930 and 1979, however, reported memories of the smells of Vick's VapoRub, plastic, Magic Markers, Play-Doh, and Sweet Tarts. Technology had replaced nature.

Exercise: Wake up and Smell the Roses

Pleasant odors, such as cinnamon and oranges, elicit positive childhood memories and other pleasant recollections in most people. You can use this process to soothe yourself the next time you're feeling down. You just need to make a few preparations first.

- Make a list of all the pleasant smell memories you can recall.
- Reproduce the fragrances.
- Make yourself a "fragrance kit" by putting these fragrances in small bottles.
- When you need a lift, expose yourself to the scents.

Apparently, "wake up and smell the roses" is a saying with hidden benefits.

Researcher Fred Bryant asked his students to recall pleasant smell memories from childhood. He then exposed them to the odors and found significant increases in the recall of pleasant memories. More importantly, he found that the enjoyable memories improved the mood of the person remembering them. Brain scan studies of olfactory memory show that pleasant odors activate the right frontal lobe, which modulates our mood and behavior, while unpleasant odors activate the amygdala, our emotional alarm system. This may be why aroma therapy makes people feel better.

In a third study researchers discovered that the memories of the odors of childhood were related to how one felt about his early years. Those with unhappy childhoods were most likely to recall unpleasant odors.

The ability to smell is often damaged in people with Alzheimer's disease. In fact, long before Alzheimer's sufferers begin to show memory impairment, they lose their ability to recognize odors.

But researcher Michael Serby felt that it was not the sense of smell itself that was defective in Alzheimer's patients. He decided to look at the ability to detect the presence of an odor compared to the ability to identify the odor. The results of his study showed that even when people were able to detect an odor, recognizing and naming it depended on memory pathways located inside the brain, rather than structures in the nose. In other words, they could still smell, but could no longer remember the identity of the particular odor.

Low levels of acetylcholine, the same chemical that transfers and stores memory, was linked to the loss of recognition of smells.

This meant that it was brain damage, not the loss of the ability to smell, that was responsible for the loss of ability to recognize smells. These findings eventually led to the smell test described earlier.

In our daily lives, odors affect us in many subtle ways. For example, there is mounting evidence that people choose their mates through the sense of smell. Chemicals called pheromones trigger the attraction of one person to another. This chemical lure is the origin of the saying that there is "chemistry" between people.

In a new study on pheromones, it was found that the human scents that people found most attractive were those that were the most chemically different than their own. In other words, the more the DNA of one person differed from another, the more attractive he or she found the other's smell. This fascinating finding is evidence that pheromones may not only contribute to sexual attraction, but may promote genetic diversity as well.

Recently it was discovered that smelling can actually improve memory. This was demonstrated in an experiment that used three different ambient odors: sweet olive, peppermint and pine. Sweet Olive was used to see whether there was a difference in performance depending on whether the smell was novel or familiar. Peppermint and pine were used to see whether the appropriateness or inappropriateness of the smell made a difference to memory.

In the experiment, subjects entered a room in which the odor was present. Attention was called to the smell. They were then asked to complete a questionnaire about the room environment. They were left alone in the room for ten minutes to promote encoding of contextual cues.

The experimenter then read out a list of 20 common nouns, pausing after each one for the subject to describe an event that the word reminded them of. Memory for the words was tested 48 hours later. Word recall was best when the unfamiliar odor of sweet olive was present. The improvement occurred only if the odor was present at the time of learning and retrieval.

Dr. Brian Lyman of the Monell Chemical Senses Center in Philadelphia says putting something with a strong odor in a shirt pocket during studying, and using the same odor when taking a test increases the amount of information remembered. A Yale University study showed that students who whiffed chocolate while studying remembered 21 percent of the words they had written down the day before compared to 14 percent for those in the control group. Researcher Frank Schab says that strong odors "piggy-back" other memories because the brain so easily remembers scent.

Visceral Memory

They may forget what you said, but they will never forget how you made them feel

Carl W. Buechner

When I was fifteen years old, I worked in a gas station. It was my job to open the station in the morning, and to do this, I had to get up at 5 a.m. Half awake, I would start each day with a bowl of corn flakes. One day as I was eating breakfast in a semiconscious state, I spooned up a large cricket from my bowl. In addition to jolting me into consciousness, this experience left me with a distaste for corn flakes that lasts to this day. The nauseating feeling I get when I look at corn flakes is a visceral memory.

Visceral memories are bundles of information about how internal organs function tied with pleasant or unpleasant experiences. Our evaluations of experiences are often based on visceral, emotionally-tinged responses. The common term for this experience is gut feeling. These primitive emotional responses often occur before we become conscious of the experiences that elicit them. At these times we may say something like, "I can't explain my reaction, but something just didn't feel right," or, "That makes me sick."

Smell, visceral memories, and taste also play a part in our dietary choices. Recent discoveries suggest that feeding experiences in childhood have an effect on adult food preferences. For example one study on dietary preferences found that the kinds of vegetables consumed by a child was partially determined by the number of vegetables liked by the mother when the child was 28 to 36 months old.

But there is also a genetic component to our preferences. A group of related chemicals, including phenylthiocarbamide (PTC) and, 6-n-propylthiouracil (PROP), are tasteless to some people and moderately bitter to another segment of the population. However, these compounds are extremely bitter to others, people who are called supertasters.

Supertasters perceive not only the most intense tastes but also the most intense oral burn from irritants, and the most intense tactile sensations from fats in foods. Family studies showed that non-tasters carry different genes for taste than do supertasters.

Why is this important? This genetic variation in taste affects health in two important ways: Reduced liking of bitter vegetables and fruits among supertasters puts them at increased risk for maladies where consumption of these foods reduces the risks of disease (for example vegetables high in antioxidant and anti-cancer properties). Reduced liking for high-fat, high-sweet foods among female supertasters puts them at decreased risk for cardiovascular diseases, an important risk factor we will discuss later with regard to memory loss.

Auditory Memory

Auditory memory is the memory for sounds. The right hemisphere specializes in perceiving and storing this nonverbal information. It is this type of memory that enables us to recognize a friend's voice, a dog barking, or a bell ringing. Auditory memory is remarkably accurate. Many of us have learned to recognize a person just from the sound of his footsteps, the way he coughs, sneezes, or how he clears his throat. This type of memory works so well that most of us never think about it.

Auditory memory also functions to record the sequence of sounds. It is in this way that we memorize songs. There is evidence that auditory memory retains very accurate storage of this type of information. In one experiment 46 subjects were asked to sing popular songs from memory. When their tempos were compared to recorded versions of the songs, seventy-two percent of the subjects came within 8 percent of the actual tempo.

People with exceptionally good auditory memory often become accomplished musicians. Arturo Toscanini, one of the greatest conductors of all time, could remember the entire score of a symphony after hearing it only one or two times. Once he had committed a score to memory, he could write it down note for note forty years later.

Studies show that about 40 percent of us are predominantly auditory when it comes to memorizing. That is, we learn best when we hear something. People with auditory preference would much rather study by listening to a taped lecture than to read notes.

The majority of us, however (about 60 percent) prefer our visual memory. This is one reason why television is more popular than radio. We like to watch something related to the information we hear, even if it's trivial. Media researchers were surprised when they found that, even though the amount of information is the same, a vast majority of people prefer to see someone reading the news on television rather than merely hearing it on the radio.

Visual Memory

The soul never thinks without images

— Aristotle

Visual memory is the ability to remember and recognize faces, places, and objects. The ability to remember faces is a very important survival mechanism. Thousands of years ago, when humans lived in huts and had to hunt for food, they needed to be able to recognize whether an approaching person was a friend or a stranger. Those that didn't do well at this didn't survive.

You know from your own experience that it's easier to remember a face than a name. In fact, you can memorize a face after seeing it for only a minute or two. We are a visually oriented species, and our visual memory is extremely accurate and permanent. You seldom hear of anyone trying to improve her visual memory.

Several areas of the brain are devoted to the processing of visual material. Some of these areas are specifically delegated to recognize faces. Damage to this part of the brain results in a disorder called prosopagnosia. People with this disorder completely lose the ability to recognize faces, even their own.

Because visual memory is our most accurate type of memory, it is the type of memory most often used in memory improvement techniques, which we will explore in chapter ten.

Sensory Memory and Language

The process of learning language begins with learning the names of objects. This is done by a parent pointing to an object and pronouncing its name. The child looks at the object and hears a sound uttered. To learn the name of an object, the child must first be able to form a mental image in visual memory. This mental image allows the child to recognize the object when he sees it again.

The next task is the tying of the mental picture to the word through the process of association. Once this association is formed, the child is able to call up the mental image just by hearing the word. You now have thousands of these image-word links stored in your memory.

Think of an elephant. A car. A dog. As you think of these words, mental pictures of the objects instantaneously appear in your mind. Later in this book, you are going to use this function of the brain to help you memorize new material.

Agnosia, (a word that literally means *without knowledge)* is the unraveling of these connections. This is often one of the symptoms seen in the early stages of dementia and in strokes. Agnosia is a glitch in the association system which disconnects the word from the image. The kind of disconnect depends on where the damage lies. For example, a gentleman in England was struck by a car and sustained minor brain damage. After recovery from his injuries, testing revealed that his brain functioned perfectly, with the exception of an inability to name fruits and vegetables!

As we age, word finding becomes more difficult. It's very common to forget a person's name. It is not common, however, to forget what a cat is. People with this kind of problem should seek help immediately.

Informational Memory

When we think of improving memory, we are usually referring to informational or declarative memory. Informational memory is the ability to recall facts and events, and this type of memory requires conscious effort. Informational memory, unlike the other types of memory just mentioned, is not a survival mechanism, and therefore doesn't work nearly as well as the other types. Until a few centuries ago, our senses were much more vital to our survival than information, so the brain's declarative memory ability is not as reliable as sensory memory. One of the secrets of improving memory, therefore, is to bypass informational memory, and memorize information using the types of memory that already work well — sensory memory.

Semantic Memory

One subcategory of informational memory is semantic memory. It is the memory of what words, gestures, signs, and cultural symbols mean to us. Alzheimer's disease causes devastating memory damage, attacking and destroying the cells that store memories. But even in those with advanced stages of the disease, about half of Alzheimer's patients still retain a good portion of semantic memory.

Skill Memory

Also called motor memory, procedural memory, or implicit memory, skill memory is the ability to remember how to do things. Complex tasks such as walking, talking, playing a musical instrument, or riding a bicycle are all examples of skill memory.

Skill memory is controlled by specific areas of the brain including the motor cortex and the cerebellum.

Once a skill is learned the memory becomes unconscious and permanent. Even if you haven't ridden a bike for several decades, you probably could get back on one and ride it with little effort. But because skill memory is unconscious, even though you can ride the bike, you cannot tell someone how you do it. Skill memory records processes, not words.

Once stored, a procedural memory is often difficult to unlearn. For example, when the transition from dial phones to touch tone phones took place in this country, many people found they had trouble remembering phone numbers. The change from manipulating a dial to pressing a series of buttons necessitated learning new patterns of movement, and new memories had to be recorded in order to recall the numbers.

Although skill memory involves recorded patterns of muscle movements, research has shown that the brain stores these programs in greater detail than just what muscles must be used. For example, when you sign your name on a check, you use your hand and wrist muscles to move the pen. Although your signature is never exactly the same, it is remarkably similar each time you write it. But it is also strikingly similar when you write it on a blackboard, even though you are now using your arm to make the movements your wrist made before. The memory program for your signature then must be more complex than just a pattern of muscle movements.

People in the early stages of dementia will forget daily events, while skill memories like writing remain intact. Writing is one of the skills that deteriorates as dementia progresses, and is sometimes used as an assessment of the severity of brain damage. Loss of this kind of memory is a sure sign of serious brain deterioration.

Episodic Memory

Episodic memory is the storehouse of our personal past. It contains all memories of things gone by. Although most people will readily admit that they have faulty informational memory, they insist that their episodic memory is perfect. Many arguments originate from disputes about who did or said something. But despite our steadfast conviction about our own memories, in reality, episodic memory is unquestionably the most unreliable. We know from years of research that eyewitness accounts of past events are remarkably inaccurate. This in part is because episodic memory is not recalled, but recreated. Instead of accessing the information like a computer does, each time we remember something, we recreate a story about what we recall.

Depending on our mood, the situation, our own beliefs and opinions, and many other factors, this story is a little different each time we recount it. Over time, our recollection of an experience may cease to have any resemblance to what actually happened. In chapter five we will discover some of the reasons that this is so.

Working Memory

The most recent memory research has focused on what scientists call working memory. It is working memory that enables us to hold part of a sentence in our minds until we get to the end. This factor of memory also allows us to keep several things in our minds simultaneously. It is also working memory that begins to slow down and falter between ages 40 and 50.

Chapter Five

The Memory Process

Just how does something become a memory? How does the experience of eating that great cheese sandwich you had last week get processed and stored, so that you can tell your neighbor about it a week later? Although researchers have been exploring this question for centuries, we still don't understand just how memories are formed. However, we do know that all information must go through a specific set of steps before it becomes a memory.

Stimulus

All memory begins with stimuli, sources of information that are new to the mind. Most stimuli originate from the outside world. Every sight, sound, taste, touch and smell is a stimulus. But memories can also be generated internally by the brain itself, as happens during dreaming, fantasy, thought, creativity, and problem solving. In fact, all of our art, science, and creativity are the end product of generating, synthesizing, and remembering newly formed internal ideas. Many groundbreaking inventions originated from remembering information that was originally generated in dreams.

Receptors

In order for any external stimulus to be recorded as a memory, it must first be processed through the nervous system. Information coming from the outside world is picked up by the millions of specialized cells in the sense organs, called receptors. Your eyes, ears, mouth and skin all contain receptors.

Although we all process this information in the same manner, some of us have a preferred mode of processing information. For example, visually oriented people would rather watch something, while people with a preference for sound would rather hear it. This preference for a specific type of information comes from your particular set of stimulus filters.

Stimulus Filters

Although we encounter millions of bits of information each day, we actually remember only a small portion of them. What we do remember is controlled by the mechanism of filtering. Like any filter, this mechanism eliminates unwanted material. Stimulus filters scan all incoming information, and allow into consciousness only the most important data.

Each of us inherits a unique set of stimulus filters. We are born with an array of natural talents and abilities that make it easy for us to remember certain types of information.

This is true in part because of individual differences in the hard wiring of the brain. Just as people differ in hair color, eye color, and height, each person's brain structure is unique. In the last few years, researchers have actually found physical differences in brain structure that correspond with different abilities and professions.

We all know people who have excellent memories for certain things. The word we use to describe our inborn abilities is talent. For example, you probably know someone with a natural ability to remember music. She can remember a song after hearing it only once. On the other hand, those born without this ability to process music, a quality sometimes called tone deafness, cannot remember a song even after hearing it fifty times. (Then there are those with no musical ability that think they have it. The term we use for this is 'painfully annoying'.)

So while some people excel in certain types of memory, others suffer specific deficits. These people are said to have learning disabilities. People with learning disabilities may be unable to process certain types of information, and therefore they cannot store it. This deficit in storage has often been mistaken for a memory problem, but it's actually a filtering problem.

In addition to inheriting stimulus filters, we form them as a result of experience. For example, if you had a history teacher that made history exciting and interesting, you'd find it easy to remember important historical events and figures. You would develop an emotional investment in history, and enjoy being able to recall this type of information.

But if your history teacher had the ability to bore you into unconsciousness, you would learn to avoid historical information and dislike history in general. Historical data slips through your memory like water through a sieve.

If you failed history, you might have a negative emotional reaction to it. From that time on you automatically tune out historical subjects, and do not pay attention to information that has anything to do with history. Your filters would shut out anything that remotely resembled your painful experience with history.

We all associate emotions with information, and if the emotions are unpleasant we'll avoid similar information in the future. Psychologists call this emotional avoidance a mental block. Conversely, it's natural to spend more time doing what we do well, because it makes us feel good. Because our stimulus filters determine what kinds of information we process, they guide our lives. A person may use his musical ability to become a composer. And one born with natural mathematical ability may use it to become a scientist. It is filtering, then, that steers us away from what we are not interested in, and draws us toward what pleases us.

Many of you have noticed this filtering process in your children. For example, if you tell a child, "The cookies are upstairs on the second shelf, and take out the trash before you leave for school," you know that they are more likely to remember where the cookies are than to take the trash out.

As adults we continue to attend selectively to things from the world, storing those things that interest us, and filtering out the things that don't. Experiments done by cognitive psychologists demonstrate this remarkably well. Researcher Donald Norman had subjects listen to two spoken passages at the same time. The subjects were asked to repeat one of the passages, as it was spoken, while ignoring the other one.

An example of this appears in Bernard Baars fascinating book *In the Theater of Consciousness.* In the following passage, the subjects were asked to repeat the words appearing here in capital letters, while ignoring those in lower case.

"MARY paper HAD A brick cream LITTLE LAMB morning ITS FLEECE day brick WAS dot WHITE flower fork AS SNOW...."

Subjects who repeated this passage found that they could attend to the story quite well, while filtering out the unwanted words. What was remarkable is that the same word repeated as many as thirty five times during a passage could not be remembered afterwards. This means that even when we are exposed numerous times to something we find unimportant, we filter it out and do not remember it later. Much of what we think of as forgetting is actually the result of filtering out what we don't care to remember.

The Orienting Response

The process by which our stimulus filters select that which is to be attended is called the orienting response. Orienting is an automatic, unconscious process. It is active even when you are sleeping. It is this reflex that allows a new mother to sleep through the noise of a police siren, only to be awakened a moment later by a slight whimper from her newborn.

While having a conversation with someone in a room full of people, we automatically focus on what the other person is saying. Without effort, all other conversations are filtered out. But if someone across the room calls our name, the orienting response refocuses our attention, and we turn our heads to see who called us. This type of selective listening is called the cocktail party phenomenon.

The orienting response is an automatic mechanism that tells us what to pay attention to at any given moment. Because we are not consciously aware of this, our attention is often diverted even when we wish it to be on the task before us. Have you ever gotten up out of your chair fully intending to do something, only to be distracted a moment later? This is the orienting response at work. When something catches our attention, we forget our previous intent.

Many things that we say we don't remember are actually never stored in our memories at all. The orienting response placed our attention elsewhere at the time of the event.

Short-Term Memory

Once a piece of information has been selected by the orienting response, and passed through the stimulus filter for processing, it enters short-term memory.

Short-term memory holds only a small amount of information, and holds this information for a very brief period of time; about twenty or thirty seconds.

You've probably had the experience of looking up a number in a phone book, walking over to the phone, dialing part of the number, and suddenly realizing that you have forgotten the rest of it.

What do you do? You look the number up again, and this time say the number over and over to yourself until you reach the phone. If you're successful in dialing the number, you finish your conversation, and hang up. But if you have to call again in a few minutes, you find you have once more forgotten the number. This happens because information stays in short-term memory for only a few seconds unless it is rehearsed. You must repeat the phone number to yourself in order to keep it active in short term memory. Short-term memory holds only enough information to store about one phone number. It's impossible to look up three or four phone numbers, and remember them long enough to dial them.

If you use a number every day, however, eventually you find that you know the number without having to look it up again. The number has now been stored in the next stage of memory — long-term memory.

Long-Term Memory

In 1890, William James distinguished between two types of memory which he called primary memory (now called short-term memory), and secondary memory, which lasts for an extended period of time (now called long term memory). But it wasn't until 1958 that the terms short-term and long-term memory were coined by David Broadbent.

Broadbent found that unlike short-term memory, long-term memory stored information in a relatively permanent fashion. It also has the capacity to hold large amounts of data — as far as we know, no one has ever come close to filling up their long term memory.

Retrieval and Recollection

The final stage in the memory process is the ability to retrieve the stored information. It is the ability or inability to access information that is the focus of most memory research.

In reality, however, most of the time the inability to remember something is caused by a failure in the storage process just described. The most common cause of not remembering is the simple failure of information being transferred from short-term to long-term memory.

One way to store information in your long-term memory is to rehearse it many times and review it frequently. This sends a message to your memory that the information is important and should be stored.

There are occasions however, that something can be stored in long-term memory without rehearsal. If you are extremely interested in something, you may store it after hearing or seeing it only once. Also, events that are unusual or emotionally arousing, such as the plot of a good book or movie, may be stored after only one exposure.

Flashbulb Memory

One morning I was walking up the stairs in my health club when I saw an amazing sight on the television in the lounge. It was a picture of the space shuttle Challenger exploding. This disaster killed seven people, and brought the entire space program to its knees. Although this happened years ago, I still have a vivid memory of walking up those stairs and seeing the ship explode. As you read this paragraph, you too may recall where you were and what you were doing when you heard this tragic news.

Scientists call this type of recollection a *flashbulb memory*. The emotional impact of these memories drive them immediately into long-term memory. Memories that are stored in this manner tend to last a lifetime.

Flashbulb memory seems incredibly accurate, but is it? Research shows that flashbulb memories select certain elements of an experience for storage, and edit out other components. For example, although I recall the picture of the exploding Challenger quite vividly, I don't remember what day of the week it was, or even what year it was.

Even though flashbulb memories seem so vivid and accurate, they actually change with time.

The day after the space shuttle Challenger disintegrated, psychologist Ulric Neisser asked his students to write a description of where they were and exactly what they were doing when they heard the news of the event. Three years later, he contacted the students and asked them to recall the same experience. Over one third of the students wrote descriptions that were totally unrelated to their original description!

What impressed Neisser the most, however, was that the students were absolutely convinced that their memories were accurate. When shown their original written descriptions of the event, some of them actually claimed that someone else must have copied their handwriting, and written the original account!

Emotion and Memory

If you look back in your life right now, you will find that much of what you remember were emotionally arousing instances, or important events such as graduating, getting married, or getting a promotion. Most people remember the last time they rode a roller coaster better then what they had to eat last week because roller coaster rides are more emotionally arousing events than meals. Even relatively unemotional events, however, are filtered through our emotional brains before they are stored. For example, the words velvet and granite each have an emotional component. You would probably rather run your hand over a piece of velvet than a piece of granite. The words pudding and blood carry emotional components also. Given the choice, you probably would rather put your hand in a bowl of pudding than a pool of blood.

While you might not have enjoyed what you just read, the emotion attached to the previous sentence increased the probability that you will remember it. If no emotion at all is attached to an event, it will not be remembered at all. It appears that emotions affect memory in several ways:

First, exciting and interesting information is stored with less effort than dull and boring information, because emotion increases our arousal. We call this emotional investment *attention*.

Second, the emotions experienced along with information determine whether we pay attention to similar information in the future. This makes it easy for us to remember the things we enjoy. We call this experience developing an *interest*.

Third, the mood that you are in when you learn something has an effect on your ability to remember it later. This is why people remember every bad thing their spouse has done when they get angry at them. This quality of memory is called state dependent memory (which is discussed later in this book).

Finally, although emotion does help us remember, research has shown us that regardless of how strongly we feel about a memory, it may be completely incorrect.

To understand better how important long term memory is to your sense of well being, you have to realize that probably the most important part of it is described in the emotional recollections you have. They extend as far back into your life as your earliest activities.

One example is the memory of a 75-year-old who told me he could recall clearly when he was five years old, the remedy his mother forced on him when he exhibited the first signs of a cold. His mother subjected him to a ceremony in the kitchen. Standing on the counter next to the sink was a bottle of castor oil. There was no way of escaping his mother's intention for him, and his brother and sister, to swallow a tablespoon of the awful stuff.

Knowing how terrible it tasted, his mother handed him, and his brother and sister in sequence, a quarter of an orange to bite into and a cup of black coffee to wash away the horrible taste. She was a firm believer in the efficacy of castor oil to ward off colds and had the wisdom to know that the coffee, never offered at any other time to her children, because it might stunt their growth, gave them a feeling of importance and helped to erase the castor oil taste.

This kind of memory, says researcher Howard Eichenbaum, a leader in the field of memory research, is an emotional memory, which fits within the broader category of long term memory.

According to Eichenbaum, "emotional memory is centralized in the amygdala of the brain. It is emotional memory that makes you nervous when you enter a dark alley; even though nothing has gone wrong at that moment, your brain associates the situation with danger and you may feel fear. Similarly, when you hear the thumping of the musical score to a scary scene from the movie *Jaws,* you expect to see a shark and your heart may start beating a little faster."

It is from emotional memory that the richness of human life is experienced by the individual and from which stems our passions, loves, hates and our cravings to understand who we are.

Another aspect of emotional memory is the fact that emotionally charged recollections stay with us much longer than those that can be classified as run of the mill.

Scientists are fascinated with the changes in the brain that occur when events bring on recollections with long term staying power that makes them unforgetable.

According to Eric J. Nestler, chairman of the Psychiatry Department, University of Texas Southern Medical Center, good or bad emotions strengthen memories in the same way that the highs produced by alcohol or heroin create addiction.

While no one would suggest that drugs of abuse are "good" for you, the brain covets them because they are intensely rewarding. Addictive drugs act on the brain's reward pathways through the actions of dopamine and other brain chemicals which trigger a switch that seems to say, "That's great. Do it again."

These same pathways, which have been stabilized throughout human evolution, also respond in behaviors such as overeating and sex drive. That the brain has evolved with such a reward system makes sense, Nestler says, because it has always been in an individual's best interest to remember where to find food for survival or mates for procreation.

The commonality among all of these types of "reward-seeking behaviors" is that they activate brain reward pathways that use dopamine, as well as other biochemical transmitters in the brain.

Chapter Six

Why and What We Forget

Memory is what tells a man that his wife's birthday was yesterday

Mario Rocco

It seems that everybody worries about his or her memory. But because we've all been taught that memory gets worse with age, it's no surprise that as we get older, we become anxious every time we forget something. Every lost pair of sunglasses or keys, every misplaced pen or forgotten promise, is seen as evidence that we are getting senile.

But actually, memory doesn't get significantly worse with age. The truth is that memory is always bad. If you think about it for a minute, you'll see this is true. If you have spent time with children, you know that their memories are terrible. Kids lose everything — their shoes, their jackets, their homework. They forget what you tell them. They forget to do their chores, they forget everything. But they have something that you don't have. They have parents in the house to remind them of things.

It's not surprising then that we continue to forget things as we get older. But things haven't changed, we just notice it more.

Now certain conditions such as nutritional deficiencies and disorders like Alzheimer's disease do cause significant memory loss. But, barring this, our memory at seventy can remain almost as sharp as it was at seven.

Even though this is true, we still forget a great number of the events in our lives. Certain experiences disappear forever. Why do we forget so much of what we experience?

Actually, the human mind is a forgetting machine. It is built to forget. To understand this, let's look at the way memory works in nonhumans.

The more complicated an animal's nervous system is, the more easily it forgets. Insects have a very limited ability to learn new behavior. Everything that they need know is programmed into them at birth. They come into the world completely equipped for survival, and they don't forget anything. But they are also incapable of learning. They cannot modify their behavior.

Birds and other animals with more complicated nervous systems are more adaptable. They are still very well equipped with the knowledge they need to survive from birth, but they have to learn some of their life skills from their parents. For example, birds are genetically programmed to sing, but they must learn the correct mating song from their parents.

But humans need to be taught everything they need to know to survive, and consequently, we must have a much larger capacity for storing memory. We also have a much greater ability to forget. Our ability to discard unwanted information allows us to adapt to new environments, developing and changing as our surroundings change. We erase old behaviors and learn new skills that help us adapt. As we change, we forget what we no longer need.

Here is an exercise in two parts. Each part will make points about different aspects of memory.

Exercise: Part One

Go back in time to your twelfth birthday. Think about that year in your life. Take as long as you need to gather your memories. Now tell a friend everything you can remember about that period.

You probably noticed several things:

- First, you will probably remember very little about that year.

- It probably took you only a few minutes to recount everything you remember.

- What you did remember probably consisted of high and low points in your life.

This shows that we soon forget much of what we do. As you learned in a previous chapter, emotionally charged events are remembered more readily.

Exercise: Part Two

For this second part, you'll need to grab your high school yearbook. Before you glance through it, begin this section of the exercise.
- Name every person you remember from high school. Take your time and list them all.
- Now open your yearbook and look through it. See how many people you still remember but were unable to recall.

This exercise demonstrates the difference between recall and recognition memory. External clues often jog memory better than internal ones.

In the previous chapter we learned that memory is a step-wise process. Each step is essential for the storage and recovery of memory. Therefore, if any one step fails, memory is not stored. Let's examine how problems in each step impede memory.

Stimulus Problems

As mentioned in chapter four, all memory begins with a stimulus. A stimulus might be a sight, sound, taste or smell, or even a complicated and delicate pattern of motion such as the graceful and beautiful movements of a ballet dancer, accomplished through the memorization of hundreds of separate movements.

For any stimulus to be picked up by the nervous system, it must be strong enough to trigger the receptor. Scientists call this minimum intensity the stimulus threshold. A mosquito is often able to land on the body, puncture the skin, and leave without our awareness because its delicate touch is below the stimulus threshold of the touch receptors in our skin. We only become aware of the insect's visit because of the itching caused by the bite.

In the 1950s, several movie theaters reported that they sold more popcorn and soda because of hidden messages flashed on the screen saying "eat popcorn" and "drink Coke." The publicity generated from this experiment launched an entire industry based on what came to be known as subliminal learning. Since that time, millions of dollars have been spent on subliminal tapes that claim to help break habits, increase self esteem, and boost productivity.

However, not one study done since the 1950 movie experiment has shown that anything can be learned subliminally. It appears that sounds too quiet to be heard are not registered or processed by the brain. So, unfortunately, subliminal tapes do not work.

To be discernable, information must also have low signal to noise ratios. This means that the information you are trying to learn should be clear and uncontaminated. This is why teachers insist that students remain quiet during class time. Too much noise makes concentration difficult.

On the other hand, too little stimulation can also lead to memory problems. It is common for people to become less active as they grow older. Older people are less physically active, less socially active, and seek out less stimulation.

Many elderly people do very little each day but sit and watch television. They are chronically understimulated. These lonely and forgotten people are seldom spoken to, seldom touched, and rarely encouraged to engage in social activity. This chronic loss of stimulation greatly accelerates memory loss. I've seen high functioning people deteriorate within weeks after they are placed in a nursing home where no stimulation is offered.

It could be said that understimulation is literally the hobgoblin of little minds. An understimulated brain eventually begins to atrophy, shrink, and deteriorate.

In fact, chronic understimulation can lead to hallucinations. The brain needs a certain amount of stimulation to function properly, and if it cannot get it from the environment, it will manufacture it. Experiments in sensory deprivation show that deprived of external events, the brain will begin to generate stimuli within a few hours.

Stimulating the brain with new experiences and novel environments actually causes neurons to grow new connections. In short, stimulation helps a brain stay healthy. The bottom line is, the more active you remain, the better your memory will function, and the more stable your identification of yourself will be.

Receptor Problems

Many years ago, children who were hard of hearing were classified as retarded. They were often shunned by society and considered unteachable. Eventually it was discovered that deaf children were just as capable of learning and remembering as anyone — they simply had a receptor problem.

As we age, our receptors begin to falter. Eyes and ears no longer function as well as they once did. This decrease in function is usually slow and insidious, and may not be noticed for a considerable time.

As hearing begins to fail, people often complain that others are not speaking clearly or loudly enough. Many people deny that they have a hearing problem even when it is apparent to others around them. Of course, when hearing fails, auditory memory suffers also. What can't be heard cannot be remembered. For this reason, some people begin to complain of memory problems when what is actually happening is a loss of the ability to detect sound. Whenever a person begins to show signs of forgetfulness, a hearing test should be done to rule out hearing loss as the cause.

It's important to be aware that many older people also lose much of their ability to smell and taste. This often results in a decrease in the pleasure of eating. When eating decreases, malnutrition may occur, which, as we will see later, can have a profound effect on memory.

Filtering Problems

Can you imagine what it might be like to remember everything? To remember every meal you've ever eaten? Every cut and bruise you've ever had? Every disappointment and loss you've ever experienced? This would crowd our minds with drivel, and make our lives miserable. The truth is that much of what we do each day is better off forgotten. Repetitive, day-to-day tasks and uninteresting experiences are soon forgotten because remembering them serves no useful purpose. Much of what we experience never enters memory at all, because our filters see it as unimportant. But when filters break down, memory suffers.

Stress

Some memory experts believe that stress is one of the major causes of forgetting. In general, the more stress that you are under, the more poorly your memory will work.

One of the reasons for this is that stress causes stimulus filters to break down. When filters break down, nothing in the environment gets filtered out.

You have probably noticed that when you're feeling stressed, every little thing bothers you. Friends bother you, kids bother you, your husband or wife bothers you — every pop, crack, and door slam makes you jump.

This causes stimulus overload. Short-term memory can't handle this much input. When this happens, you find you can't pay attention to anything, and therefore you are unable to transfer the information into long-term memory.

The net result is that short-term memory stops processing new information. Later on, when the stress is over, you find that you can't remember much of anything that went on during the time that you were stressed.

When people start feeling stressed, they instinctively try to get away from the noise and distraction they can no longer filter. They attempt to "get away from it all" by taking a vacation.

Stress also makes it more difficult to remember things that you already know. When you are stressed, you find that your mind is filled with concerns about the fact that you are under pressure, and this preoccupation interferes with your ability to recall information (state dependence, which is discussed below, is also partially responsible for this lack of recall).

Even worse, several studies suggest that stress is one of the causes of brain-cell death. Chemicals called free radicals which increase during stress, can actually destroy cells in the amygdala and hippocampus.

Most adults have read about how stress can do harm to the body if it is prolonged and is produced on a consistent basis in the life of an individual. Americans in particular have demonstrated an attitude that stress is just part of the price a person has to pay to be successful at his job and to endure the faster pace of life at home with the increasing demands to provide children with a variety of educational, social and athletic opportunities.

Recent research on stress, however, was reported in the *New England Journal of Medicine* in 1998. Significant in the report, authored by Bruce McEwen, Ph.D., of Rockefeller University, was the fact that a group of successfully aging elderly people were studied for three years. They were monitored and given common tests to measure blood pressure, blood glucose levels and cortisol and cholesterol levels.

McEwen introduced the concept of *allostatic load,* which is the price our bodies pay for the ability to adapt to stress. Measurements were made to determine how the "allostatic load level" of the participants influenced their health.

"Even the brain can be affected," McEwen reported. "In fact," he said, "results from studies on aging animals and humans suggest that a lifelong allostatic load may accelerate changes in the brain that can lead to memory loss." In the group McEwen and his associates studied, they found that those with the highest allostatic loads were most likely to develop newly-diagnosed cardiovascular disease and were significantly prone to show declines in mental and physical functioning.

"What it tells us," McEwen says, "is that from the standpoint of health, what is even more important than how we feel about the stressful events in our lives, is how our bodies react to the stress hormones they produce. Stressful life events — loss of a loved one, divorce, job loss, severe disappointment or chronic depression — as well as the daily wear and tear of living, such as traffic jams and family disagreements, set off the release of stress hormones that help our bodies charge up to meet the challenge.

"During episodes of acute stress, stress hormones provide a protective junction by activating the body's defenses," McEwen said.

"But when these same protective hormones are produced repeatedly, or in excess, because of chronic stress, they create a gradual and steady cascade of harmful physiological changes."

Higher levels of allostatic load leads to bone loss, muscular weakening, arterio atherosclerosis and increased insulin levels that produce elevated levels of fat deposition in the body, especially around the abdomen. "People end up with that apple body shape that researchers have shown over and over again predisposes us to heart disease," he pointed out.

The conclusions reached as a result of McEwen's findings were recommendations that the concept of allostatic load may provide physicians with the basis for a more comprehensive assessment of major risks in the aging process. His antidote for stress is moderate, but consistent exercise.

Robert Sapolski at Stanford University has spent several years undertaking studies that suggest that a family of hormones called glucocorticoids can kill brain cells. These hormones are designed to mobilize glucose during the fight or flight response, but repeated stress overloads cells in the hippocampus with these substances, and kills them.

The hippocampus is the part of the brain that is responsible for the transfer of short-term memory to long term memory.

It has been estimated that as we age we lose from 10 to 40 percent of our hippocampal cells. Memory impairment begins when about 15 percent of the cells are lost. According to Sapolski, stress can kill these cells.

Aging also reduces the effectiveness of the immune system. As people grow older immune function may be as low as 15 percent of its original capacity. Science has learned, however, that the brain and the immune system continuously signal to each other, which may explain how state of mind influences health.

A rapid and protective immune response is dependent on immunological memory. This memory also decreases with aging. In some instances, as we age, our immune system mistakes our own cells for those of foreign origin invader cells, resulting in "auto-immune" diseases.

Stress hormones, especially cortisol, (the stress hormone that produces the "fight or flight" response) injure the brain and immune system.

High levels of allostatic load also lead to suppression of the immune system which leaves us open to infection and infectious diseases. As people grow older immune function may be as low as fifteen percent of its original capacity. Science has learned, however, that the brain and the immune system continuously signal to each other, which may explain how state of mind influences health.

Immune responses are mediated by numerous types of white blood cells including B and T lymphocytes. Some middle-aged persons, and the elderly with impaired immune functions, demonstrate an increased susceptibility to infection and decreased response to vaccines.

The cumulative effect of everyday stressful events leads to this deterioration. Therefore, Sapolski suggests, the best method of prevention is to learn coping skills and stress reduction techniques.

Techniques such as relaxation training, meditation, and problem solving skills can lower these stress hormones to an acceptable level. Reduced cortisol has been associated with heightened immune response, and increased brain function.

The manner in which people deal with life — with effective coping techniques — affects how we age and how we allow aging to influence our behavior. This concept was basic to a follow-up of the nun study, by Deborah Danner, Ph.D., of the University of Kentucky. She found that the nuns who penned words like "joy" and "thankful" lived up to 10 years longer than their sister nuns who expressed negative emotions. Danner is currently analyzing data indicating that nuns who smile more may also live longer.

Other studies suggest that prayer and meditation decrease stress and increase immune function. Oxygen consumption, brain activity, and immune function are enhanced by both prayer and meditation. For example, a study of 60 African American men and women with hypertension was conducted over 6–9 months. The meditation group had 5–8 hours of instruction on TM techniques, while the other group was given the same amount of instruction on exercise and proper diet.

Ultrasound was used to measure fatty deposits on the arterial walls. The meditators showed a decrease of .098 mm in the arterial wall thickness while those in the health education group had an increase in thickness of .054 mm.

Previous studies show that meditation can decrease blood pressure, reduce stress hormones, and decrease the oxidation of lipids.

Music can also mitigate stress. In one study of drummers, it was found that they had heightened levels of immune cells, called natural killer cells, that seek out and destroy cancer cells and those cells infected with viruses.

Worry

Still another reason that certain items are forgotten has come to be known as the Ziegarnick Effect, named after the researcher who studied it. Zeigarnick gave subjects twenty simple tasks that each took only a few minutes. She interrupted the subjects during half of the tasks, and did not allow them to complete them. When the subjects were done, they were asked to recall as many of the tasks as possible.

She found that 68 percent of the uncompleted tasks were recalled as opposed to 43 percent of the completed ones. The Zeigarnick effect then is the propensity to recall uncompleted tasks more easily than completed tasks.

In part, this is useful. The effect makes it more likely that you will remember chores that have not been completed than ones that have been finished. For example, if I ask you to think about your bills, do you think about the ones that you have paid, or the ones that you haven't paid? The Zeigarnick effect helps you focus on what must be done, rather than what you have done.

On the down side, however, unfinished business tends to stay on your mind and fill your consciousness. The popular term for this is worry.

Beyond question, worry interferes with concentration. It fills your mind with the flotsam of unfinished business and unresolved conflict so that nothing else is allowed to enter.

In addition, people who worry become so filled with anxiety that stimulus filters break down, and we've already seen that filter malfunction means memory loss.

Here is a five step method for reducing worry:

1.   Write down all of your worries.

2.   After you have completed the list, read it over and decide which items on your list are within your power to change.

3.   Write a plan of action for facing these challenges, and commit yourself to a time and place to resolve them.

4.   Let go of the worries that you have no power to change. Thinking about them is a waste of time.

5.   If you still feel that you need "worry time," set aside 15–30 minutes a day to do nothing but worry. When that time is over, enjoy yourself.

Overload

Overload occurs when information is coming in at too rapid a rate. What happens is that the new data "bumps out" the information already stored in your short-term memory, and prevents it from moving on to be warehoused in long-term memory. Effectively your memory system goes on strike. This is why we find ourselves saying, "Whoa, slow down!" when someone is giving us too much too fast.

The best way to avoid overload is to take information in at the rate in which you can process it. If someone is giving you too much information too quickly, it is perfectly proper to ask them to slow down.

Interference

When information comes in from several sources at once, only a small portion of it is allowed into short-term memory. As we have seen, stimulus filters block out all but the most important and interesting data. This is why it's not a good idea to study while listening to the radio or when watching your favorite television show.

As mentioned earlier, the older we get, the more sensitive we become to the disruption of interference. Our ability to filter becomes impaired. Therefore, the older you are the more it becomes necessary to keep unnecessary input at a minimum.

Research has shown that you can increase your ability to remember something if you review it right before going to bed at night. This is because the information is the last thing you see before you fall asleep. No other information competes with it.

This allows the information to be stored in long-term memory during your slumber (a topic that is further explored in chapter eleven).

Exercise: Picturing a Penny

Here is an exercise based on research by Adams and Nickerson which will illustrate how the stimulus filters block information that is deemed insignificant. This exercise may have you searching for a penny to check the right answers, but don't peek until you've reached the end.

- Without looking, draw a picture of the face side of a Lincoln-head penny.
- Which way is the former president facing?
- What words hover above him?
- What words or information appear on either side of him?

You may be surprised to find that although you have looked at these copper-colored coins thousands of times, you have some doubts about what is really on them. The reason you're unsure is that you never considered this information important, and therefore you never stored it.

Okay, it's all right to check your answers against a penny now.

Storage Failure

Because we do not have to remember everything to survive, we filter out what does not interest us, or that we don't consider important. This again is a function of our stimulus filters and our emotions.

Of course, any item that is filtered out does not get stored in long-term memory. If you are asked to remember it, you find that you can't. This is not because your memory is bad, but because you never stored the information in the first place.

An experience that is not stored in long term memory is not an experience at all. In fact, you have no knowledge that it ever happened. When someone suggests that you did or said something that you have not stored, you will deny it with complete conviction.

Have you ever picked up a valuable object, put it away, and then completely forgot where you put it? This is storage failure at its worst!

Lack of Use

A phenomenon that scientists call passive decay suggests that unused memories become less available to us as time passes by.

For example, you may call a good friend on a regular basis. Because you call her a lot, you find it easy to remember her telephone number. However, if she moves to a different town, and changes her phone number, you've got to learn the new number. Over time, you forget the original number because you no longer use it.

As time passes we forget much of what we learn because of the process of passive decay. Many of us at some time during our school years, were required to memorize the names of the presidents, or the names of all the states and their capitals. How many of them can you remember now? Unless you used a memory system to store these things, you've lost this information through passive decay.

Memory researchers have found some evidence that this process may be caused by the actual dissolving of old connections between neurons in order to make new ones, much in the same way that an old building is torn down to make room for a new one. It seems that memory is constantly under construction.

Have you ever known someone who tells you the same stories again and again? The reason is that this is what they remember about their life, and they remember it because they have told the story so frequently. As they have done, you can prevent passive decay by rehearsing important information frequently. In this way the information stays at the threshold of consciousness.

Most memory researchers have adopted the slogan, "Use it or lose it!" Of course, they are referring to brain activity in individuals.

Repression

Simply put, repression is the process of avoiding unpleasant memories. It is an automatic forgetting mechanism that allows us to ignore things that don't agree with our self-image.

This process sometimes spawns arguments, as when someone accuses you of having done or said something, and you vehemently deny ever having done it.

Even though you may not remember these things, the emotional component of the memories are not forgotten. And these emotions affect your ability to record new information about yourself.

For example, if you see yourself as an intelligent, sensitive, emotionally mature individual, you tend to repress every stupid, insensitive, immature thing that you have done.

Conversely, if you see yourself as an incompetent fool, you will repress all the intelligent and successful things you have done, and remember your blunders.

Unpleasant emotions cause you to avoid situations that you remember as painful. Therefore, you may shy away from learning something because of the anticipated pain.

Some fears and phobias may be caused by repressed experiences. There is evidence, for example, that some agoraphobics lost a parent or loved one during their childhood. The forgotten trauma of the loss later manifests itself in panic attacks whenever the traumatized person is away from a loved one. Often, when this is pointed out, the phobia goes away.

Contrary to popular belief, repression does not wipe out memories of trauma, or erase entire sections of a person's life. Research suggests that the repression of painful memories is actually caused by the avoidance of thinking about them, not by an active process called repression. The human mind does not hide memories from itself.

The rash of "repressed memory therapies" that exist today are based on the false assumption that abuse memories can be pushed into the unconscious, and that therapy and hypnosis can "de-repress" them. This is absolutely untrue. There is simply no method known to science to recover a lost memory.

Motivated Forgetting

Have you ever forgotten a dentist appointment, a promise, or someone's birthday? If so you may have experienced motivated forgetting. This type of forgetting is based on the desire to forget. Motivated forgetting involves pushing hurt, anger, or fear into the unconscious. These emotions are then dealt with by forgetting material related to them.

This differs from intentional forgetting, where there is a deliberate effort not to remember. Motivated forgetting happens "by accident." The desire to forget is not focused or conscious. This process always involves a negative emotion that has not been acknowledged.

If this concept is difficult to understand, it may help to think about it in terms of motivation to remember. For example, when I was discussing this problem in one of my memory seminars, a student interrupted me and said, "Wait a minute. I forgot to go to my best friend's birthday party a few months ago. I love this person. Are you telling me I deliberately forgot?"

My answer was "Yes." Now, imagine that one of your friends called you and said, "My birthday party is next Tuesday at three o'clock. If you will be there at three, I will give you a cashier's check for $100,000." Do you think you would forget this party? In this case you would be highly motivated to remember.

The things that you forget can be those you decided not to remember. My student may have forgotten the party because she unconsciously decided to dismiss it from her mind. This may have been because of some unconscious hurt or anger towards her friend. She may have avoided discussing this feeling because of fear of hurting her friend, or because of guilt about being angry at someone she obviously loved.

This type of forgetting has been referred to as having a mental block. One patient of mine forgot his wedding anniversary several years in a row. When he was able to recognize and resolve his anger toward his wife, his memory immediately improved.

Intentional Forgetting

Yet another cause of forgetting unpleasant memories is a similar process called intentional forgetting. This is similar to repression, except that it is deliberately controlled. When you have been hurt emotionally or when you have done something embarrassing, you often try not to think about it. This helps you to forget the incident. Sometimes you do this by forcing yourself to think of something else. This helps you to forget by preventing you from reliving the memory, which then allows it to fade through passive decay.

Psychologists suggest that an effective way to forget something is through a process called thought stopping. This involves yelling, "Stop!" whenever you notice yourself thinking an unwanted thought. The emotional intrusion of yelling "stop" prevents the thought from being rehearsed.

The differences between repression, motivated forgetting and intentional forgetting are subtle and unclear. The defining differences involve the automatic nature of repression, the lack of awareness in motivated forgetting, and the deliberate, conscious effort of intentional forgetting.

However, regardless of how the process takes place, the results are always the same — that which is not thought about is eventually forgotten.

Interestingly, intentionally forgotten material disappears from recall, but not from recognition memory. This means that even if you forget an event, you will recognize it the next time it occurs.

Retrieval Failure

All of us have experienced retrieval failure as the "tip-of-the-tongue" phenomenon — that uncanny feeling of knowing that you know something, but not being able to recall it.

This phenomenon shows us that memory retrieval is not an all-or-nothing process. For example, you may see a picture of an actor, and be able to recall the titles of several of his movies, but not his name. Or you may be able to say what letter his name begins with, but not remember the name itself.

This suggests that memory is stored in many different categories, and that each memory may be stored in segments which are distributed in many locations in our brains. We may be able to retrieve one segment, while the other pieces elude us.

It also illustrates that there is a difference between availability and accessibility of information — you may know that you have the information available, you know that you know it, but you just can't seem to make it available to yourself at the time you want it. Memory researchers call this the "feeling of knowing" phenomenon.

This phenomenon also tells us that retrieval of information is not always a conscious process. You know from your own experience that when you encounter a tip-of-the-tongue episode, if you stop trying to remember and go on about your business, the desired information eventually pops into your head.

Retrieval failure is one of the components of memory that increases significantly with age. While psychologists still do not fully understand what causes retrieval failure, one possible reason for it is a process called state dependence.

State Dependence

State dependence is the process of associating emotions, moods, and surroundings with the things that you remember. This means that if you were in a bad mood when you learned something, you will recall it best the next time that you're grumpy. If you were happy when you studied something, you will recall it best the next time that you're feeling cheerful.

If you think about this for a while, you will see how this principle works in your own life. When you are furious at a friend, don't you find it easy to remember everything that he or she has ever done wrong? When you are feeling anxious, don't you find it extremely easy to find things to worry about? When you are depressed, doesn't the world seem to be full of troubles? And when you are feeling good, doesn't the world seem full of great and inspiring things?

Many students have noticed that the minute they leave a classroom after a quiz, all of the answers they couldn't remember popped back into their heads. If this has ever happened to you, you may have said to yourself, "Why couldn't I answer that question? I knew the answer all along!"

The anxiety you felt while taking a test put you in a different state of mind. When you left the room you became more relaxed, which was most likely the state that you were in when you learned the information in the first place.

How many times have you gotten up out of your chair to go do something, only to find yourself standing in the middle of the kitchen without the slightest idea of what you are doing there? Besides feeling very foolish, what did you do when this happened? If you're like most people, you returned to where you started. As you sat down, you immediately remembered why you got up.

When you were seated again, you recreated the state dependent variables under which the thought occurred to you, and this helped you to remember it.

Understanding state dependence can assist you in improving your ability to remember. For example, you can improve your ability to recall test answers if you learn to relax while studying, and to remain calm when you take a test.

You will also increase your ability to remember answers if you take state dependent variables into account when you study. This means becoming aware of what you do while you are studying. It is not a good idea to smoke, drink, or eat, or take any kind of medication while you are studying unless you intend to do the same thing when you take the exam, because all of these things become state dependent variables. (State dependent variables are discussed further in chapter seven.)

What We Forget

It is a lazy Sunday afternoon. You and your family are in the den watching a great old black-and-white movie. Suddenly, onto the screen walks one of your favorite actresses of all time. You look at the screen, turn to your family and say, "Look! That is … Oh! You know,… Oh, you know she was married to that guy … that guy! What's his name? Oh, you know, we saw them both last week in … that movie. What was it?"

By now you are beginning to panic. As the blood leaves your brain and rushes to your face your entire mind goes blank. You can't remember anything.

You do a quick check: "Who am I? Where do I live? Okay I still know that … I guess I'm all right. But what is her name?"

By this time you are on a mission to remember it. You challenge yourself. You go through the entire alphabet. Does it start with A? No! B? You reach Z empty minded. At this point, somebody offers you a Frito, and you forget the whole thing.

It is now Monday afternoon. You are walking down the produce isle of the supermarket. Because you now fear your memory is deteriorating, you carefully check items off your grocery list.

You pick up a head of red cabbage and put it in your cart, but as you glance at the cabbage you suddenly have a flash. Forgetting where you are and what you are doing, you cry loudly, "Marlene Dietrich!"

Several shoppers stop, look at you, look at the cabbage, and say, "I don't see the resemblance." But you don't care. You are filled with relief that the lost name, and your sanity, has been recovered. Take heart, you are not senile. This happens to everyone. In fact surveys show that the most common memory problem is remembering names. But why?

First, names are slippery. They lack semantic links, that is, there is no intrinsic meaning for a person's name. Concrete nouns, such as tree, house, and car have corresponding mental images. Speak or think the word, and a mental picture instantaneously appears. Words like hunger and fear have corresponding feelings. We all know what we mean by these terms. And some names do have this quality. For example, the name Elvis conjures up a picture also. But we may not know a Willy or a Sam and consequently, the words are labels with no meaning.

Remembering names also seems to be affected by brain-cell loss. For some reason, as we age, the part of our brain that retrieves names is the first to falter. Remembering names involves face recognition, face-name linking, reaction time, vocabulary, education, familiarity, storing cues, and retrieval. According to memory researcher Thomas Crook, name recall drops significantly after 40, but from 40 to 60 conjuring names remains stable. After 60 it drops off again. Even with this drop off, we do seem to remember names of people we have seen many times. Very few of us would have difficulty recognizing Bill Clinton.

Lack of Cues

In fact the ability to remember names is facilitated by repeated exposure, which leads to what memory experts call *cue density*. Repeated exposure in many contexts causes cue density. As we are repeatedly exposed to a person's name and face, a group of associations form an internal construct. Over time there are so many paths to this construct that finding our way to the information is effortless.

And this is the secret of recalling someone's name. When you find yourself struggling to recall a name, make a conscious effort to relearn it. Reassociate the name with several cues, and add as many links as you can. Once you have forged new pathways, the name will come effortlessly.

A memory occurs when it is triggered by a cue. For example, if someone begins to talk to you about an old friend, hearing his name triggers memories about your experiences with him.

In everyday language, cues are often called reminders. The string tied around a finger is a popular image of this. A cue might be thought of as a hook that a memory hangs on. For this reason, memories that have many hooks are more easily retrieved than those that have only a few.

If the friend being discussed is a lifelong friend, there may be hundreds of cues that trigger memories about him. But if you only met him a week ago, these cues are few, and memory may be faulty. Of course, this means that the more cues you can attach to a piece of information, the easier it is to remember, and that is one of the cornerstones to memory improvement.

Distortion

Because of our differing individual stimulus filters, we do not see things accurately, but distort them through the lens of our expectations, prejudices, and beliefs. This causes us to modify what actually took place.

Attorneys are very much aware of this phenomenon when it involves eyewitness testimony. They try to get as many witnesses as they can, because they know that several people seeing the same event will have different interpretations of what they saw.

In addition to this immediate distortion, scientists have found that memory is not as permanent and immutable as we once thought. As time passes, memories distort and change radically. This process can cause us to remember something the way we wanted it to be rather than the way it really happened. It can cause us to omit certain facts from a memory and include others, and it can cause us to remember things that never really happened at all.

Have you ever had an argument with someone because you remember them saying something, and they deny saying it? Usually in these cases, the discussion elevates into a shouting match about who was right, and nothing ever gets settled. Both of you insist that you remember things correctly. What has actually happened is that both of you recalled the stored information to the best of your ability, but distortion caused your mind to record things the way that you wanted them to be, rather than the way that they actually occurred.

Scientists believe another cause of distortion is that every time you tell a story, you reconstruct it from your memory. However, you also add knowledge about the world that you have acquired subsequent to the event. This means that a fifty year old person recalling an event that happened when he was five will tell the story in words, phrases and perspectives learned as an adult. This means the story gets edited every time you tell it. Once you have told the story, you re-store it in a new part of the brain. The next time you tell the story, you will recall the most recent version of it. Over time, after many editions, the story may have little resemblance to the actual event. The common phrase we use to describe this is "the big one that got away."

Exercise: Beginnings and Endings

Memory stores information in categories, and tags each item with cues. Here's an exercise that demonstrates how important cues are.

Name the following items that begin with the letter shown:

a flower	P_____
a vegetable	T_____
a girl's name	T_____
a metal	T_____

Name the following items that end with the letter shown.

a flower	_____T
a vegetable	_____S
a girl's name	_____N
a metal	_____R

You probably discovered that the first letter of a word is a much more potent cue than the last letter.

In this chapter we have explored the ways that a normal healthy brain forgets. In the next chapter, we will look at some more serious memory problems. You may wish to test yourself for memory problems with the following questionnaire if you have serious doubts about your memory retention abilities.

Memory Problems Questionnaire

I forget:

1. The name of a movie star I see on television.
2. The name of an old friend.
3. The name of someone I am introducing.
4. The name of someone to whom I was just introduced.
5. The name of an object I am talking about.
6. The name of one of my children.
7. The title of a book I recently read.
8. The title of a movie I recently saw.
9. To take my vitamins.
10. Whether I have taken my medication.
11. Why I just walked into a room.
12. To buy items at a store that I went there to get.
13. To bring important material to a meeting or event.
14. To defrost food for a meal.
15. To keep commitments or promises.
16. To return a phone call.
17. To keep appointments.
18. Where I parked my car.
19. To pay bills on time.
20. To do important tasks and chores.
21. What time it is.
22. Where I put an important object.
23. To turn off my headlights.
24. What I was about to say to someone.
25. Where I was born.
26. If I have already told someone a story.
27. The details of a story I am telling.
28. What day of the week it is.
29. What month it is.
30. Where I am.
31. The plot of a book or movie I have read or seen.
32. Whether I have eaten.
33. A close friend's or relative's birthday.
34. Instructions I have just been given.
35. A good friend's telephone number.
36. To whom I lent something.
37. What I have just read.

This questionnaire is only effective in relationship to the qualitative activity of an individual's brain. Many people who use their minds on intense study or problem solving, are so centered with their thinking that they often become "absent minded." This does not mean they are suffering from incipient Alzheimer's. However, if you answered yes to questions 2, 5, 6, 17, 25, 26, 29, 30, 32, or 35 you should seek further testing.

Chapter Seven

How to Learn New Information

Old minds are like old horses; you must exercise them if you wish to keep them in working order.
John Quincy Adams, U.S. President.

Study is the deliberate effort to memorize or learn new information. The goal of study is to be able to recognize, recall, and reproduce what you have learned.

Why Learn New Information?

This question may seem absurd, but the truth is the majority of us stop learning new information, with the exception of anecdotal bits and pieces and "little facts" the minute we finish school. This is unfortunate because hundreds of research papers have proved that studying and learning new skills is one of the most powerful ways to maintain a healthy memory.

For this reason, I highly recommend that you make a commitment to learn something new each day. Pick a subject you know very little about, and make the decision to master it. Take a class, read a book, attend a seminar — do what ever you like the most — but learn something new.

Don't tell me that you're too old to go to school. When I was in graduate school, a lady in my class got her doctorate at 73 and set up a private practice. You're never too old to learn something.

Why is this so important? Researchers like Marian Diamond have shown clearly that the more the mind is challenged to learn new things, the better that memory functions. Studies show that learning actually increases the number of connections between brain cells, and causes the cells to remain healthy and active.

More recently researchers, at the Albert Einstein College of Medicine in New York City (in a study which took place over a 21 year span) found that participants in the top third in mental activity had a 63 percent lower risk of dementia than those in the bottom third. Scientists at the Rush Alzheimer's Disease Center and Rush-Presbyterian-St. Luke's Medical Center in Chicago found that a mere one point increase in mental activity had a 33 percent reduction of risk for Alzheimer's. Clearly, learning is one of the most important and effective ways to maintain a powerful memory

Even though this is true, it's a sad fact that most of us hate to study. Why is this so?

It isn't that we hate to learn — learning is fun — it's studying that we hate. We hate feeling stupid. We hate the frustration that comes when we can't understand something. We hate having to spend hours on something that we aren't interested in and don't care about.

No matter how long it's been since we went to school, most of us associate studying with school, homework, and taking tests. For these reasons, study seems like drudgery. Everyone remembers walking away from a study session feeling that they hadn't learned anything.

People dislike studying because studying:
- is seen as punishment.
- makes people feel stupid.
- makes people feel frustrated.
- provokes the feeling of failure.
- was never learned properly.
- destroys self esteem.

But take heart. If you follow the suggestions in this section, your ability and desire to learn and explore new exciting fields of knowledge will open mental vistas that you never imagined. Also your desire to study will improve. Consider each one of these suggestions, as they are all proven techniques for improving your study habits. Once you have become an expert at studying, you will enjoy it more.

People who have lived beyond expectation say studying is good because:

- it is stimulating to learn new information.
- you will gain a sense of accomplishment as you begin to master a new subject.
- you will have the feeling that you are doing something good for yourself.
- a class can be a social event where you meet new people.
- this is an opportunity to challenge yourself again and again.
- the class will give you something to share with your friends and loved ones.
- you will keep your memory sharp.

The McArthur study, published in the journal *Psychology and Aging,* investigated more than 1,000 people between the ages of 70 and 80. One of the scientists leading the project was Marilyn Albert, Ph.D., Professor of Psychiatry and Neurology at Harvard Medical School and Director of the Gerontology Research Unit at Massachusetts General Hospital.

Dr. Albert found that continuing education and mental activity, repeated rehearsal of information, and the development of critical thinking skills promote plasticity in the brain. This increases both the number and the strength of synapses (electrochemical connections between neurons). This finding, she pointed out, may explain why people with college degrees consistently appear to be less vulnerable to memory loss and dementia than those with less formal education. These people consistently traveled, played word games, read, and participated in other types of mentally challenging activities throughout life.

As I reported earlier, a *Psychology Today* article by Terry Needles described a woman 105 years old who has learned the value of keeping mentally busy: "Lily Hearst is trim, fit and trilingual. She practices piano an hour a day, a passion she has indulged since she first learned the instrument 99 years ago. At lunchtime she visits the local senior center in Berkeley, California, where she gives regular concerts. She enjoyed rock climbing and skiing when she was younger and now swims for 20 minutes every day. 'At my age, I'm glad I can do that,' says Hearst, who turned 105 in 2002.

"As a centenarian, Hearst belongs to an elite club whose numbers are swelling: There are about 75,000 Americans age 100 and up, and the U.S. Census Bureau projects that figure will rise to some 800,000 by the year 2050. Like many centenarians, Hearst attributes her longevity to good genes and healthful habits. Her parents remained vigorous into their 80s; her sister to age 90. She eschews wheelchairs, eats well ('a grapefruit every morning'), drinks socially and doesn't smoke. Add to that a healthy dose of optimism, and her *modus vivendi* starts to jibe with current findings about lifestyle choices and sustained vitality.

Researchers confirm that genetics need not be the decisive factor in determining how long and how well we live. And a growing body of research suggests that sustained cognitive activity may hold the key to how well we age.

Your immediate goal then, is to make a commitment to keep your mind stimulated. Turn study skills into habits. Once you have done this, you'll automatically do the things necessary for learning effectively.

Structure Your Time

The first and most important factor in learning something new is the structuring of time. Most of us take on new projects thinking we can do a great deal more than we actually can do. This is because we always have more enthusiasm when we begin a project than after we're halfway through it. So don't overload yourself; take on a project you can handle.

Overloading the day ruins the enjoyment of it. Obviously, if you have more things to do than you have hours to do them in, you won't get all of your work done. But in addition to not completing your work, you rush through the work you do attempt, feeling distracted and anxious.

When you overload your day, you end up doing poorly in everything. Instead of concentrating on the things you are doing, you worry about what you still need to do, and feel guilty about what you didn't do. And at the end of the day, you can't remember anything that you did. If you've ever reached the bottom of a page only to realize you have no idea what you just read, you know how preoccupation destroys concentration.

It is important to get a realistic picture of how long it takes to accomplish certain tasks. Experience with hundreds of people has taught me that most of us are very bad at estimating how long things take.

The best way to find out how long a task actually takes is to do the task and time yourself. For example, find out how long it takes you to read a page in a book, or find out how long it takes you to do the laundry.

Don't fret if it takes you longer to do something than it takes someone else. No matter how much time it takes you, if you organize your time well, and don't take on more work than you can handle, you'll have enough time to finish everything.

Make a structured daily schedule of activities. This schedule should include study time and your activity schedule for each day.

Don't forget to schedule in fun along with daily and weekly obligations. No one looks forward to a day that contains only work.

People tell me that they object to scheduling their entire day. They claim that schedules are too restricting. They want to be able to be free to do what they want to do when they feel like it.

This sounds good, but it just isn't true.

First of all, it is you who is making this schedule, so you actually do decide what you will do and when. Second, you already know that you do put off or forget to do things you don't like to do. So, if you wait until you feel like doing it, it never gets done.

Third, you will find that after you begin to schedule your time, you will actually feel more free to do the things you want to do. It is much easier to enjoy leisure time when you don't have that guilty feeling in the back of your mind that your obligations haven't been met.

Fourth, scheduling improves self-esteem, reduces stress, is an effective antidepressant, and greatly improves memory.

Even if you are retired, schedules are important. As you check off the things you do each day, you get a feeling of accomplishment and satisfaction. You feel productive. This is very different from the feeling of rushing through a day, forgetting important things, going to bed each night wondering where the time went, and feeling like the day was wasted.

Planning the day has long term effects too. Keeping a schedule allows you to look back over the weeks and months to remind yourself of all the things you have accomplished. This helps you deal with that "where did the time go?" feeling.

Most importantly, schedules reduce anxiety and improve the ability to concentrate, learn, and remember.

Although keeping a schedule may be a bother at first, after a few weeks of scheduling, planning the day will become a natural thing, and you won't think of it as a chore.

School as a Source of Learning

Taking a class is one of the most effective ways to keep your memory sharp. The stimulation of new information, new skills, and new people keeps the mind alert.

If you decide to take a class or seminar, go to all of the sessions. Even if you don't enjoy a certain session, resist the temptation to skip it, and show up every time. Remind yourself of the reason you took the class in the first place — to improve your memory. Don't worry about how well you do in the class. Remember that your goal is to learn something, not to be the smartest person in the room.

Prepare a Study Environment

Where and when you pursue learning is just as important as how you absorb new information. Studying should be done in a quiet, private place where there are no distractions or interruptions. If you study at home, find a place away from other family members and other distractions, such as the TV or radio.

Tell friends, neighbors and relatives that you have set aside a certain time to study, and you don't wish to be disturbed. This is sometimes not enough, however, and people may still drop over or call you during your study time. Make a firm commitment not to answer the door or telephone during your study time. After everyone realizes that you are serious about not being disturbed, they will quit interrupting you, and your time will be your own.

I strongly recommend that you do not have a TV or radio playing when you are studying. Although you may be used to this and enjoy it, it detracts from the absorption of new learning, and it will break your concentration.

If you have taught yourself to study or read with the radio on, it may be a tough habit to break. However, after a few weeks of practice, you will get used to the silence, and have better results in learning and retention.

Research on aging and memory shows that the older we get, the more difficult it becomes to filter out distractions, so minimize them.

Study Do's and Don'ts

- Do structure your time, using a realistic assessment of how much you can accomplish.
- Don't miss classes.
- Do create a quiet place for study where you will not be disturbed.
- Do sit at an uncluttered desk or table as you study.
- Do try to study at the same place at the same time each day.
- Don't skip meals.
- Do study at the times of the day when you naturally have more energy.
- Don't skimp on sleep.

Create a Study Space

Study at a desk or table, and sit in a chair. Don't study standing up, lying down, or sprawled out on a bed. Although these positions may be appealing to you, you will tire faster than you will sitting in a chair at a study table, and you'll get less done. Have you ever fallen asleep while reading? Sitting up makes this less likely.

Make sure that your study table or desk is large enough to hold all the materials that you need. See that your table or desk does not face an open window or door, both of which can be a source of distraction. However, some learning experts recommend a viewing window on a quiet garden scene is conducive to quiet inspiration. Have all of your materials and study tools such as pens, pencils, erasers and rulers, available to you before you begin studying. This eliminates interruptions in your work because you are looking around for the item you need.

Clear the desk of everything that isn't needed for the subject you are studying. Clutter makes it hard to concentrate, and if you put other unrelated material on your desk, it will be a constant reminder of what you have not yet finished.

Make sure that the lighting is adequate, and that the room temperature is comfortable. You will have less ability to concentrate in a room that is too cold, or too warm.

Go to the Library

If you don't have a good study space in your home, consider studying in your nearest library. Surveys show that people learn more effectively when they study in libraries.

There are several reasons why a library is a good place to study:

• Studying in a library gets you out of your house. It's a way to break the habit of isolation and boredom, as well as getting you away from all the distractions you find at home, such as television, the refrigerator, or a friendly looking couch.

• Because you are away from home, you are less likely to be interrupted. People rarely drop by the library just to visit you.

• A library is a place of learning, and just walking into a library puts you in the right frame. Those who study in libraries find that they get more done in less time for these reasons.

Develop a "Study Set"

Study the same subject in the same place, at the same time of day if possible. Doing this will allow you to develop what psychologists call a response set, that will help put you in the right frame of mind to study. Objects in your environment, and feelings that you experience at a certain time of day can act as cues to tell you that it is time to study. This will happen in the same way that turning on the television prompts some people to think that it is time to eat. Once you do develop this study habit, sitting down at your desk at three o'clock will automatically put you in the mood to learn.

Food and Learning

What and when you eat can have an effect on your ability to learn. It is not a good idea to study right after you have eaten a heavy meal, as this tends to make you feel tired and sluggish, and you won't pay attention to what you are studying. On the other hand, it is not a good idea to skip meals in order to try to get more done.

Skipping meals can result in low blood sugar. Low blood sugar makes it harder to concentrate, makes you easily irritated and frustrated, and will cause you to walk away from your study session with the feeling that the work is too much to deal with.

When the negative feelings caused by low blood sugar happen at the same time that you are studying, you'll associate those feelings with what you are studying, and you'll avoid that subject in the future, without ever really knowing why you don't like it.

Meals high in carbohydrate can make you drowsy, while a high protein meal can sharpen your mind. It's also been shown that eating immediately after you study can improve memory storage. Researchers have found that eating causes the release of the hormone cholecystokinin, which improves memory.

As mentioned earlier in this book, fragrances become associated with information and can be used as a study aid. Smelling citrus, mint, or chocolate that you have placed in your pocket while you study can help you recall information when you use the same scent during a test.

Drugs and Learning

During an intense study period, some people smoke cigarettes and drink a lot of coffee. Both of these drugs affect your memory and your ability to study. When you study under the influence of drugs such as nicotine, caffeine, or other stimulants, you create a situation that is called state dependence.

State dependence is the phenomenon of not being able to recall material that you learned while in a certain state of mind until you are in that state again. If you're using stimulants while studying, you will have trouble remembering what you studied unless you use the same stimulants again. This makes you dependent on a drug to be able to recall what you have learned, which is a less than desirable situation. For this reason, you should try to avoid studying while under the influence of any drug. (More information on caffeine and smoking appear in a later chapter.)

Biological Clocks

Whenever it's possible, arrange your study time to fit your energy cycle. All of us have a natural daily energy cycle. For most of us, this cycle has two peaks, one in the morning, and one in the evening. There is usually a slump between the peaks, which occurs in mid-afternoon, often about two o'clock. If you are a morning person, the best time to study is before noon, when you are at your energy peak. If you are a night person, the best time to study is in the evening, usually somewhere between three in the afternoon and ten at night.

For most of us, the time period from about noon to three is our midday slump. During this time of day the ability to concentrate is low. Studying during your midday slump will result in poorly learned material, or an unintended nap! Scheduling your study time to match your energy peaks will increase your ability to concentrate, and increase your tolerance for frustration. (More about this in chapter eleven.)

Sleep and Memory

The amount of sleep that you get can also affect your ability to absorb and retain new information. Lack of sleep makes for inefficient study and poor memory. Many people get into the habit of studying late at night, when things are quiet, and others are sleeping.

Aside from the fact that your energy and tolerance for frustration are lower at night, if you study late, and have to do something important in the morning, you won't get enough sleep.

Lack of sleep results in chronic fatigue, and this lowers your resistance to illness. It also can result in extreme nervousness and irritability and interferes with the ability to concentrate.

Each of us has a minimum number of hours required for proper rest. While a few people can get by on as little as six or seven hours of sleep a night, others need as much as ten hours of sleep each night in order to feel rested.

Don't feel guilty or lazy if you require more sleep than some of your friends. Your sleep habits are set biologically, and it is a myth that we all need eight hours sleep. Robbing your body of as little as a half hour's sleep can impair concentration.

Daniel Press at Beth Israel Deaconess Medical Center has found that sleep deprived subjects could not properly store new memories. Subjects who were deprived of adequate sleep showed no improvement in learning over a five day period, while those who got adequate sleep improved each day,

If you require an alarm clock to wake you up each morning, you may in fact not be getting enough sleep. People who shortchange themselves on sleep experience sleep rebound, which causes a strong urge to fall asleep during the day, interferes with attention, and increases sleep need the next night.

If you are not getting enough rest, and are trying to concentrate when you are tired and irritable, you may begin to associate the subject that you are studying with the irritability. Later you may find yourself avoiding that subject, thinking that it is the cause of the irritation. In reality you are irritated merely because you are tired.

The Study Process

You will become a better learner and enjoy the process more if you consider the following crucial factors:

Intend to Remember

When you want to record something in your memory that you don't find interesting, you must do so with conscious, deliberate intent. To do this, prepare yourself for memorizing, by telling yourself that you are going to remember. If possible, sit quietly for a few moments before you start, and relax. Take a few deep breaths, clear your mind, and tell yourself that you are about to memorize something, and that you are going to remember it perfectly. While this might seem silly, think of what you normally do. Many people prepare for memorizing by saying things like, "Boy, this stuff is boring. I'll never remember it!" That sounds even sillier. Since you already talk to yourself, learn to do so in a positive manner.

Write it Down

Writing something down triples the odds that you will remember it. Writing involves visual, motor, and informational memory, and forces you to pay attention to what you want to learn. People who take notes learn significantly faster than those who don't.

Get Organized

How you structure your learning sessions affects how much you accomplish during that session. Once you have a place and a time in which to study, make a study plan. Know in advance what it is you intend to accomplish during your study session, and write these things down.

If you are planning to study more than one subject, tackle the most difficult one first. In this way your energy level and tolerance for frustration will be higher when you are working on difficult material. If you save the most difficult subject for last, you'll be tired before you even start, and the work will seem more difficult than it actually is. When this happens, you'll give up too easily, and avoid the subject completely.

Keep Focused

When interest is low, the human attention span is quite short. The brain has an automatic mechanism which diverts attention from unimportant information. (See the section in chapter three on the orienting response.) The way to force yourself to pay attention is to read the material out loud, and write down what you want to remember. Doing this forces you to pay attention.

Educators have discovered that the most effective way to learn something is by using the spaced practice method. Spend a short time reading the material, take a break, and look at it again. Do this many times throughout the day.

During your allotted study time, break up your study sessions into short periods of time — about twelve to fifteen minutes each. This is the best time span for maximum concentration.

When you find your attention repeatedly wandering, take a break and try again later. Separate different subjects with breaks also. This will allow you to prepare yourself mentally for the next subject.

Set Reasonable Goals

Set a learning goal for each short study period. For example, tell yourself that in the next hour you will have memorized and learned how to use five French verbs if a foreign language interests you. Don't expect to memorize an entire book at one sitting. You will set yourself up for failure. At the end of that study period, test yourself to see that you've accomplished your goal. If you find that you are not reaching your goals, set them lower.

Make Sure What You're Learning Means Something

It's more likely that you will remember a sentence spoken in English than one spoken in Russian. The things we remember easily are things that we already understand.

For example, if you are a baseball fan, you can watch a game on television and later tell your friends about it in vivid detail. You can do this because you already have an understanding of the rules of the game. On the other hand, you might attend a lecture on theoretical physics and walk away not remembering a thing.

Because memory works on the principle of association, it is important that you understand something about the material before you can memorize it. This enables you to associate the material with something you already know.

For this reason, it's important that you develop a broad background on the subject that you need to assimilate. This means that you must spend some time learning the basics about that subject before you attempt to memorize the new information. One of my clients was a secretary in a company that sold hydraulic equipment. One of her duties was to read reports that came to the office, and give her boss a verbal summary of what she had read. She was having a terrible time doing this because she could not remember the technical terms in the reports.

Upon my suggestion, she bought an introductory textbook on hydraulics, and read it every night after work. As she began to understand the theory of hydraulics, she was able to remember the terminology, because now she understood what the words meant.

Become an expert in the area that you want to master, and you will memorize new material easily. Take pride in your expertise, and it will motivate you to remember.

Repeat and Rehearse

You know that if you see or hear something enough, you remember it whether you want to or not. Just think of all the TV and radio commercials you've learned without any conscious effort. Use the principle of overlearning. Tape the information and play it to yourself twenty times a day. Put it on flash cards and tape them up everywhere.

Test Yourself

Using self tests is an excellent way to discover how much you have learned. It also allows you to eliminate studying material you already know. Flash cards are a good system of self-testing. But the best way to verify that you have learned something is to explain it to someone else. If you can put what you have learned in your own words, you know that it has been stored in your long term memory.

Above All, Have Fun

The learning methods you've read about in this chapter will indeed help you absorb new material more quickly and effectively. However, the whole idea about learning is to stretch your mind and imagination to improve your memory and, above all, to keep that magical brain of yours active. Unchallenged, unused for *investigative thinking,* your brain, like the tires on an old car which hasn't been driven for a long time, will lose air and become soft.

So, the most important message of this chapter is for you to investigate subjects to learn about that really intrigue you. As you gain knowledge from your learning you will discover new meaning in your life, new excitement and new horizons to explore that are not barred to you at any age.

Chapter Eight

How to Stop Losing and Forgetting Things

How many hours of your life have you wasted looking for lost sunglasses, car keys, your shoes, or your wallet or purse? Time management experts say that the average person spends about four weeks per year looking for misplaced objects!

Looking for lost objects is not only time wasting, it's also frustrating. So why do you find yourself doing this again and again?

You lose things for three reasons.

First, you have never made a commitment to fix the problem. In fact, you only become aware of the problem when it's happening. What you need to do is make a commitment right now to stop losing things.

Second, without being aware of it, you've developed habits that help you lose things. For example, you put your keys down wherever you feel like putting them. You set your sunglasses down anywhere when you take them off. You put important papers on any available flat space.

Third, you put things down without paying attention to what you are doing. You remember only what you consciously pay attention to, so it's not surprising that you can't remember what you've done. For this reason, many inanimate objects seem to roam aimlessly around the house.

You will stop losing things when you foster habits in yourself that help you find them.

Here are some solutions:

- First and most importantly, make a list of the things that you keep losing. Next to each item on the list, write down what you intend to do to stop losing it. Write down the place where you will store each item. Keep this list posted where you can see it so that it becomes a reminder of where things are.
- Establish a specific place for each item, and always put things in their place. Doing this involves breaking old, unconscious habits. To break these habits, put signs up around the house to remind you to put things in their proper place. For example, make a sign that says "The bills go here."
- Put labels on cabinets and drawers that tell you what is to be stored in them. Label storage boxes and canisters also, so you know what they contain.
- Use clear plastic storage boxes for small items like screws and buttons, and label them also.
- Put labels with your name, address and phone number on objects that you often take out of the house, such as umbrellas and glasses. This increases the odds that you will get them back if you do forget them.
- When you are out of your house, carry everything in one bag if possible, and attach the bag to your clothing so that you can't lose it.
- When you sit down in a restaurant, put the bag on the table so it is in plain sight. This makes it hard to forget. If you must carry several items with you, know how many items you left with, make a checklist of them before you leave the house, and look at the list each time you leave a location.
- Teach yourself to look at what you are doing, and say out loud exactly where you are putting something. When you put your keys on the coffee table, say out loud, "I'm putting my keys on the coffee table." Verbalizing what you are doing insures that you are paying attention to your actions. While you might laugh at this idea, when you put it into action, you will be surprised at how few are the things you lose in the future. Practice recalling where you put things just to make sure you remember.
- Whenever possible, buy several of what you often lose. This works well for items like pens, scissors, tape, glue, batteries, and other

utility items. Put some of the items in several places around your house and office. It will save you hours of frustration. For example, if you have a pair of scissors in every room in your house, you won't have to wander from room to room looking for them.

- Protect yourself from family thievery by buying a set of household items for each family member. Make each member responsible for his or her own scissors, pencils, and glue.

- When you are parking your car in a large parking structure, write down where the car is parked on the parking ticket, and put the ticket in your pocket. Look around the area and make a mental note of any landmarks that you can associate with the car's location.

- Finally, don't loan anyone anything you value without writing a dated note to yourself about to whom you've loaned an item. If you don't do this, you may never see it again, and you won't know who to ask.

- If you have lost something, go back in time to the last time you remember seeing it. Retrace your steps until you happen upon it. If this doesn't work, imagine where you would put the item if you had it, and look there. Start with the obvious places, and work towards the less likely spots.

- If you have to do this with an item more than once, add it to your list of frequently lost items.

Exercise: Hide and Seek

Here's an exercise to test your ability to remember where you put things.

Put about ten items away one evening.

Before you go to bed, write down where you stowed these objects.

The next day, attempt to recover all of the items without looking at the list.

This exercise will help you get into the habit of making mental notes about where you put things.

Have you ever had someone tell you, "It's right under your nose."? Psychologist Yvette Tenny researched people's experiences searching for lost objects. She discovered that many times the object was in fact in the very place a person had looked. he had simply failed to recognize it. The older a person is, the more likely this will occur. She felt that this experience was caused by a decrease in perceptual ability that occurs with age. There is nothing alarming about this, but it helps to know that it happens. Dr. Tenny's findings suggest that the next time you lose something, you might try looking in the same spot twice.

How to Stop Forgetting Things

Now that you are armed with ideas that will help you stop losing things, here are some additional tips that will help you kick the habit of forgetting:

- When a thought occurs to you that you should do something, do it immediately. If you do not, you will forget. If you cannot do it immediately, write it down in an appointment book, so that you will see it later that day. When this idea occurred to me, I immediately wrote it down in this book.
- Use a daily medication and nutritional supplement box to insure that you have taken the proper pills each day. Fill the box at the end of each week.
- Use an alarm clock to remind you to do important things. Set several alarms around the house as reminders for important events. For example, if you need to call someone at seven, set the alarm for that time. If needed, put a note next to the alarm so that when you shut it off, you will remember why you set it.
- Use an appointment book whether you work or not. The book adds structure to your day and reminds you what you need to do, and what you have done.
- Record your thoughts, ideas, and things to do on tape. Establish a time of day to play the tape back and write the material down in your daily planning book.
- When writing notes to yourself, compose them as if you were writing them to someone else. This will allow you to understand them when you read them later. For example, instead of writing

"Call Dick at 7:30," write, "You talked to Dick Smith today about the computer he wants to sell. Call him at 7:30 on Tuesday, April 20, and tell him when you will pick it up."

- Attach your car keys to items you need to take with you when you leave the house. This way you cannot leave without them.
- When you are cooking, do not answer the door or telephone, or go into another room to watch television. Stay at the stove and you won't burn things (including your house!).
- Whenever you are cooking something that must be timed, use a timer with an alarm. Don't rely on remembering to look at the clock — you are asking for trouble, and you will spoil your meal.

With a little added effort you can greatly reduce the amount of things you lose and forget. You'll feel less frustrated as a result. And think of all the time you will save yourself.

Remembering Names

Because forgetting names is the most common memory problem, I'd like to review some tips for correcting it. The trick is to make a special effort to remember them.

Before you go to any social gathering, review the names of the people you expect to see. If you can't bring the names to mind, ask someone else for the information. You might even call your host and get a guest list. Rehearse the names in your mind several times. Before you arrive at the event, form memory links by linking things you know about the individual with her name. Gather personal information about new people you meet, and form a link between the data and the name. For example, Barry is a golfer, so think of him burying his clubs after a bad game. When possible, collect business cards from each person you meet. Write information about the person on the back of the card to remind you who he is.

Keep a small "name bank" book with the names, descriptions, and personal information about people you will see again. Make a habit of reviewing the book frequently.

Everyone has said at some time, "I can never remember his name." If you repeatedly forget a certain person's name, resolve to fix the problem. Take a few moments to visualize the person. Rehearse the name several times. Think of someone else with the same name and say to yourself something like, "His name is Jerry, just like Jerry Clark next door."

Chapter Nine

Factors for Maximizing Memory

I know of no more encouraging fact than the unquestionable ability of man to elevate his life by conscious endeavor.
— Henry David Thoreau (1817–1862)

Whenever you're having difficulty remembering anything, ask yourself the following questions.

Am I Paying Attention?

Make a conscious effort to focus on the material you wish to memorize. One way to do this is to say out loud whatever you wish to remember. Saying things out loud forces you to pay attention.

Am I Interested?

Interest in the subject is the most important deciding factor as to whether or not you will remember something. The more interested you are in something the easier it is to remember. You can increase your interest in something simply by learning more about it. For example, sports fans remember a remarkable amount of information about sports figures and scores because they are emotionally invested in them. Because they already know a lot about the field, new information comes easy.

Is it Arousing?

The things that we are interested in stir our emotions. This is why you are able to remember the plot of a good movie more easily than a chapter in your history book. If you absolutely can't get aroused about the material, get aroused by challenging yourself to remember it. Dare yourself to remember.

Is it Important?

Most of us have no trouble remembering to pick up our paychecks. We remember things that are important to us. You can increase the importance of something if you focus on the benefits of remembering it. In other words, what's the payoff?

Am I Motivated to Remember?

If you know that you will benefit by remembering something, you are more motivated to remember it. For example, if someone told you that she would pay you $5,000 for remembering her name the next time you saw her, you would most likely make a special effort to remember it.

If you can't clearly see the payoff for remembering something, use the information as an opportunity to practice the memory techniques you learned in this book. Another way to get motivated about remembering something is to think of the consequences of remembering or forgetting it.

For example, if you need to get a few things from the store after work, think of the benefits of remembering to do it. If you do remember, you will save yourself an extra trip. Now think of the consequences of not remembering. If you forget, you must go back to the store, and besides wasting time, you might make someone angry. In other words, remembering will make things easier on you.

What Is My Attitude?

A negative attitude about a piece of information lowers your chances of remembering. A negative attitude can cause you to ignore something that might be important to remember. You may even actively avoid the subject you need to remember. Have you ever found yourself saying, "I keep forgetting to do such and such," or, "No matter how much I promise myself I won't forget it, I still do." This kind of negative programming is like a self-fulfilling prophesy. If you tell yourself that you can't remember something, you probably won't.

Is it Weird or Different?

You remember things that are unusual or out of the ordinary. For example, if you meet ten people a day, you might have trouble remembering their names, but if one of them was seven feet tall with green hair, you will remember her because she was different.

You can make an ordinary thing novel by learning it a new way. For example, one of my students was studying accounting. She made it interesting by cutting her textbook into pieces, and sticking the pieces up all over her house.

Did I Write it Down?

You will triple the odds of remembering something simply by writing it down. Writing involves focused attention, motor memory, and visual memory, three things that insure memory storage.

Did I Repeat it?

Advertisers know that repeated messages are remembered. Use this fact to insure memory storage. Repeat the desired material several times during the day, and it will record itself in long term memory.

Am I Using a System?

Research studies show that the older one gets, the less likely it is that they use a memory system. Learning and using memory systems can double your memory in just a few days. For information on memory systems, read the next chapter.

Factors Affecting Memory

External Factors

- The amount of interfering stimuli
- The novelty of the event
- The emotional impact
- The complexity of the event
- The structure of the event (is it logical or chaotic?)
- The number of times the event occurs

Internal Factors

- Interest in the event
- Deliberate intent to remember
- Paying attention
- Your personal level of background knowledge
- Level of arousal
- Your internal model for organizing the data
- Your mood

Chapter Ten

Memory Systems

Almost every survey of memory problems shows one major difference between people over forty and the younger population — the majority of people over forty do not use memory systems. In fact, most adults in the over-forty group have never been taught these systems, and have little interest in learning them.

This is unfortunate, because when researchers looked at the differences between older people with memory problems and those who had superior memories, they again found one glaring difference — those with good memories used memory systems.

Even though most adults have never heard of these systems, they are far from new. In fact, most memory systems date back at least to the era of ancient Greece.

Before paper and the printing press were invented, all important information had to be memorized. Early Greek and Roman teachers and orators were able to memorize large amounts of information by using some simple memory techniques. Most of these techniques are still in use today.

Although there are many different kinds of memory systems, all take advantage of the basic properties of memory — association and visualization.

Association

When you are exposed to a new piece of information, your mind automatically executes a search for associations. You make associations through the applications of several principles: similarity, contrast, contiguity, continuity, and synesthesia.

The quality of similarity insures that our minds automatically link any bits of information that share characteristics. These similarities may be obvious, as linking words that rhyme, or may be as subtle as your Uncle Oscar's resemblance to Victor Mature.

The quality of contrast causes us to link things with their perceived opposites. For example, the word "hot" instantly brings to mind "cold."

The quality of association by *contiguity* occurs when two or more things happen together in time and place. Even though they have no intrinsic similarity, they become associated because they happened together. Advertisers have used this quality of the mind for years — the shiny new car will get us the pretty girl. And even though we say we know better, our mind makes the link.

This is also why cars are often named after exotic animals like Jaguar, Mustang, and Cobra. We know the car is not the animal, but the association makes them attractive. This is why you will never see a car called the Ford Pig.

Information presented out of context often lacks contiguity and bewilders us. Most likely you have had the experience of passing a person on the street, recognizing them, but not being able to remember who they are. Later on, you see them where they work, and immediately remember who they are. This has sometimes been called the *butcher-on-the-bus phenomenon.*

This shows us that there is a difference between two qualities of memory — familiarity and recollection. Familiarity occurs by exposure, but recollection occurs by association.

Associations based on *continuity* are similar to contiguous associations. With continuity things become linked because of their order and sequence. Obvious examples of this are the alphabet and the number system. We know the sequence of our alphabet and number system not because of any intrinsic need for the letters to be in a certain order — we just learned them that way. If you don't believe this try reciting the alphabet backwards.

Our language contains specific structures also. A sentence is comprehensible not only because we understand the words, but because we anticipate its structure. A string of words out of sequence is much more difficult to remember than a proper sentence or a rhyme.

Less obvious are things like story-telling. In our culture, we learn to tell stories in a specific way, with a clear beginning, middle, and end. Stories in which one element is missing, or where the parts are out of sequence, are much harder to comprehend and remember. By the time we are four years old, we have learned how to structure a story properly.

Synesthetic associations are those that cross over sensory boundaries. People who have a highly developed synesthetic sense can literally see noises, taste colors, and feel music.

These types of associations make no intrinsic sense, but are very real and often quite vivid. For example, a woman I was working with told me, "My boyfriend reminds me of mashed potatoes." She could not tell me why, but every time she thought of him, mashed potatoes came to mind. And ever since I was a kid, Frankie Avalon has reminded me of Vienna sausage.

Since memory already makes these kinds of associations unconsciously and automatically, it makes sense to start deliberately and consciously using this ability to help memory. Therefore, the first key to remembering is to use these innate linking propensities. When you are confronted with a new piece of information, ask your self. "What does this remind me of? What can I associate it with?"

Here are some examples of how association helps memory:

Read the following number:

$$1\ 7\ 7\ 6\ 1\ 9\ 8\ 4\ 2\ 0\ 0\ 1\ 1\ 0\ 5$$

Now close your eyes and repeat the number.

You probably could not do this. One of the reasons for this is that 15 digits is too much for you to store in your short-term memory.

One way to remember this number is to cut it into pieces. This cutting of information into digestible segments is what memory experts call *chunking*.

Scan the number and associate it with things that you already know. In my memory seminars, some of the attendees usually notice that the first twelve digits contain dates which are the titles of movies:

1776 1984 2001

That's a great way to remember these numbers. Now for the last three digits, 105, visualize yourself wearing a pair of Levi's 501's backwards.

To remember the whole number, think of yourself seeing the movies, 1776, 1984 and 2001 while wearing your Levi's 501's backwards (for 105).

Let's do it another way, by cutting the number into five pieces. Five is less than seven, the maximum number you can process with your short term memory.

Here are the chunks:

177 619 842 001 105

Now let's make a specific association with each chunk. Look at the first three digits, 177. Here's an association one of my students gave me. He said that's what he drank every day after work: one seven and seven.

The second three numbers, 619, is the area code for San Diego. If you live in California, this association is immediate.

The third three numbers, 842, can be remembered as "ate for two." The fourth three digits are 001, which is James Bond's grandfather. The fifth three digits, 105, is a pair of blue jeans backwards (again think of Levi's 501's).

Now let's take this second group of associations and link them together. To do this, we'll use the second automatic property of memory, visualization.

Visualization

Visualizing is the ability to form pictures in your mind. Some of you know that you are good visualizers, and some of you believe that you are poor at visualizing, or that you can't visualize at all. For the majority of us, visual memory is the most effective type of memory. Because of this, most memory systems are based on visual processing.

For reasons not yet completely understood, as people age, they use their visualization skills less. This loss of visual imagery is a major contributor to age associated memory impairment. Everyone has this ability, and everyone can improve it with practice.

In order to demonstrate that this is true, I'm going to ask you to participate in a little experiment.

Close your eyes, and count the number of windows in your house. Take a moment to mentally travel from room to room, and tally the number of windows that you see.

How many windows did you count? In order for you to do this exercise, you had to form a mental picture. This means that you are able to visualize, and it also means that you will be able to use the memory systems that I am about to describe.

The Link System

The link system of memorization uses visualization and association to link together unrelated items on a list. Telling a story is more interesting than memorizing a list, and enhances your ability to memorize any list of words. The link system uses visual links to tie together unrelated items. Here's how it works.

Let's go back now to that 15 digit number. In your imagination, see a man at a bar drinking one seven and seven. He picks up the phone on the bar to call San Diego. After he ate for two (see him sitting with a huge pile of food in front of him), he becomes upset when he sees James Bond's grandfather thrown out of the bar for wearing his Levi's backwards.

You now have formed a visual memory of the number. Once these pictures are in place, this number will stay in your memory forever.

Now, take a moment to read the following list of words:

1.	Fish	6.	House
2.	Bed	7.	Fork
3.	Table	8.	Window
4.	Bottle	9.	Knee
5.	Paper	10.	Fly

These words are not related to one another in any logical way. There is no similarity or contiguity. They do not tell a story, and would be difficult to remember without a system. But by using the link system, the words will become indelibly associated forever. As you read each item do the following:

1. Fish. See a six foot tall albacore tuna walking through his house.
2. Bed. The fish walks into his bedroom, and plops down on his California king size water bed.
3. Table. His wife comes in carrying his breakfast on a small table, and places it on his bed.
4. Bottle. On the table is a small brown wine bottle.
5. Paper. Out of the neck of the bottle sticks a rolled up sheet of paper.
6. House. Imagine taking the paper out of the bottle and flattening it out. On the paper is a picture of Mr. and Mrs. Fish's house.
7. Fork. You immediately notice that there is a 27 foot fork sticking out of the top of the house.
8. Window. When you look closely at this giant fork, you notice that cut into the end of the handle is a window.
9. Knee. Sticking through the window is a large human knee.
10. Fly. On the kneecap is a fly.

Once you have formed these associative and visual links in your mind, you have memorized the list. Not only that, but you will probably discover that you can now recite the list forwards and backwards. Try it.

The Locus System

The locus system involves associating the things that you wish to remember with familiar landmarks in your environment. For demonstration purposes, let's memorize a short shopping list. It consists of ten items. Without a memory system, it is difficult for you to remember ten items, because your short term memory can only hold seven or eight items.

See how many of the items on the shopping list you can remember without writing them down.

- broccoli
- lettuce
- mayonnaise
- hot dogs
- peanut butter
- potato chips
- tomatoes
- hamburger
- a copy of the Enquirer
- a jar of mustard

A moment ago you counted the windows in your house. Now, associate each item on the list with a window in your house. Get a clear picture of the item in the window. Once this picture has been solidified, a mental walk through the house will remind you of the items. (If you live in a place which doesn't have enough windows, you can use items of furniture.)

Reading to Remember

How many times have you found yourself at the bottom of a page, with absolutely no memory of what you have just read? Although we have all done this when reading for pleasure, it is even more common when reading a textbook. People hate to read textbooks because many of them are boring and complicated. You will save time and increase your comprehension of your reading material if you approach reading with a plan.

Most people object to plans, and prefer to read a chapter as they would a novel. They unrealistically hope that one reading will allow them to absorb all the information. Others use a high-lighter to mark the things they feel are important. Most do this with the intent to read the chapter again later. Of course, they rarely do, and all they get for this effort is a book full of marks.

Taking notes while you read eliminates these problems. Taking notes forces you to pay attention to what you are reading. And reading your notes is much easier than rereading an entire chapter.

A chapter of text is prestructured, but you can impose your own structure on the material. For example, history is the study and interpretation of the past. Important information in history consists of names, dates, deeds and events. Divide a piece of paper into four columns with the headings:

NAMES   DATES   DEEDS   EVENTS

Now skim through the chapter and list all material that belongs under each of these headings. In this manner, with one reading, you've extracted all the important information from the chapter.

I also find it very useful to use a tape or digital recorder when I am reading to retain information. Every time I come across a point I feel I should remember, I record it. When I'm finished reading, I have an audio summary of what I want to know. In addition I can play it back in my car as many times as necessary to memorize it.

The Key Word System

The key word system is used in memorizing reading material and speeches. It involves extracting key words from the text to act as hooks to recover the material. This is similar to making an outline. Doing this doubles the probability that you will remember the material. For example, take the paragraph topics of the chapter or the speech, and then connect them using the link system described earlier in this chapter. This simple tool can prevent you from losing your train of thought when giving a presentation.

The Phonetic Code System

The phonetic code system is one of the most widely used memory techniques. It involves assigning a number value to the consonant sounds in the English language. In this manner, long strings of numbers can be transformed into familiar words. This technique allows you to memorize long numbers almost instantly. See the chart for the letter codes on the next page.

Through the use of this system, any number can be converted into a few words that result in effortless recall.

To use this system, simply assign the appropriate letters to the number you wish to memorize.

For example, my phone number is 310-230-2601. Possible corresponding letters to this number are MDS-NMS-NJST. You might remember this by the sentence Memory Doctor Says No More Senility Now Just Start Trying. I know this sounds stupid, but that's one of the things that will help you remember it. You might think that this extra effort is a waste of time, but taking the time to convert a number into a sentence like this *triples* the probability you will remember the number later.

The Phonetic Code System

Number	Code	Explanation
0	s, z, soft c.	A "Zero" has almost the same sound as these letters.
1	t, d, th	The letters "t" and "d" both have one downstroke. "Th" has a similar sound to these letters.
2	n	The letter "n" has two downstrokes
3	m	"m" has three downstrokes.
4	r	"R" is the last letter in the word "four."
5	l	The capital letter L is the Roman numeral for 50.
6	j, ch, sh, soft g, dg	The letter "j" is the mirror image of the digit 6; the other letter combinations all have basically the same sound.
7	k, hard c, q, hard g,	The written capital "K" looks like a seven
8	f, v, ph	The cursive "f" in script looks like an 8.
9	p & b	The letter "p" is the mirror image of the digit 9; and the letter "b" is an inverted "p".

The Peg System

The peg system is an extension of the phonetic code system. It is composed of ninety-nine words that use the letters in the phonetic code. Using the peg system involves memorizing the pegs. This is not as hard as it seems if you already know the phonetic coding system previously discussed in this chapter. Each word begins with its phonetic code letter. For instance, the first word begins with a "t" which is associated with the number 1. The two digit numbers use two code letters. The list of 99 words I have provided on the next page is widely used, but you can make up your own words if you prefer.

You can use the peg system to memorize lists of items by attaching each item to its peg word.

For example, let's go back to the list we used for the locus system.

- broccoli
- lettuce
- mayonnaise
- hot dogs
- peanut butter
- potato chips
- tomatoes
- hamburger
- a copy of the Enquirer
- a jar of mustard

To use the peg system, attach each item to a numbered peg word. See a stalk of broccoli wearing your favorite tie. Now get a picture of Noah chewing on a head of lettuce. See your "ma" spreading mayonnaise on a sandwich (remember that Mayonnaise begins with "ma") and put the hot dogs on rye.

Now see yourself breaking the law by throwing a jar of peanut butter through a window. Then you get a cramp in your jaw from eating a whole bag of potato chips. You shove your car key through a tomato, and throw a pound of hamburger at someone you hate (a foe). You then catch your "pa" actually reading a copy of the Enquirer, and cover his toes with mustard.

Stop for a moment now, close your eyes and remember the words.

If you've formed the links properly, the words will come immediately to mind.

The 99 Peg Words

1.	tie	34.	mower	67.	chalk
2.	Noah	35.	mule	68.	chef
3.	ma	36.	match	69.	ship
4.	rye	37.	mug	70.	case
5.	law	38.	movie	71.	cot
6.	jaw	39.	mop	72.	can
7.	key	40.	rose	73.	comb
8.	foe	41.	rat	74.	car
9.	pa	42.	rain	75.	coal
10.	toes	43.	ram	76.	cage
11.	tot	44.	rower	77.	coke
12.	tin	45.	roll	78.	cave
13.	tomb	46.	roach	79.	cob
14.	tire	47.	rock	80.	fuse
15.	towel	48.	roof	81.	fat
16.	dish	49.	rope	82.	fan
17.	dog	50.	lace	83.	foam
18.	dove	51.	lad	84.	fur
19.	tub	52.	lane	85.	file
20.	nose	53.	lamb	86.	fish
21.	net	54.	lair	87.	fog
22.	nun	55.	lily	88.	fife
23.	name	56.	leech	89.	fob
24.	Nero	57.	log	90.	bus
25.	nail	58.	lava	91.	bat
26.	notch	59.	lip	92.	bone
27.	neck	60.	cheese	93.	bum
28.	knife	61.	sheet	94.	bear
29.	knob	62.	chain	95.	bell
30.	mouse	63.	chime	96.	beach
31.	at	64.	cherry	97.	book
32.	money	65.	jail	98.	puff
33.	mummy	66.	cha-cha	99.	pipe

Chapter Eleven

Sleep, Biological Rhythm and Memory

I don't feel old. I don't generally feel anything until noon; then it's time for my nap.

Bob Hope (1903-2003)

A good night's sleep is something that everyone desires. Each of us is born with a requirement for a certain amount of sleep. While some can get by with just three or four hours sleep per night, others need as much as ten hours per night in order to feel rested. It is a popular myth in our culture that everyone needs eight hours sleep to stay healthy.

Here is how it breaks down statistically: about 80 percent of Americans doze an average of 7.5 hours per night, while another 15 percent need only 6.5 hours of sleep to feel rested. About 1 percent of the population requires less than 5 hours of sleep per night, while another 1 percent actually needs up to 10 hours.

If you are convinced that you should get eight hours of rest every night, but your body actually needs ten hours, you will be constantly depriving your body of the sleep it needs. This will result in being perpetually fatigued. Fatigue lowers your tolerance for frustration, and impairs your ability to concentrate. In addition, when you're tired your stimulus filters don't work, which will make you easily distracted.

On the other hand, if you are a person who actually requires only four hours of slumber to feel rested, but you force yourself to sleep longer, you will upset your natural biological rhythm. This will decrease your ability to concentrate.

Recent studies have reinforced the old adage "early to bed and early to rise" Subjects who went to bed an hour earlier than their normal bed time and awoke at their regular time showed an increased ability to concentrate the next day. This was seen as evidence that these people were chronically depriving themselves of sleep by staying awake too late, and then forcing themselves to awaken each morning by the sound of an alarm clock.

Studies on modern American lifestyle indicate that many of us are short-changing ourselves on sleep by staying up late and then forcing ourselves to get up before we are rested. In his book, *Sleep Thieves,* researcher Stanley Coren concurred and reported that even one hour of increased sleep at night can improve your memory. Several sleep and memory studies suggest that a person who gets enough sleep does not need an alarm to wake them.

Sleep Problems

As we age, we naturally need less sleep. In addition, it's common for older people to wake up several times during the night. While less sleep and nighttime awakenings are normal, many people worry about this, and begin to believe that they have insomnia.

Insomnia is by far the most common complaint about sleep, and about half of the population over 50 complains about sleep problems. There are three basic types of insomnia. The first is called sleep onset insomnia, and is characterized by the inability to fall asleep. People with this type of insomnia may lie in bed for over an hour before falling asleep.

The second type is sleep maintenance insomnia, characterized by the inability to stay asleep. People suffering from this type of insomnia may wake up many times a night. The third type is early morning awakening, in which the person awakens before they wish to, and cannot return to sleep.

To Sleep, Perchance to Remember?

So why is sleep important to memory?

First, sleeping too much can impair memory. As mentioned above, as people age, they need less sleep. In a recent report, a 59-year-old retired physician came to a clinic for medical help because of mental confusion. It was found that the cause of the problem was merely that he was sleeping too much. When his sleep time was temporarily reduced to 3 hours 45 minutes, the confusion cleared. One treatment for depression involves keeping people awake for extended periods of time. Like the gentleman just mentioned, depressed people often sleep too much.

Second, dreaming is essential to memory. During slumber, the body goes through a cycle consisting of alternate periods of light sleep, deep sleep, and another type of sleep called rapid eye movement or REM sleep. We do much of our dreaming during REM sleep.

While in REM, hands and feet may twitch and eyes dart around under eyelids. If you have ever watched someone else sleep, you may have seen this happening.

Studies on sleep and memory show that information gathered during the day is categorized and stored in long term memory during sleep. If you are a person who remembers dreams, you might have noticed that the activities of the previous day show up in your dreams. Dream theorists call this the day residue.

In 1978, Howard Roffwarg conducted a fascinating study which helped explain how day residue is incorporated into our dreams and our memories. During the day, nine college students wore special goggles that colored everything red. After a few hours, the subjects soon became acclimated to a "goggle-colored" world. On the day that they started wearing the lenses, all of their visual input was tagged with color.

Roffwarg reasoned that whatever information was processed during REM sleep would include the colored goggle world input. Each night the subjects slept in a sleep lab, where their EEGs and eye movements were monitored. They were awakened during REM sleep and asked to report their dreams. The subjects experienced four REM periods each night. On the first night, goggle material began to enter their dreams, but only during the first REM period.

In the subjects' first dream of the night, about half of the scenes contained red information. On succeeding nights, however, red scenes appeared in later and later dream periods. By the fifth night scenes from all REM periods contained goggle-colored material. As the red color moved into later dreams, it also increased in the first dream period, so that by the fifth night the first REM period contained 83 percent red scenes.

This study suggests that material appearing in dreams later in the night comes from earlier memories, which suggests that past material is mixed with recent material during sleep. In this way we weave present experiences to past memories which gives our life a sense of continuity.

A growing body of evidence suggests that sleep is essential to memory. At Harvard Medical School, neuroscientist Robert Stickgold asked volunteers to master a visual learning task. They were then tested every three hours to see if their performance had improved. Over time they showed no improvement. However they all performed significantly better after one night's sleep.

Conversely, if subjects were deprived of a night's sleep, they performed the task as poorly as those who had never done it before.

German scientists Steffen Gais and Jan Born have been researching other reasons why adequate sleep may improve memory.

Two distinct stages of brain activity called rapid eye movement (REM) or dream sleep, and slow wave sleep (SWS) play a part in memory storage.

Gais and Born found that the different sleep stages affect different kind of memory. Slow wave sleep occurs predominantly in the first half of the night, and strengthens informational memory. Dream sleep strengthens skill memory, and also seems to convert new memories in to long term-abilities.

This may explain the findings of other sleep researchers. Learning is improved if you read the material you need to remember immediately before going to sleep.

Since it appears that memory is categorized and stored during sleep, lack of sleep means impaired memory storage. For this reason, it's important that you get adequate amounts of sleep each night.

Most sleeping medications on the market today prevent you from getting adequate REM sleep. Alcohol can also have this effect. If you are taking sleeping pills on a regular basis, or if you drink every night. you are impairing your ability to store information in your long-term memory. If you are having trouble sleeping at night, it is a good idea to find the cause of your insomnia, and correct that problem, rather than drugging yourself to sleep.

If you have been taking sleeping medication for some time, do not attempt to stop without consulting your doctor. Sudden withdrawal from sleeping medication can cause serious health problems.

Finally, here's another reason that sleep is essential to brain function. Several sleep laboratories have established that poor or inadequate sleep impairs the immune system. At the UCLA Neuropsychiatric Institute, researchers found that insomniacs showed increases of norepinephrine and decreases of natural killer cell responses, which impaired immune function, which predicted cardiovascular disease and an increase in mortality.

If you are having trouble sleeping try the following:

Establish a regular sleep schedule. Go to bed and get up at the same time each day, including weekends.

Establish a regular routine of exercise. Exercise is one of the most effective remedies for insomnia. (Do not exercise right before bedtime, as the simulation will keep you awake.)

Get exposure to sunlight each day. If you can't do that, get some natural light bulbs, which mimic the effects of sunlight. Sunlight helps regulate your biological clock.

Avoid caffeine and other stimulants. Caffeine takes a long time to metabolize. A cup of coffee in the morning may actually be keeping you awake that night. In fact caffeine is one of the most common causes of insomnia.

Don't use alcohol to help you sleep. Alcohol causes insomnia, especially sleep maintenance insomnia.

Develop a bedtime ritual. Do the same things each night before bedtime, as this will cue your body that it's time to sleep. Use your bed only for sleeping. This makes getting into bed a sleeping cue.

For more information about sleep problems, contact the Better Sleep Council, PO Box 13, Washington DC 20044. Web: http://www.bettersleep.org/

Also write to the Wakefulness-Sleep Education and Research Foundation, 4820 Rancho Drive, Del Mar, CA 92014, and ask for information about purchasing *101 Questions About Sleep and Dreams*. Because this is such a common problem, there are dozens of books and websites that will teach you how to get better sleep.

Biological Rhythm

My aunt Lucille could tell herself to wake up anytime of the day or night. She could say she would be up at 6:52, and when the time arrived, her eyes would open. People like Aunt Lucille who can do this have learned to pay attention to subtle cues from their biological clock.

All living things have a biological clock within them, and human beings are no exception. In concert with the earth's rotation, we exhibit a daily rhythm known as circadian rhythm. The word "circadian" comes from the Latin term *circa dies,* which means "about a day."

Our biological clock is located in a tiny bundle of cells (about 10 thousand neurons) called the suprachiasmatic nucleus, which is part of the hypothalamus. The hypothalamus also regulates hunger and thirst, body temperature and sleep and wakefulness.

This inner clock is responsive to external changes in light and darkness. Disruption of this clock impairs our feeling of well-being and our mental and physical performance. People notice this when they cross time zones — a feeling of fatigue we call "jet lag".

This brain area also times the release of melatonin; a hormone found in the pituitary that increases during sleep. This is why many people use melatonin to help with jet lag and to improve sleep.

Each day, our bodies go through a complex biological cycle which alters moods, tastes, opinions, and beliefs — how we see the world at ten o'clock in the morning is much different than the way we see it at ten at night.

This rhythm also alters our tolerance for foods and drugs, and this is why cocktail hour is in the evening. The body has a much greater tolerance for alcohol in the evening than it does in the morning. This circadian rhythm is also why certain foods taste better in the morning than at night, and why we have specific foods for breakfast, lunch and dinner. For example, cereal, pancakes, and eggs are breakfast foods, while pasta is not.

For most of us, this rhythm begins at a low point in the morning when we first awaken, and reaches a peak some time in mid-morning. We then experience a slump in midday, usually somewhere between noon and three in the afternoon. We reach another energy peak in mid-evening, and then our energy decreases steadily until bedtime.

These rhythms fall into two categories, one with its highest peak in the morning, and the other with its highest peak in the evening. People who have a high energy peak in the morning are of course called "morning people," and people who have their highest peak in the evening are called "night people." You are probably aware of your own type of rhythm.

Morning people wake up immediately, feeling rested and energetic. Morning people usually prefer to wake up between 5 a.m. and 7 a.m., and go to bed between 9 p.m. and 11 p.m. They do their best work before noon. They are tired by the end of the day, and are not much interested in night life.

Night people, on the other hand, find it difficult to wake up in the morning. It sometimes takes them several hours to really get going. They find that they do their best work in the evening, and usually enjoy staying up late. Night people prefer to wake up from 9 a.m. to 11 a.m, and go to bed between 11 p.m. and 3 a.m.

Morning people tend to be more rigid in their schedules, while night people are more flexible and make adjustments to new schedules somewhat easier.

This rhythm also modifies our ability to remember. Our ability to put things into, and get things out of, our memory depends on our personal biological rhythm. If you are a morning person, your ability to learn is greater in the morning, and if you are a night person, it is greater in the evening.

Most of us experience a mid-day slump. This is that time of day when we feel tired and foggy-minded, and it is not a period in which to memorize new material, hold an important meeting, or take a class.

Since memory is a function of our ability to focus, we find it more difficult to remember things that are experienced during this time period.

Becoming aware of your own biological rhythm will help you increase your ability to learn and remember. Choose your peak time of day to learn new material.

Don't attempt memorization when you're tired. Your stimulus filters do not work well at these times, and easy tasks seem overwhelming when you are exhausted. However, it helps to review study material right before bedtime, because the information is stored during your dreams.

Ultradian Rhythm

The human cerebral cortex (the outer layer of the brain) consists of two identical looking hemispheres. In 1972, a series of studies done by researchers Goldstein, Stoltzfus and Gardocki demonstrated that the cerebral hemispheres alternate in dominance on a 90-minute cycle. This cycle is akin to the 90-minute sleep cycle and is known as ultradian rhythm. Two other brain researchers, Klein and Armitage, discovered in 1979 that the 90 minute oscillations actually affected cognitive style and mental activity.

Then, in 1981, Debra Werntz found that the 90-minute rhythm was associated with the nasal breathing cycle. When the left nostril is open, the right hemisphere of the brain is dominant. Further research demonstrated that cerebral dominance could be altered by changing the nasal breathing pattern. Psychologist Ernest Rossi found that one way to do this is to lie on your side — lying on your left side activates the left hemisphere because the right nostril is open.

Because the hemispheres differ in the type of information they store and process, it is possible to increase access to the information by activating the proper hemisphere.

These findings suggest that ultradian rhythm is one explanation of the "tip of the tongue" phenomenon. As discussed earlier, this is the temporary inability to retrieve information from memory, even though we are sure we know it. Waiting a short period of time, or closing one nostril for a few minutes allows the brain to shift hemispheres, and access the desired information. Try it! It works!

Chapter Twelve

Brain Function and Blood Flow

To lengthen thy life, lessen thy meals.

Benjamin Franklin (1706-1790)

Although the brain weighs in at only 2 percent of our body weight, it consumes 20 percent of the oxygen we use. In children, the oxygen use of the brain can actually be as high as 50 percent.

Doctors calculate the overall oxygen absorption in the body by using a measure called VO2max. VO2max is highest in adolescence, and declines with age. In adults, VO2max declines about 1 percent a year, and decreases about 23 percent between the ages of 33 and 61.

The brain cannot store oxygen. Because of this, it must rely on a constant supply of oxygen delivered through the blood stream. A decrease in oxygen dispensed to the brain results in an immediate impairment in brain function, and a change in blood supply is felt almost instantly. You may have experienced how fast a drop in blood flow can affect your consciousness if you have ever stood up too fast.

Less oxygen means impaired thinking. In fact, an Italian study revealed that people who suffer from chronic obstructive pulmonary disease (COPD), including bronchitis and emphysema, show significant cognitive impairments. When the researchers compared the mental abilities and verbal memory of patients with COPD with two groups of healthy people and a group of patients with Alzheimer's, they found that only 20 percent of the COPD sufferers performed at the normal level for their age group. In addition, 16 percent of the COPD subjects performed at the same level as the Alzheimer's patients.

In healthy people, the total blood flow to the brain is remarkably constant. The blood supply to the brain doesn't significantly increase during exercise, and doesn't drastically decrease during inactivity or sleep. Normal blood flow to the brain is about 50ml. per minute. Slight fluctuations may go unnoticed, but if the flow of blood is decreased to 30ml. per minute, mental confusion and even loss of consciousness may occur.

In a healthy, middle-aged person, a drop of blood pressure below normal usually has no effect, but in an elderly person the brain is especially dependent on a strong blood supply. If blood flow is reduced too much, the brain cells become starved for oxygen, causing an impairment in thinking, or in extreme cases, a stroke. A chronic lack of oxygen to the brain can cause confusion and symptoms that mimic dementia

Water Level

The amount of water stored in the body has an important effect on the brain's blood supply. In younger people, water balance is maintained adequately, but as we age the total amount of our body fluid decreases. Body water level actually falls from 62 percent at the age of 25, to 50 percent at the age of 75. This lower fluid level means that there is less room for altering body water levels without affecting brain function.

To make matters worse, many older people decrease their fluid intake, because they have lost their taste for liquids and because they simply forget to drink enough water. In addition, older people avoid drinking fluids because it increases their need to urinate.

Because the fluid levels are lower in elderly people, the circulatory system becomes extremely sensitive to changes of both water and salt levels in the body. Diuretics, which are drugs used to lower blood pressure, reduce the body's salt and water levels. If the dosage of these drugs is too high, the drugs may lower blood pressure to such a degree that the fluid level of the body becomes low enough to cause dizziness and confusion.

Although it is not often pointed out to patients by their doctors, one of the most common side effects of blood pressure medication in the elderly is memory loss.

The Arteries

The blood vessels that supply oxygen to the brain are called arteries. The wall of an artery consists of several layers of smooth muscle. Arteries actually manufacture cholesterol, but at the same time prevent the cholesterol from accumulating on the surface of their walls.

Blood is supplied to the human brain by four major arteries. The two internal carotid arteries supply about 85 percent of total blood flow to the brain. The vertebral arteries supply the remaining 15 percent. If these vessels become blocked or clogged with plaque, blood flow to the brain is diminished, and this condition must be corrected to restore proper brain nourishment.

The Carotid Arteries

Two large arteries, called the carotid arteries, supply blood to the cerebral hemispheres. There is one carotid on each side of the neck.

A small branch of the carotid supplies blood to the artery of the eye. If this branch of the carotid artery becomes narrowed by atherosclerosis, and part of the plaque breaks off and travels to the brain, the afflicted person may experience a temporary loss of vision to one eye. People who have experienced this describe it as having a curtain drawn in front of their eye. These episodes may occur several times a day.

People over 40, particularly if they have diabetes or high blood pressure, should have their carotid arteries checked regularly. Through the use of a stethoscope your doctor can diagnose whether narrowing of the carotid artery has occurred. If a murmur (called a bruit) is heard to be located over the carotid artery in the middle of the upper portion of the neck, narrowing has happened. More sophisticated testing includes X-rays with the use of dye, and computer analysis. The most recent technique for diagnosing carotid narrowing is sonar examination.

Blockage of the carotids is serious. If the carotid artery becomes so blocked that blood flow to the brain is impaired, surgery may be required. The operation, called an endarterectomy, is similar to roto-rootering the artery. If the damage to the artery is severe, doctors may replace a portion of it with a vessel from another part of the body, often from the leg.

Some doctors claim that neurological deficits and cognitive functioning improve after the procedure, because of improved blood flow to areas of the brain which were impaired before the operation. If the blockage is not too severe, aspirin can sometimes be used as a substitute for this surgery, because it impedes the formation of blood clots.

The Basilar Artery

At the base of the brain is the basilar artery. This artery furnishes the brain stem and the merging cranial nerves with blood. Patients with atherosclerosis in the basilar artery complain of vertigo and nausea. Vertigo is the very unpleasant feeling of spinning around in space. Often the person has the feeling that everything around him is spinning uncontrollably. This feeling can be very uncomfortable, and can sometimes cause vomiting.

Patients with blockage in the basilar artery frequently complain of having tingling sensations around their mouth, and may have difficulty pronouncing words. They may also have swallowing problems.

When the blood flow through this artery is interrupted, the person may suffer a brief loss of consciousness, or may fall down. There may also be a loss of equilibrium, staggering, and behavior that mimics drunkenness. Some people with this problem are not able to walk at all.

Many of these symptoms can also be caused by an infection of the inner ear, and should not be confused with basilar artery problems. Also, a rare congenital disorder called Arnold-Chiari's malformation has been known to cause similar symptoms. These things should be ruled out before basilar artery damage is considered.

Atherosclerosis

As we age, the blood flow to our brain decreases, often caused by the blockage of blood flow in the arteries themselves.

The medical term for any type of hardening of the arteries is arteriosclerosis. Atherosclerosis is a form of arteriosclerosis in which the layers of the artery become thickened and irregular. This gradual blockage is caused by debris, by deposits of cholesterol, and by other fatty deposits that build up in the arterial wall, just as sludge builds up in a drainpipe. These deposits narrow the arteries and impede blood flow. The medical term for these deposits is atheromas.

Clogged arteries and capillaries cannot deliver adequate oxygen and nutrients to the brain cells. As a result, the brain cannot function properly.

Normally the arterial walls are smooth and clean, but high blood pressure puts stress on the arterial walls, which can cause small tears in the arterial surface. Cholesterol then collects in these tiny tears. Once this process has begun, the cholesterol eventually builds up into hard deposits called *plaque.*

As this process progresses, the artery becomes thick and hard and loses its elasticity. A diseased artery can actually change from the consistency of a rubber hose to that of a hard, plastic pipe.

The process of arterial blockage begins much earlier than you might think. In fact, many people begin developing blockage by age 15. Medical tests show that in most people over 20, the intima and the media, the inner and middle layers of the arteries, have already begun to become packed with cholesterol.

Plaque can form in any artery, but it is particularly dangerous when it collects in the arteries in the brain, where the buildup can lead to strokes, or in the coronary arteries, which can cause heart attacks.

It's obvious that adequate blood flow is vital to good health. William Faloon, in a commentary in the May 2001 edition of *Life Extension Magazine* describes the critical elements in maintaining cardiovascular health.

"For the last 50 years, doctors have concentrated on control-ling blood pressure as the primary method of preventing stroke. While guarding against even borderline hypertension is critical in reducing stroke risk, there are factors that can be tested in the blood to further determine stroke risk. Everyone over age 40 should have their blood tested to make sure their homocystine, fibrinogen, C-reactive protein, LDL-cholesterol, etc. are in the safe range.

"If any of these risk factors for stroke are elevated, they can be safely lowered with therapies that are proven to work. Since these same risk factors also predispose one to heart attack and other diseases, anyone concerned with living a long and healthy life should keep them in the optimal ranges.

"Based on the sheer number of people suffering neurologic deficits caused by "silent" strokes, protecting the brain against the effects of reduced blood flow is now even more important for aging people to consider.

"All of this new research points to the fact that the most common forms of mental impairment, disability and death in the aging population (vascular dementia and stroke) are potentially avoidable. While conventional doctors focus solely on blood pressure control, they are failing to recommend important blood tests, drugs and supplements to reduce the stroke epidemic that continues to plague the aging human population."

Talk to your doctor about these tests; copy this page and take it with you for him to read. You may be saving a stroke later on.

Cholesterol

In our bodies cholesterol acts as a biochemical building block in the manufacture of a number of hormones, bile, and cell walls. It is a lipid (meaning a fat) and is unable to dissolve in the blood, which is mostly water.

In order to be transported throughout the bloodstream, cholesterol binds to proteins, which are designated by their different densities. The two categories that affect blood flow are high density lipoprotein (HDL) and low density lipoprotein (LDL). (To remember that HDL is good cholesterol, and LDL is bad, just remember that feeling high is good and feeling low is bad.)

The highest concentration of cholesterol in the body is found in the brain.

Foods and Nutrients that Lower Cholesterol

- A glass of red wine a day
- Two apples a day
- High fiber diet
- Pectin
- Lecithin
- Skim milk
- Grapefruit
- Garlic and onions
- Vitamins C and E
- Coenzyme Q10
- Evening primrose oil
- Niacin

- Lemon grass
- Cold water fish
- Soy products
- Beans
- Two carrots a day

- Chromium
- Folic acid
- Omega-3 fatty acids
- L-Carnitine

In spite of the importance of this substance, elevated cholesterol plays a crucial part in atherosclerosis. Buildup of plaque generally begins to occur in the brain when total blood cholesterol is above 260mg.

The higher your serum cholesterol, the greater your risk of developing atherosclerosis. In fact, people with cholesterol above 260mg. have a three to five times greater chance of developing arterial clots than people with cholesterol below 200.

According to data from the Framingham Heart Study, persons with total cholesterol levels above 260mg./dl. had a 33 percent risk of death versus 15 percent in persons with levels below 18mg./dl. over a period of 30 years In that thirty year period 85 percent of the patients with baseline cholesterol levels below 180mg./dl. were still alive, while one third of those with baseline cholesterol levels above 260mg./dl. had died.

While most of the cholesterol in our bodies is actually manufactured by the liver, 20 or 30 percent of it comes from dietary sources, and we now know that arteriosclerosis can be slowed, stopped, and can even be reversed through dietary modification.

Although there is a lot of controversy about how dietary cholesterol affects atherosclerosis, it's generally agreed that the less cholesterol in the diet, the lower the risk of atherosclerosis. Dr. Dean Ornish in his book, *Eat More, Weigh Less,* has shown that eating a no-fat diet can prevent, and in some cases actually reverse cardiovascular disease.

C-reactive Protein

Cholesterol is not the only culprit. Many studies show a strong association between C-reactive protein (CRP) — a chemical released in the body because of inflammation — and coronary artery disease. It's also been found that baseline CRP level is a good predictor of future cardiovascular events such as heart attack and stroke.

In fact, a recent study published in *The New England Journal of Medicine* identified elevated CRP levels as a stronger predictor of heart attacks than elevated cholesterol levels. In a survey of 388 British men aged 50-69, the prevalence of coronary artery disease increased 1.5 fold for each doubling of CRP level. The authors recommended a CRP and cholesterol screening for accurate assessment of cardiovascular disease.

CRP and cholesterol levels seem to be unrelated, which suggests that there may be a whole new way to control the risk of heart disease. This may also explain why almost half of all heart attacks occur in individuals with normal cholesterol levels.

C-reactive protein is released by the body in response to acute injury, infection, or other inflammatory stimuli. A study published in the Journal of Periodontology reports that inflammatory effects from periodontal disease, a chronic bacterial infection of the gums, cause oral bacterial byproducts to enter the bloodstream and trigger the liver to make proteins such as CRP that inflame arteries and promote blood clot formation. Periodontal disease is now considered as a major contributor to increased levels of CRP.

Dr. Gordon Douglass, president of the American Academy of Periodontology has stated "I foresee patients receiving routine CRP testing in their dentist or periodontist office in the near future. This could help early diagnosis of potential heart disease sooner rather than later, as most people see their dentist or periodontist at minimum two times a year."

It is now thought that the reduction in risk of a first myocardial infarction associated with aspirin is directly related to CRP levels. Such results may indicate a possible role for anti-inflammatory drugs in preventing cardiovascular disease.

Other studies have further indicated that statins, which are now commonly used to lower LDL levels, have the additional and independent effect of reducing coronary heart disease risk in people with high CRP. A recent study has shown that treatment with pravastatin (Pravachol) in addition to lowering cholesterol, appears to reduce levels of CRP.

Statins

There is no doubt that statins are the most powerful cholesterol lowering drugs on the market today. Depending on the dosage they can lower LDL from 20-60 percent. Fluvastatin (Lescol®) appears to be the least potent, decreasing LDL levels by only 22-36 percent at the maximum recommended dosage. Up to now Atorvastatin (Lipitor®) has been the most potent, reducing LDL levels by 39-60 percent with a dosage range of 5-80mg./day.

As of this writing, Rosuvastatin (Crestor®) is the newest member of this class approved in August, 2003 in the United States. It appears to be even more potent than Lipitor. In several studies, rosuvastatin dosage of 20-80mg./day reduced LDL up to 65 percent, and 65 percent of patients reached target LDL levels. Statins also have modest effects on HDL, raising levels by approximately 5 percent. Crestor may be slightly better than other statins at raising good (HDL) cholesterol

In November 2000 researchers compared 24,480 patients from 50 to 89 years of age who had received at least one prescription for a statin medication at any time to 11,421 patients who had hyperlipidemia but had not been treated with lipid-lowering drugs. A control group of 25,000 patients in the same age range was also included.

All three groups were followed for six years to monitor the development of dementia. During that period, 284 patients developed dementia. Each of these patients was matched by age and sex with up to four control patients from the same practice. The authors found that the risk of developing dementia was reduced by 37 to 70 percent in patients 50 years and older who use statin medications. Other studies have shown similar results.

As well as reducing cholesterol, statins may also reduce dementia by reducing inflammation. In Sweden's Goteborg University, researcher Magnus Sjogren found that 19 Alzheimer's patients taking statins had significantly reduced amounts of amyloid plaques in their brains. The progress of the disease was thought to be slowed by the statin's anti-inflammatory quality.

So should you be taking statins? Maybe not. Statins seem to be very effective in lowering dementia risk. But they do carry their own risks. In fact, the dangers of statin drugs are manifold, including liver failure, weakness, immune system suppression, an increase in cancer risk, muscle aches and deterioration.

In August 2003, Baycol, a statin drug marketed by Bayer, was pulled off the market. It had been linked to 31 U.S. deaths. Bayer would not disclose the total number of deaths worldwide, but at least nine more fatalities abroad are known.

Baycol was found to cause a serious degenerative muscle condition called rhabdomyolysis It also displayed compounded toxicity when used with other drugs.

A study published in the December 2002 *Journal of the American Medical Association* examined the effect of statin drugs versus natural methods such as improving diet and exercise. The statin group did lower their bad cholesterol levels significantly more than the usual care group. However, both groups had the same rates of heart disease and death.

Another study, published in *American Journal of Cardiology* found that lowering bad cholesterol with statin drugs did not reduce the rate at which plaque builds up in arteries.

This finding contradicts the accepted medical stance that lowering LDL cholesterol is the best way to reduce arterial plaque. As in the previous study, subjects in this study taking statins lowered their cholesterol. However, all the groups had an average increase in arterial plaque of 9.2 percent.

Almost all health practitioners agree that lowering cholesterol is good for you. But how to do it is open to question.

Treating high cholesterol with statins does not address the cause of the problem. Some people actually see statins as a way to eat more fat with less risk.

Natural methods such as diet, physical activity, and natural products have all been shown to be effective, and less dangerous than statins.

Red Yeast Rice

For many years, red yeast rice, a dietary supplement from Asia has been used successfully as a cholesterol lowering nutrient. The substance is made by fermenting a type of red yeast (Monascus purpureus) on a base of rice. This nutrient worked because the fermentation process created significant amounts of natural statins.

A study done at the UCLA School of Medicine and published in the *American Journal of Clinical Nutrition* in 1999, confirmed that the supplement lowered cholesterol levels by an average of 40 points in 12 weeks when combined with a low-fat diet.

In 2001, approval for this extract was withdrawn by the FDA. The agency had decided that red yeast rice was, chemically, too similar to the prescription statin medication Mevacor, and thus should be classified as a drug, not a nutrient. As a result of this decision red yeast rice supplements are no longer available in retail stores.

NuSkin International, who was the retailer of the popular red yeast rice product *Cholestin,* has now reformulated their product. They replaced the yeast with a substance called policosanol, derived from sugar cane, which also has a cholesterol-lowering effect. Like red yeast rice, policosanol acts on the liver to reduce cholesterol production. However, it is significantly different, biochemically, from the statins.

Gugulipid

Gugulipid is another natural product that lowers cholesterol. Also called Gugul, this substance is an extract of the *Commiphora Mukul* tree, a traditional Indian medicinal plant. Gugul appears to an effective lipid-lowering agent, which means it decreases both cholesterol and triglyceride levels.

Proponents state that gugul is effective because it brings down LDL cholesterol while elevating HDL. Studies show that gugul prevents atherosclerosis and aids in the regression of pre-existing atherosclerotic plaques.

In addition to its effect on cholesterol, gugulipid also appears to prevent heart damage from free radicals, and improves the metabolism of the heart. It also mildly inhibits platelets from clumping together in blood vessels.

In addition it's been shown that gugul has an ability to stimulate the thyroid function. This thyroid-stimulating effect may, in fact, be responsible for some of Gugulipid's fat-lowering ability.

A survey of research studies on this product showed equivocal results — some studies touting its benefits while others showing no effect. However, this is typical of medical research, so I would still consider this substance to be an alternative to statins.

Alfalfa

Alfalfa is rich in molecules called saponins (chemicals that are also used to make soap). Saponins bind cholesterol in the gut to prevent absorption. Studies conducted on the cholesterol lowering properties of alfalfa suggest that it does work. Some researchers believe that in addition to the saponins, other as yet unidentified components of alfalfa may also play a part in its cholesterol lowering ability, and that alfalfa seeds contain more of the active ingredients than the plant itself.

Niacin

Niacin, or vitamin B3, reduces triglyceride levels and raises HDL. It's also one of the most inexpensive ways to do this. The problem of some people is side-effects, which include flushing in the face and neck, headache, and dizziness. Most people find that after a time the side effects subside.

Getting Tested

You can measure your propensity towards atherosclerosis through a blood test. The blood test should include measures of total cholesterol, C-reactive protein, triglycerides, high density lipoprotein (HDL), and low density lipoprotein (LDL), DHEA, iron, glucose, homocystine, and fibrinogen, as all of these factors play important roles in cardiovascular health.

For information on lowering your cholesterol, contact the National Heart, Lung, and Blood Institute, NHLBI Health Information Center, POB 30105, Bethesda, MD 20824-0105 Phone: 301-592-8573 Web: http://www.nhlbi.nih.gov/about/ncep/

Another source of information is the American Dietetic Association, Consumer Nutrition Hotline, 120 South Riverside Plaza, Suite 2000, Chicago, IL 60606-6995 Phone: 800-366-1655 Web: http://www.eatright.org/public/.

For information about the new synthetic fat substitutes on the market, request *Sorting Out the Facts about Fat,* Publications Department, International Food Information Council (IFIC) Foundation, 1100 Connecticut Avenue, NW, Suite 430, Washington, DC 20036 Phone: 202-296-6540 Web: http://ific.org/about/index.cfm.

Transient Ischemic Attacks

Tiny strokes, called transient ischemic attacks (TIAs), mimic strokes in their symptoms, causing numbness, nausea and dizziness. But unlike actual strokes, which can cause permanent disability, TIAs last only up to 24 hours. TIAs are caused by a temporary decrease in the blood flow to different parts of the brain. When this occurs, there's often a loss of motor ability and thinking capacity that lasts several minutes to a day, and then disappears.

Other symptoms of TIAs include brief flashes of numbness in the face and the arms, or sudden weakness of an arm or a leg with the inability to move.

The major cause of TIAs is atherosclerosis of the arteries supplying the brain. Other less common causes include episodes of irregular heartbeats, low blood pressure and brain tumors.

If the blood flow to a part of the brain called the hippocampus is blocked during a TIA, memory loss will occur. Repeated episodes of TIAs over time may cause dementia.

Having a TIA is a very terrifying experience, but between these little attacks, the sufferer feels fine. For this reason, people often fail to go to the doctor to have them checked out.

Even though people with TIAs may have no signs of heart disease, they should have a thorough cardiac workup, because many also have hardening in the arteries of the heart. In fact, the cause of death in people with TIAs is usually heart attack.

In 1978, the Mayo Clinic reported that one-third of patients with TIAs will suffer a stroke within five years of the first attack.

Unfortunately, 20 percent of those experiencing TIAs will suffer stroke within one month of the initial attack, and 50 percent will suffer a stroke within a year. As we shall see, strokes can be devastating and sometimes fatal events, but they are, in part, preventable.

The Major Causes of Stroke

- High blood pressure
- Heart disease
- High cholesterol
- Overweight
- Smoking
- Alcohol
- Lack of exercise
- Diabetes

Stroke

A stroke is the destruction of brain cells caused by an interruption of blood flow to the brain. Strokes are the leading source of adult disability, and the number three cause of death (after heart disease and cancer). They afflict about 500,000 Americans each year.

Eighty percent of stroke victims survive, but they often suffer permanent loss of function, such as the loss of the ability to speak (called aphasia) or paralysis of part of the body. Strokes are also called cerebral vascular accidents (CVAs) but they are, in fact, not accidents; to a great degree, they can be predicted and prevented.

The number of strokes in the United States has decreased almost 50 percent in the last thirty years. This is attributed primarily to the medical control of high blood pressure. Still, almost a half million people a year in the United States suffer from strokes.

Researchers have found that a brain chemical called calpain may cause brain cell damage after a stroke. Normally calpain cleans up blocked receptors in neurons and facilitates memory transfer, but too much calpain in the system kills neurons.

When a stroke occurs, it is followed by the release of glutamate, another chemical that causes brain damage. This phenomenon is called a *glutamate cascade*. Under normal conditions, glutamate is a neurotransmitter required for memory storage. But after a stroke, excess amounts of glutamate over-excite the cells. This over-stimulation results in large doses of calcium rushing into the neurons, destroying them.

Some researchers believe that Dextromethorphan, a substance found in most cough syrups, can protect the brain against stroke damage. In animals, high doses of the drug administered after a brain injury reduced damage by 80 percent. It reduced brain swelling by 85 percent.

It is known that nitric oxide, a substance released by glutamate, can cause stroke damage. FK 506, *(Tacrolimus)* an immunosuppressant drug, blocks nitric oxide damage and also enhances nerve regeneration. This drug, brand named Prograf, is used primarily to prevent organ transplant rejection.

GPI-1046, a related compound which possess the neuron protecting properties of FK-506, but doesn't have immunosuppressive activity, has also been found to improve nerve regeneration.

Both of these drugs attach themselves to molecules in the brain called immunophilins. Scientists at Johns Hopkins University and Guilford have discovered that drugs that bind to immunophilins, such as Tacrolimus and GPI-1046 protect the brain primarily by enhancing nerve growth. This is considered to be a new approach to the treatment of brain damage (as occurs in strokes) and other neurodegenerative disorders such as Parkinson's disease. GPI-1046 is the first orally administered drug that can stimulate regrowth of damaged dopamine neurons in Parkinson Disease.

Strokes occur in three major ways. As mentioned earlier, plaque is the debris that blocks arteries in atherosclerosis. A blood clot that completely clogs an artery and causes a stroke is called a thrombus, and the incident is called a thrombic stroke. When a bit of plaque, called an embolus breaks off and clogs a smaller vessel or capillary, it is called an embolic stroke. When an artery in the brain actually bursts, and spills blood on the brain, the incident is called a hemorrhagic stroke. This type of stroke usually occurs from a combination of atherosclerosis and high blood pressure. About 80 percent of strokes are of the thrombic type.

In the past few years, it's been discovered that injections of a clot-dissolving drug called tissue plasminogen activator (TPA) can dramatically improve the chances of stroke patients recovering with few lasting effects. In a study of 624 stroke patients, victims were randomly assigned to get either TPA or a placebo. After three months, doctors judged the patients' conditions on four scales of stroke symptoms. Depending on the measure used, those getting TPA were between 30 percent and 50 percent more likely to have full or nearly complete recoveries.

On the most conservative of these scales, the doctors found that 31 percent of the patients receiving TPA showed no permanent disability, or were left with minor symptoms such as slight weakness in one arm. By comparison, only 20 percent of those in the untreated group were this fortunate.

TPA is not a cure-all. To be effective, it must be administered within the first three hours of the onset of symptoms. Furthermore, all patients must be given a CAT scan first to make sure that the stroke is from a blood clot in the brain and not from a broken blood vessel. Since prompt treatment is essential, strokes are now considered emergencies by ambulance crews and hospitals.

TPA does carry a high level of risk. Giving TPA too late in the course of a stroke may trigger bleeding in the brain, causing further damage. These hazards were illustrated by a major study in which European doctors gave TPA to patients six hours after stroke symptoms began. Among victims who already had large areas of dying brain tissue, TPA increased the risk of death by two-thirds.

Even when the drug is used properly, it increases bleeding in the brain in 6 percent of patients. However, the study concludes that this hazard is offset by the reduction in symptoms among stroke survivors. When given to the right person at the right time, it can prevent lifelong disability.

Black Tea and Stroke

According to an article in the *Archives of Internal Medicine,* regular, long-term consumption of black tea, and other substances containing a family of chemicals called flavonoids may protect against stroke.

Sirving O. Keli, M.D., Ph.D. and his colleagues studied 552 men, aged 50 to 69 years, between 1970 and 1985, to test a theory that the dietary antioxidant vitamins and flavonoids in fruits and vegetables shield against stroke. The major source of flavonoids consumed was from Black tea (70 percent), while apples contributed about 10 percent.

The study showed an inverse association between tea consumption and stroke risk. Men who drank more than 4.7 cups of tea per day actually had a 69 percent reduced risk of stroke compared with men who drank less than 2.6 cups per day. Tea also contains other antioxidative compounds which may contribute to this effect.

The researchers concluded that, "long-term intake of flavonoids and consumption of black tea may protect against stroke."

In addition to black tea and apples, onions, kale, green beans, broccoli, endive, celery and cranberries all contain high levels of flavonoids.

Carnosine

In a study published in the November 2000 issue of *Brain Research Bulletin* rats were subjected to 45 minutes of reduced blood flow (ischemia) to the brain. This resulted in massive cell damage and decreases in cerebral enzyme levels. As a result of the damage 67 percent of the animals died. However, in a group of rats pre-treated with carnosine, only 30 percent died in response to ischemic injury. The study showed that carnosine protects rat brains against the effects of oxygen starvation

I know you are not a rat. But several dozen published studies demonstrate beyond doubt that carnosine protects the brain from stroke damage in humans. A stroke victim taking carnosine could potentially reduce brain damage by more than 50 percent. In addition, there is increasing evidence that carnosine has beneficial effects in the treatment of congestive heart failure, arrhythmia, and peripheral vascular disease as well.

For more information about strokes, contact

The American Stroke Association, National Center, 7272 Greenville Avenue, Dallas, TX 75231 Phone: 888-478-7653 Web: http://www.strokeassociation.org/

National Stroke Association, 9707 E. Easter Lane, Englewood, CO 80112 Phone: 800-STROKES Web: http://209.107.44.93/ NationalStroke/

Maximizing Blood Flow

It's clear that healthy arteries and unimpeded bloodflow are vital to proper brain function. Fortunately, scientists have found several ways to increase blood flow to the brain, and reduce the risk of stroke.

Numerous studies have demonstrated that exercise slightly increases brain blood flow. However, even this small rise is enough to improve mental abilities. These studies show that people who make even a modest effort do better at memorizing and processing information, than those who have not increased their activity level.

Exercise also helps to reduce the stress and tension in your body, and enhances your ability to concentrate. In general, the more physically active you are, the better your brain works. Some studies show that exercising at least three times a week can increase brain oxygen uptake by as much as 30 percent.

Exercise also can affect cholesterol levels. It can keep LDL down, while maintaining high HDL levels.

In a recent study done at Stanford University, 377 men and women with moderately high LDL (bad) cholesterol and moderately low amounts of HDL (good) cholesterol, who added an exercise program to a low-fat diet plan for one year lowered LDL cholesterol two times as much as did people who used diet alone.

Women who added exercise to low-fat eating lowered their LDL about 12mg./dl. more than people who did nothing. Men on the same program lowered LDL by about 15mg./dl. more than those who did not change their habits. Eating less than 25 percent of calories from fat without exercising changed LDL only about 5 to 6mg./dl. for both men and women. It's important to note that exercise alone had no effect on cholesterol levels. Both exercise and fat reduction are necessary to get a significant result.

It is thought that exercise lowers LDL by facilitating weight loss. Abdominal fat in particular is a problem because the blood circulating through it drains directly into the liver. The liver, receiving fat-laden blood from the abdomen, then manufactures LDL. When abdominal fat is reduced, the liver has less raw material with which to create LDL. Studies show that staying at your ideal weight is linked to lower LDL.

A study from Barcelona looked at HDL (good) cholesterol. Of 537 men studied, those who worked out for 15 minutes at a rate of 420 calories per hour had HDL levels about 2mg./dl. higher than those who worked out at a more moderate rate.

A study published in *Medicine and Science in Sports and Exercise* demonstrated that exercise also sharpened brain function. In this study 32 subjects were given a battery of tests for mental function. They then took a ten week program in physical fitness. When they were tested again, there was a significant improvement in intelligence. This means exercise alone increased their I.Q.!

The American Psychologist reported that people over 60 who took a daily stroll of 6 to 10 miles experienced increased brain function in only 26 days. In another study, reported in the journal *Psychosomatic Medicine,* college students who attended a 14-week swimming class reported less tension, depression, and confusion. Various measurements showed that swimming increased blood flow, oxygen uptake, and availability of nutrients to the brain.

There is another reason why the activity of swimming brings brain benefits. Researcher Win Younger suggests that holding your breath under water increases the amount of blood that travels to the brain by expanding the carotid arteries. If the swimming routine is performed regularly, the increase can become permanent, which can improve mental capacity.

As mentioned above, cleaning out the carotid arteries through surgery removes plaque, but it's been shown that certain tropical fruits help tidy up arteries too. Bananas, kiwis, papayas, mangoes and pineapples, all contain bromelain, a substance that keeps arteries clean. Bromelain is a natural blood thinner and an effective anti-inflammatory. Because it has blood thinning properties, bromelain should be avoided if you are already taking blood thinners. You can purchase bromelain supplements in any nutrition store.

Grapefruit and apple pectin also help by lowering cholesterol. One study demonstrated that eating 12 grams of grapefruit pectin a day over four months brought down cholesterol by 17 percent. Like bromelain, you can buy grapefruit pectin in health food stores in tablet form. One gram of vitamin C per day can also lower your cholesterol.

Several studies show that thyroid imbalance can affect the condition of your arteries. William Kountz found that 288 low-thyroid patients all had high cholesterol. Stephen Langer in his book, *Solved: The Riddle of Illness,* suggests that a kelp tablet a day can balance the thyroid in many people.

Coffee and Cholesterol

There are several studies that suggest moderate to heavy coffee drinking can cause a significant rise in cholesterol levels. Norwegian researchers examined the relation between coffee consumption and levels of total serum cholesterol, high-density-lipoprotein (HDL) cholesterol, and triglycerides in a population of 7,213 women and 7,368 men between the ages of 20 and 54. They found that moderate coffee drinkers (those drinking four cups or less a day) had cholesterol levels 5 percent higher than non-coffee-drinkers.

People who drank five to eight cups a day had cholesterol levels 9 percent higher, and those who drank more than nine cups of coffee per day had cholesterol levels 12 percent higher than non-coffee-drinkers. The researchers stated, "… the present finding of a coffee-cholesterol association … is strong and consistent, and its magnitude makes coffee one of the strongest determinants of serum cholesterol levels in the present population."

Researchers at Stanford University also studied the effects of coffee on "bad" LDL cholesterol and apolipoprotein B (apo-B), a fat molecule which attaches itself to protein. In this study, male university employees between the ages of 30 and 55 who drank more than 2 to 3 cups per day had elevated plasma concentrations of three cardiovascular risk factors: total cholesterol, LDL cholesterol, and apo-B.

At the University of Texas, researchers also found a coffee-cholesterol link. In their study, serum cholesterol rose from 205.3mg./dl. in women who drank less than a cup of coffee a day to 223.1mg./dl. among those who drank eight or more cups. Serum cholesterol in men rose from 206.7mg./dl. for those who consumed less than a cup of coffee daily to 226.5mg./dl. among those who downed eight or more cups.

Researchers are not sure how coffee drinking or associated factors spur this increase in cholesterol. Neither the cream in the coffee, nor stress, nor cigarettes appear to be behind this cholesterol effect. However, studies suggest that oils found in coffee such as cafestol and kahweol may be responsible for its lipid elevations. Theses oils may increase the formation of cholesterol by decreasing excretion of bile acids and neutral sterols. The amount of oils in a cup of coffee depends on the preparation method. Boiled or French-pressed coffee retain more oil than filtered or drip coffee, possibly explaining the meta-analysis findings that boiled coffee had a greater cholesterol-raising effect. Other studies show that if the coffee is filtered, the toxic components are eliminated.

In a 30 year study at Johns Hopkins, published in the *New England Journal of Medicine* in 1986, subjects who consumed five or more cups of coffee per day had the highest cumulative incidence of coronary artery disease (10.7 percent). This group of coffee drinkers was compared with subjects who drank three to four cups a day (8.8 percent were found to have heart disease), one to two cups per day (a 5.1 percent finding), or no coffee (a 1.6 percent incidence).

Several recent studies have failed to replicate these results, so the coffee cholesterol link remains controversial. Even though the evidence is conflicting, those with high cholesterol might quit coffee for a while to see if it helps.

Coffee can also cause irregular heart beats and several studies have demonstrated a significant increase in blood pressure after drinking a cup. Go easy on coffee.

Chelation Therapy

Chelation therapy utilizes a substance called ethylene diamine tetra acetic acid (EDTA). This is a protein like molecule that binds to metal ions such as lead, mercury and calcium, and makes them soluble in the blood. This allows the kidney to eliminate heavy metals from the body. Chelation therapy has been the treatment of choice for heavy metal poisoning for years.

Dr. Norman Clark began researching chelation therapy in the early 1950s. He felt that because calcium was deposited in cholesterol plaques that plugged arteries, it made good sense that EDTA, which removes calcium, could soften the plaques and lead to a reversal of the cholesterol deposits. When he began to use the treatment for this purpose, Dr. Clark found that infusions of EDTA improved symptoms in as much as 80 percent of his patients.

Since that time, traditional medicine has decided that chelation therapy is an ineffective treatment for unclogging arteries. But even though most doctors claim that chelation is worthless, there are several hundred physicians in the U.S. that swear by it as an effective cure for cardiovascular disease, and to reverse some symptoms of dementia.

For more information on chelation therapy, and a list of physicians in your area who use it, contact the The American College for Advancement in Medicine (ACAM), 23121 Verdugo Drive, Suite 204, Laguna Hills, CA 92653 Phone: 714 -583-7666. Web: http://www.acam.org/

Chapter Thirteen

Blood Pressure

Low Blood Pressure

Although most people worry about high blood pressure, low blood pressure is more common than previously suspected, and can cause many problems with memory, thinking, and concentration. The medical term for low blood pressure is hypotension, a condition which can occur because of chronic blood loss, inadequate fluid intake, excessive vomiting, heart attacks, heat exhaustion, endocrine diseases or abnormalities in thyroid function.

In elderly people, low blood pressure is responsible for a variety of brain problems. For example, the hippocampus, which is a part of the brain that allows us to store memories, is notoriously prone to damage from insufficient blood supply, inadequate oxygen levels, or deficits in nutrients.

Because of the odd geometry of its blood vessels, the hippocampus is highly prone to damage from hardening of the arteries. Low blood pressure can starve these tissues of oxygen and nutrients, further damaging this delicate tissue and causing permanent memory problems.

Dehydration is another cause of lowered pressure. This condition is often worsened by taking diuretic drugs. For this reason, maintaining adequate fluid intake is essential.

Some of my patients with low blood pressure suffer from congestive heart failure. There is evidence that Coenzyme Q10 may improve this condition. Others experience low blood pressure from medication problems. In these cases, when the person stops taking the problem-causing drug, blood pressure often returns to normal.

Many elderly people experience hypotension because of blood loss from ulcers and other lesions. This condition is made worse by taking too much aspirin, a drug which frequently causes internal bleeding. A test for occult blood can diagnose this problem.

In addition, it appears that low blood pressure raises the risk of Alzheimer's in the elderly. Findings reported in the December 23, 2003 issue of *Neurology* suggest that diastolic blood pressure, below 70 mm. Hg. is associated with an increased risk of dementia in people over 75 years of age. For each 10-mm.Hg. drop in diastolic pressure, the risk of dementia increased by 20 percent. The risk was highest in subjects with persistently low blood pressure, and was linked only to Alzheimer's type dementia, not vascular dementia.

In the study 406 healthy community-dwelling elderly subjects were followed for up to 21 years. During a median follow-up period of 6.7 years, 122 subjects developed dementia. Individuals with consistently low blood pressures throughout the first two years of the study were twice as likely to develop dementia.

High Blood Pressure

High blood pressure is also known as hypertension. Basically in cases of hypertension, the tension inside the blood vessels is too high. Although this is a common medical term, some people still misunderstand its meaning, and wrongly conclude that hypertension means that you are more tense emotionally than you should be.

We've known for years that high blood pressure is a major factor in the acceleration of arteriosclerosis. When high blood pressure is decreased, the incidence of strokes, atherosclerosis and dementia is greatly reduced.

Researchers have found that men with high blood pressure are significantly slower in searching their short-term memory than those with normal blood pressure. The authors of the study that reported these results believe that decreases in cerebral blood flow could be the cause. Many other studies show that untreated high blood pressure does indeed impair memory.

For example, a study reported in the journal *Stroke* showed that high blood pressure hastened the loss of memory and other cognitive abilities in the elderly, and actually caused their brains to shrink in size. In 1997, researchers at the National Institutes on Aging in Bethesda, MD compared otherwise healthy people with long-standing histories of well-controlled high blood pressure in two age groups (56-69 and 70-84 years of age) with people of the same age who had normal blood pressure. Each participant received brain-imaging scans and a battery of neuropsychological tests.

Even though none of the patients with high blood pressure had ever had a stroke or other medical condition, they had more brain atrophy and impairments in memory than those with normal blood pressure.

The effect was worsened by aging, that is the older the person was, the more damage had been done. Nevertheless, the study concluded that although aging alone causes some loss of cognition, the loss of memory is significantly accelerated when blood pressure is high. Furthermore, the changes seemed to occur even in patients receiving blood pressure medication.

These results suggest that this is a type of brain deterioration that is different from Alzheimer's disease. In addition, it appears that the medical treatments now used to lower blood pressure in the elderly may not be sufficient to ward off the combined effects of high blood pressure on the brain.

Although at least 35 million people in the United States are known to have hypertension, most are unaware that they have it. High blood pressure usually has no symptoms, and therefore it has come to be known as the silent killer.

High blood pressure affects over 20 percent of the adult white population in the United States and over 30 percent of the adult black population.

However, in higher age groups, these percentages increase significantly. About two-thirds of the people between ages 65 and 74, and three-fourths of the people over 75 have high blood pressure.

Even though high blood pressure usually has no symptoms, there may be some warning signs. These include a rapid pulse, feelings of dizziness, chronic headaches, sweating, problems with vision, and shortness of breath.

Another factor contributing to high blood pressure is the epidemic of obesity in America. A recent medical report announced that two-thirds of all Americans are now classified as obese. Since obesity, and lack of exercise contributes significantly to the onset of type 2 diabetes, the combination is a realistic threat to maintaining cognitive ability.

Two following studies demonstrate the harmful effects of sugar on memory and how the control of diabetes and high blood pressure keeps memory functioning.

The first study, published in the *Proceedings of the National Academy of Sciences,* found that people's memory may be harmed long before they develop full-fledged diabetes — and that it's a problem of fuel, not plumbing.

One researcher studied 30 non-diabetic middle-aged and elderly people. He measured how they performed on several memory tests, how quickly they metabolized blood sugar after a meal; and, using MRI scans, the size of the hippocampus, the brain region responsible for recent memory.

He discovered that the slower those outwardly healthy people metabolized blood sugar, the worse their memory was — and the smaller their hippocampus was. Unlike most other tissues that have multiple fuel sources, the brain depends on blood sugar for almost all its energy. The longer glucose stays in the bloodstream, instead of being metabolized into body tissues, the less fuel the brain has to store memories.

Dr. Convit's study sheds important light on yet another risk of high blood sugar, said Dr. Fran Kaufman, president of the American Diabetes Association. But she cautioned that it was a small study that requires confirmation before doctors test glucose solely for memory complaints. But if it is confirmed, the same advice for lowering people's overall diabetes risk — drop a few pounds and do exercise as simple as walking 30 minutes a day — apparently would help to protect people's brains as well, Kaufman said.

Diabetes can have a "memory effect" whether you are "elderly" or otherwise. When blood sugars are high, dehydration occurs. It takes six molecules of water to move one molecule of sugar through the bloodstream. Fuzzy, tired thinking is often the result. Diabetes left unchecked over the years produces complications that affect most of our systems. In essence, we are not operating with a full deck.

In the second study, diabetes and hypertension were tied to cognitive decline. This was a study conducted at the University of Minnesota, and researchers found that participants with diabetes or high blood pressure showed a greater rate of decline in mental ability. The full study was reported in the January 9, 2001 issue of *Neurology*, the journal of the American Academy of Neurology. The study looked at changes in mental ability over six years and included more than 1,000 participants between 40 and 70 years of age. The results showed that while all participants showed a degree of decline the subjects with diabetes and high blood pressure had a more significant decline in mental ability. The participants with diabetes showed a higher rate of decline after the six-year period of the study even in the group that was younger than 58 years of age.

Researchers stated they were not certain how diabetes and high blood pressure affect cognition, but do theorize that, "It could be due to micro infarctions (mini-strokes), that cause tiny areas of brain damage." The author of the study suggests that the results point to the need for more aggressive treatment and control of diabetes and high blood pressure earlier. By controlling these diseases before age 60, there may be a lower rate of cognitive decline in the later years. This translates into quality of life and lower healthcare expenditures as people age.

A new study shows that there is a loss of brain tissue among patients with childhood-onset diabetes which may lead to cognitive problems. Previous research suggested that many people with juvenile-onset insulin-dependent diabetes also have cognitive problems.

Researchers at the State University of New York studied 100 patients, aged between 18 and 50. All of these individuals had had insulin-dependent diabetes for at least ten years. Their brain scans were compared with those for 100 matched healthy individuals. The study revealed that nearly 90 percent of those with diabetes had a lower brain tissue volume than their healthy controls. Further research is underway to determine how this brain atrophy impacts upon cognitive perform-ance. There is a smattering of evidence that suggests it is the hypo-glycemic episodes of diabetes that impair the brain.

Hypoglycemia may preferentially harm neurons in the medial temporal region, specifically the hippocampus.

One of the important mechanisms reducing brain metabolism in AD relates to inappropriate responses to insulin. In studies where impairments of brain metabolism were artificially induced, changes in brain function that mimic the disabilities in AD, appeared. Preliminary results from several units suggest that treatment directed at the restoration of brain glucose metabolism can improve cognitive function in AD patients.

What is the Solution?

Both diabetes and hypertension (high blood pressure) need to be diagnosed early and kept in tight control with diet, exercise and the appropriate medications.

- All adults should have a yearly checkup that includes measuring blood pressure and lab tests to evaluate blood sugar levels. This is especially important for people with a family history of diabetes.
- Have a yearly eye exam. Subtle changes in eyesight may indicate that measures to control diabetes are not as effective as they should be.
- People with diabetes should check their blood sugar daily, or more often when they are under stress or have an infection (like a cold or flu). Both stress and infection can cause blood sugar to rise out of control.
- Control your weight. Many people with high blood pressure have achieved lower blood pressure and have even been able to eliminate the medications they were taking by losing weight.
- If you have high blood pressure, take your medications as ordered. If you experience symptoms, such as dizziness, changes in urination that you think may be caused by the medication contact your doctor. It may be a temporary effect or may mean you need a change of dosage.
- Control is the word. Blood pressure less than 120/80 and blood sugar in the normal range will help to maintain memory, cognitive function and quality of life.

Measuring Blood Pressure

In his excellent book *Aging Myths,* physician Sigfried Kra points out that to get an accurate measure of your blood pressure, it's important to measure it in both arms, and to take readings while sitting and while standing.

Particularly in older people, atherosclerosis may involve the arteries of only one arm. If the blood flow is impaired in one arm, the affected arm will show a lower blood pressure reading, while the blood pressure in the other arm may be high. If both arms are not measured, the high blood pressure may go undetected.

What levels are considered high blood pressure?

Blood pressure is measured by getting two numbers called systolic and diastolic levels.

The National High Blood Pressure Education Program Coordinating Committee searched for and analyzed studies on blood pressure and health from 1997 to April 2003. Based on this newer evidence, the committee replaced the previous 1997 guidelines with new standards for the identification, prevention, and treatment of high blood pressure.

The upper range of what was considered 'normal' in the old guidelines (140/90 mm.Hg.) now falls into a new category, 'prehypertensive.' Prehypertension is defined as having a systolic reading (the top number) anywhere between 120 and 139, or a diastolic (the bottom number) reading of 80-89 mm.Hg. Prehypertensive individuals are at an increased risk for progression to hypertension. A reading of less than 120/80 mm.Hg. is now considered 'normal.'

Diastolic Pressure

Diastolic blood pressure is the pressure in your blood vessels when your heart is not pumping. As mentioned above, diastolic blood pressure less than 80 is now considered normal. From 85 to 89 is considered high normal. From 90 to 104 is called mild high blood pressure, and over 105 is referred to as moderate high blood pressure. If your diastolic pressure is 115 or higher, you have severe high blood pressure and are in some medical danger.

Systolic Pressure

Systolic blood pressure is the high point of your blood pressure, and occurs when your heart is pumping. Systolic pressure less than 120 is now considered normal. Pressure from 140 to 150 is called borderline systolic high blood pressure. Systolic pressure of 160 or higher is known as isolated systolic hypertension. This last type of high blood pressure is often found in elderly people, where the diastolic pressure is normal.

The Dangers of Hypertension

The cardiovascular system consists of the heart and blood vessels. During an average lifetime, the heart pumps more than 60 million gallons of blood through more than 60,000 miles of blood vessels! The blood is responsible for taking oxygen and nutrients to every single cell in the body.

To understand what high blood pressure is, think of water running through a hose. The more water that runs through the hose, the higher the water pressure is going to be. If you squeeze the hose down so that the opening is smaller, the pressure gets higher. Blood vessels act just like a hose, and blockage or constriction of the blood vessels is what causes high blood pressure.

Constant high blood pressure is a medical emergency. It can damage blood vessels along with the organs that they feed. In extreme cases, blood vessels may even rupture. As we discussed previously, a blood vessel that ruptures in the brain causes a stroke.

High blood pressure is dangerous for several reasons. First, it's a leading contributor to atherosclerosis or cardiovascular disease, sometimes called hardening of the arteries. High blood pressure puts strain on the arteries and causes tiny breaks in the artery lining. This causes them to become scarred, stiff and hard. When this happens, small deposits of fat called plaque build up in the arteries, blocking them.

A healthy artery is as pliable and flexible as a rubber hose, but hypertension can damage an artery to the degree that it becomes as stiff as a piece of dry spaghetti. Arteries that become hardened and blocked are one of the major causes of strokes.

Fatty blockages and plaque in arteries, along with fluid buildup due to sodium retention or mineral imbalances, further elevate blood pressure. This makes the heart work harder and harder to pump the blood, and can eventually lead to heart failure or heart attack.

People over age 45 with high blood pressure are three times as likely to have a heart attack than those with normal blood pressure, and are five times as likely to have a stroke than those with normal blood pressure.

High blood pressure is the foremost cause of stroke, and is one of the major causes of death among the elderly. The higher a person's blood pressure, the more likely it is that they will have a stroke. Even though women are less likely to have heart attacks then men, when it comes to strokes, women are just as vulnerable.

High blood pressure causes increased pressure in the internal organs and can promote damage to your kidneys, liver, and brain. Injury to the internal organs from high blood pressure happens silently, slowly, and without symptoms. But once it leads to a serious condition, the symptoms become very apparent.

People with high blood pressure have life spans on the average of 10 to 20 years shorter than people with normal blood pressure.

At the present time, no one knows for sure why people develop high blood pressure, but we do know that high blood pressure is one of the most treatable and preventable disorders.

Treatment for High Blood Pressure

Because hypertension is the major contributor to cardiovascular related deaths, doctors have for years looked for ways to effectively lower blood pressure.

People with severe high blood pressure must take antihypertensive drugs. In such cases, the benefits of the drugs far outweigh the side effects. However, people with mild hypertension have the option of trying non-drug therapies.

Even though it's been shown clearly that dietary modification alone is often just as effective as many hypertensive medications, the majority of hypertensive patients are given prescription drugs to lower blood pressure without being offered any alternatives.

Unfortunately these drugs sometimes cause more problems than they cure. For example, several studies have shown that taking medication designed to lower blood pressure can actually increase the risk of having a heart attack.

In addition, many people fail to control their blood pressure with medication because they forget to take it. Because high blood pressure has no symptoms, people don't notice that they have skipped taking their medicine. Others stop taking the medicine because they don't like the side-effects.

The drugs that are particularly toxic are the diuretics and the beta-blockers.

Beta-blockers

Beta-blocking drugs, such as propranolol (marketed under the brand name Inderal), are some of the most widely prescribed drugs in the United States today.

Beta-blockers lower blood pressure by decreasing the heart rate and the cardiac output. These drugs have many side effects, the most serious of which is congestive heart failure. Other common side effects include light-headedness, depression, memory loss, fatigue and sexual impotence.

It's also known that beta-blockers can trigger a rise in the level of cholesterol and triglycerides in the blood. This effect may explain why patients on beta-blockers have a higher incidence of heart attacks than high-risk patients not taking any medication.

It's been known for some time that several types of high blood pressure medication impair memory and intellectual capacity, but beta-blockers, such as propranolol and atenolol, may decrease memory performance more consistently than anti-hypertensive agents that act through other mechanisms.

Diuretics

As mentioned above, the other major class of hypertensive drugs are the diuretics. Like the beta-blockers, these medications have also been shown to increase the risk of heart attack.

These drugs lower blood pressure by removing water from the cells and passing it out of the body through urination. Kidneys monitor blood chemistry and make sure that the balance of water, waste products, and electrolytes is precisely maintained. But diuretics override this system. As well as removing water, they increase the excretion of calcium, magnesium and potassium. This is an unfortunate side-effect, as these minerals actually lower blood pressure and prevent heart attacks. In addition, diuretics sometimes raise cholesterol levels.

Diuretics are used for a specific purpose — to get water out of the body. The result of the lower water level is reduced fluid tension in the blood vessels. But, unfortunately, fluid tension in every cell in the body is reduced.

This means that diuretics cause brain cells to excrete water, which under normal conditions, happens only in an extreme emergency. This loss of fluid causes people to feel dizzy and drowsy, and to have memory problems.

In most cases, these problems are bothersome but not serious. However, in older people, who already have less water in their tissues, further water excretion can cause brain function to be thrown off. For example, if an elderly person drinks alcohol, even in moderation, they can become so confused that they forget to consume enough water or to eat properly. This then leads to malnutrition and dehydration. In fact, some doctors believe that the dehydration induced by diuretics combined with alcohol or tranquilizers is A leading cause of death among older Americans.

While all of the above mentioned problems are called side effects of diuretics, they are not side effects at all, they are the main effect of the drug. A diuretic works by grabbing onto sodium atoms and causing the body to excrete extra salt. This in turn brings down the water level in all tissues, since water is bonded with the salt in the body.

Because potassium is close to sodium in its atomic structure, diuretics also cause the body to excrete potassium. Loss of potassium can lead to weakness, fatigue, and leg cramps.

Besides these common signs of potassium deficiency, there can be other complications. For example, digitalis, a drug given to heart patients to relieve their chest pain, becomes more toxic if the body is low in potassium.

There is some evidence that potassium deficiency is linked to high blood pressure, which means that a diuretic may actually be promoting the very condition that it's meant to cure.

All people taking diuretics should take a potassium supplement. Eating a diet high in potassium is not enough. It would take a truckload of bananas to replace the potassium lost from taking diuretics.

Seeking Non-Drug Alternatives

There are many ways to lower blood pressure without medication. However, before you try any of them, heed the following words of caution.

All of the information in this chapter has been gathered from research studies, magazine articles, and books on blood pressure. Don't take anything you read as gospel — research it yourself. New research may show that some of this information is incorrect.

Also, never stop taking any prescription medication without consulting your doctor. Before you decide to undertake any dietary modification, lifestyle alteration, or a change in your medication, consult your doctor first, and let him or her know exactly what you intend to do.

The irony behind these sometimes dangerous medical treatments is that non-drug therapies are supported by most medical authorities, especially for mild and moderate hypertension.

There have been numerous studies that show that the harmful side effects of beta-blockers and diuretics outweigh their therapeutic effects. These studies support the fact that effective lifestyle changes work as well as taking drugs.

Many doctors, including those on the Joint National Committee on Detection, Evaluation and Treatment of High Blood Pressure, recommend that most people with high blood pressure not be placed on drugs, but instead say these patients should be encouraged to make dietary and lifestyle changes.

Drugs that Raise Blood Pressure

- Alcohol
- Oral contraceptives
- Decongestant nose drops
- Anti-inflammatory drugs
- Estrogen
- Steroids
- Medicine containing sodium
- Ibuprofin

Factors that Raise Blood Pressure

Food Allergy

Several studies have shown that blood pressure can be raised by food allergies. If you have a history of allergies or if there is a history of allergies in your family, it may be worthwhile to engage in an elimination and allergic rotation diet to find out if it can lower your blood pressure. Several studies have shown a positive relation between food allergies and a rise in blood pressure. For information on elimination and rotation diets, consult an allergist. More information on allergies can be found in the book *Brain Allergies,* by W. H. Philpott, M.D., and D. W. Kalita, Ph.D.

Sugar

In one experiment, the blood pressure of twenty healthy men was examined after they consumed various sugar solutions following an over-night fast. Drinking sugar raised their blood pressure for two hours. Eating sugar produced a significant increase in blood pressure that lasted for an hour. In light of these results, it may be a good idea to minimize your sugar intake.

Alcohol

Medical evidence shows that drinking more than three beers a day, more than three glasses of wine daily or three mixed drinks in a 24 hour period raises blood pressure.

However, drinking moderately can be good for you. There is some data that suggest drinking a glass of red wine a day can actually lower moderately high blood pressure. Keep in mind that alcoholic beverages are very high in calories, so if you are trying to lose weight, alcohol is not going to help.

Red wine has an added benefit. It contains substances that may have positive effects on brain health. Resveratrol, the most studied and probably the most active of these substancesis a naturally occurring compound present both in wine and grapes. It is a powerful antioxidant. Several studies have shown an inverse relationship between moderate wine intake and dementia, which suggests that components of wine (not alcohol) may have a protective effect on the brain, and increase blood flow through relaxation of the blood vessels. (There is also some evidence this substance inhibits the growth of breast cancer cells.)

Smoking

If you're a smoker, quit. This is absolutely essential. Smoking drastically increases your risk of dying of cardiovascular disease. Smoking also causes an immediate temporary increase in blood pressure during the time a person is smoking the cigarette. But because of its negative effect on the cardiovascular system, the long-term effect of smoking may be permanent hypertension.

Licorice

Although most licorice flavored products in this country contain artificial flavor, real licorice contains a substance called glycyrrhizic acid which can increase blood pressure.

This substance causes the body to retain sodium and excrete potassium. In addition, licorice can increase the side effects of diuretics. Real licorice is found today in some laxatives, natural licorice candy, some tobacco products, and in many natural cough remedies. Check labels before using these products.

Lead

Lead levels that were previously considered safe are now found to be associated with increased blood pressure. Eliminate all sources of lead and cadmium in your diet and, if necessary, get chelation therapy. (For more about lead, see chapter eighteen, Neurotoxins and Memory.)

Cadmium

People with hypertension show blood cadmium levels three or four times higher than those in matched people with normal blood pressure. Cadmium is found in high levels in cigarettes. It's been found that taking zinc supplements counteracts the effect of cadmium toxicity that raises blood pressure. This does not offset the other negative effects of smoking, however.

Salt

The average American consumes about two to two and a half teaspoons of salt a day. That's more than twenty times the amount of salt the body actually needs. In Japan, citizens consume enormous amounts of salt, perhaps the highest in the world. Jane Brody's *Nutrition Book* states that stroke caused by high blood pressure is the number one cause of death in Japan. And it's been found that 40 percent of the people in Japan have high blood pressure.

Conversely, in New Guinea, in the Amazon areas, and in the highlands of Malaysia, where people eat very little salt in their diet, there is no hypertension.

When you eat something salty, you get thirsty because extra water is needed to dilute the salt. The extra salt causes the body to hold water, and causes the volume of blood to rise. Blood vessels become water-logged, and they then become more sensitive to nerve stimulation, which cause them to contract. As more blood has to go through the contracted smaller vessels, blood pressure increases.

Even though salt usually raises blood pressure, it affects some people differently. Over half of the people with high blood pressure are salt sensitive. Adding salt to their diet makes blood pressure go up significantly. Salt sensitivity is found more commonly among blacks, individuals that are overweight, and those that have a genetic family history of high blood pressure. If you fall within one of these categories, salt should be avoided completely.

Other people with high blood pressure are salt resistant. Their blood pressure does not change when they vary the amount of salt they eat.

There is a small amount of people who are reverse salt sensitive. In these people blood pressure increases when they reduce salt.

If you decide you must eliminate salt from your diet, remove the salt shaker from your table. Cut out foods like ham, bacon, hot dogs, shell fish, cheeses, avocado and all processed foods. Also avoid antacids and laxatives that are high in sodium. Become aware of the hidden salt in fast food and prepared foods. Read labels very carefully.

You can lower the salt content in prepared food and canned goods by simply rinsing them in water. For example, in one study, the salt in a can of tuna rinsed in water for one minute was reduced by 79 percent.

Talking

Strange as it may seem, it has been found that talking causes a temporary increase in blood pressure. In fact, some people with normal blood pressure have been diagnosed in the doctor's office as having hypertension merely because they were talking while their blood pressure was being measured.

Snoring

Earlier in this book we looked at a case where sleep apnea was mistaken for dementia. Sleep apnea, a disorder that blocks the flow of air through the esophagus, also causes a significant rise in blood pressure, and can be potentially dangerous.

In fact, men who snore frequently actually have a 50 percent higher risk of having high blood pressure, a 70 percent increased potential for heart disease, and a 40 percent higher risk of stroke than those who do not snore. Women who snore are 30 percent more likely to have elevated blood pressure.

This condition also causes sleep deprivation and constant fatigue, because the person wakes up each time the airway becomes blocked.

There are now several simple non-medical and surgical techniques that can eliminate this problem. If you are a chronic snorer, see a specialist who can offer you several remedies for the problem.

Nutritional Factors in Lowering Blood Pressure

Water

Some research suggests that increasing the amount of water that you drink can lower blood pressure. Dr. F. Batmanghelidj, in his book, *Your Body's Many Cries for Water,* feels that dehydration is a major cause of high blood pressure, and that increased fluid intake is the cure.

He also recommends that you avoid all foods that contain caffeine, such as coffee, tea and soft drinks, because caffeine has diuretic properties. He suggests that every person should drink six to eight glasses of water per day.

Weight Reduction

It is clear that one of the most powerful contributors to high blood pressure is excess weight. This is evidenced by the fact that 70 percent of people with hypertension are overweight.

High blood pressure is more common in overweight people than in those of normal weight because every extra pound of body fat requires an additional mile of blood vessels to feed the cells. This extra mileage forces the heart to work harder. Obesity, as I pointed out earlier, is at epidemic proportions in the United states and is a prime cause of high blood pressure, as well as a condition favorable to the onset of type 2 diabetes.

The good news is that weight-induced high blood pressure can be reduced dramatically through weight loss alone. Several studies suggest that overweight people can decrease their blood pressure eight to ten points just by losing twenty pounds.

The most effective way to lose weight and consequently lower your blood pressure is to permanently increase your physical activity and eliminate all fat from your diet.

Low-Fat Diet

Eating a low-fat diet reduces blood pressure, even if body weight remains the same. In one particularly interesting study, thirty five healthy, middle-aged men and women changed their diet from one in which nearly 40 percent of calories were from fat to a regimen that included only 20 percent fat.

After six weeks on the reduced fat diet, diastolic blood pressure was lowered by an average of nine points.

A diet high in fresh fruits and vegetables which includes only low-fat meats, such as chicken, turkey and fish, lowers fat intake dramatically.

Various Cuts of Chicken and Turkey and Their Fat Content
(3 ounces for each except thigh as noted)

1/2 Chicken Breast without skin	4.0 grams
1 2-oz. Chicken Thigh without skin	5.7 grams
1 Chicken Leg w/ Thigh and no skin	8.0 grams
4 Chicken Wings	6.8 grams
Turkey White Meat	2.7 grams
Turkey Dark Meat	6.1 grams

A Dozen Types of Fish and Their Fat Content
(3 ounces for each)

Cod, Atlantic, cooked	7.0 grams
Flounder, cooked	11.7 grams
Haddock, cooked	7.5 grams
Halibut, cooked	18.9 grams
Mackerel, Pacific, raw	28.8 grams
Monkfish, raw	18.0 grams
Orange Roughy, raw	50.4 grams
Salmon, Atlantic, raw	40.1 grams
Sardines, Atlantic, canned in oil	50.4 grams
Sea Bass, cooked	18.8 grams
Shark, raw	30.8 grams
Trout, Lake, raw	40.0 grams

Vegetarianism

People who eat vegetarian diets have significantly cleaner arteries and lower blood pressure than meat eaters. Doctor Ross Trattler in his book, *Better Health Through Natural Healing,* states, "Over 85 percent of the people with high blood pressure can be treated without drugs. In most cases, dietary modification is all that is needed." He recommends the most effective way to treat high blood pressure is a vegetarian diet.

Melvin Werbach has spent years researching the nutritional influences on illness. Werbach recommends above all, an increase in fiber intake. He cites various studies that show that fiber decreases blood pressure. Like Trattler, Werbach suggests that the best way to achieve this is through a vegetarian diet.

Raw Foods

Studies show that people who increase the amount of raw foods in their diet can actually lower their blood pressure significantly. In addition, several studies have revealed that increasing the amount of raw food in the diet resulted in weight loss and a spontaneous decrease in the consumption of nicotine and alcohol. It seems that the improvement in nutritional status of the body reduces the craving for these substances.

Fruit

In his book *How to Develop a Sky High I.Q.,* Jeffery Bland states that certain tropical fruits clean out arteries. These include bananas, kiwi, mangoes and papaya. An enzyme in these fruits, called bromelain, is responsible for this effect.

Grapefruit and apple pectin lower cholesterol and keep arteries clean. In one research study, people who consumed twelve grams of grapefruit pectin a day lowered their cholesterol by 17 percent. Grapefruit pectin capsules are available in health food stores.

Eating fruit is important. For example, it's been shown that just eating one serving of fruit per day can lower stroke risk by as much as 40 percent.

Olive Oil

Certain types of fats, called polyunsaturated and monounsaturated fats, are found in fish, vegetable oils, seeds and nuts. These fats lower blood pressure and neutralize the negative effects of saturated fats. The most highly unsaturated or monounsaturated fats available are olive oil and canola oil. One teaspoon of olive oil per 1,000 calories of intake reduces blood pressure as much as 10 points.

Fish Oils

Ocean fish are high in omega-3 fatty acids. Two of the fats, (docosahexaenoic and eicosapentaenoic acids) are found in oily fish. Studies indicate that they may have benefits for many medical conditions, including hypertension. Fish high in omega-3 fatty acids include mackerel, sardines, salmon and haddock. (Of course, you'll want to combine any high-fat content fish with low-fat food items for a healthier diet.) You can also buy omega-3 fatty acids in concentrated form in your health food store.

It appears that fish oils lower blood pressure by decreasing the viscosity of the blood and making it flow more smoothly through the blood vessel. When fish oil is eaten, it is immediately taken up by blood platelets and red blood cells. The oils reduce the tendency of the platelets to stick together, which prevents clots. The presence of the oils in red cells makes the cells more flexible, and the increased flexibility makes them more slippery. (There is more information on Omega-3s in chapter twenty-four.)

Fiber

Eating a diet high in plant fiber can lower blood pressure, although the mechanism is not clearly understood. Some studies show that by tripling the amount of fiber in the diet, people have reduced their systolic blood pressure by as much as 11 percent.

It's thought that increased fiber has this effect because it regulates changes in insulin levels. There is some evidence that high levels of insulin contribute to high blood pressure because it's a salt retentive hormone. High fiber foods include all vegetables and fresh fruits and whole grains.

Nutritional Status

Studies show nutritional differences between people with normal blood pressure and high blood pressure. People with high blood pressure tend to have lower levels of vitamin A, vitamin B complex, vitamin C and vitamin D. This suggests that supplementing all of these vitamins would lower blood pressure.

Coenzyme Q10

Another nutrient that's been shown to be deficient in high blood pressure patients is coenzyme Q10. The recommended daily allowance for lowering of blood pressure with coenzyme Q10 is 60mg. per day. It is said to take four to twelve weeks for this nutrient to lower blood pressure.

Potassium

As mentioned previously, diuretics leach potassium from the body. Anyone taking diuretics should also take a potassium supplement.

Supplementing your diet with potassium can reduce blood pressure. Studies show that potassium supplements have little effect on people with normal blood pressure, but they do reduce blood pressure in people with high blood pressure. Winter squash, cantaloupe, avocados, orange juice, bananas, potatoes, and tomatoes are all high in potassium.

Julian Whitaker, in *99 Secrets for a Longer Healthier Life,* says the following about blood pressure: "It's not just the amount of salt that we take in every day that causes high blood pressure, but it's the ratio of sodium to potassium. In our culture, potassium is reduced in our diet by food processing and sodium is added to our diet by food processing. By increasing your potassium intake, you can lower your blood pressure without reducing sodium."

Here are several ideas for increasing your potassium intake. You can use one or more of these suggestions each day.
- Drink an 8-ounce glass of orange juice daily.
- Eat a salad of uncooked, fresh vegetables every day.
- Eat two apples a day.
- Use a potassium-based salt substitute.

If you have a kidney problem, check with your doctor before attempting to increase the potassium you take in. Potassium salt substitutes are found in grocery stores under the names Morton's Salt Substitute, Nu-Salt and No Salt.

Calcium

Calcium is found in dairy products, all of the bean family, and in leafy green vegetables.

It's been determined that people with high blood pressure consume less calcium than people with normal blood pressure. In a study at the University of Oregon, hypertensives were given 1,000mg. of calcium a day. At the end of eight weeks, twenty one of them had reduced their blood pressure by ten points or better.

Calcium helps lower high blood pressure by aiding in the excretion of excess sodium, it also relaxes the blood vessels.

Magnesium

Magnesium is another important nutrient to lowering blood pressure. Magnesium is found in nuts, brown rice, milk, wheat germ, bananas, potatoes, molasses and soy products. Low levels of magnesium in the diet have been shown to increase blood pressure. Magnesium acts in concert with calcium in regulating blood pressure.

Some new drugs on the market are called calcium channel blockers. These drugs work by altering the access of calcium into the cell. These medications relax smooth muscle in the artery wall and cause a patient's blood pressure to fall. Taking magnesium causes the same type of thing to happen, with none of the side effects. It might be called a natural calcium channel blocker.

Taking 1,000mg. of magnesium every day has been shown to relax blood vessels and reduce peripheral resistance. It's thought that one of the reasons magnesium lowers blood pressure is because this compound is a vasodilator. This means that it can widen the diameter of a blood vessel. Magnesium is able to accomplish this task by removing calcium from the smooth muscle cell surfaces inside the blood vessels.

Dr. Julian Whitaker has a specific approach to treatment for severe cases of hypertension. He uses injections of 2 grams of magnesium sulfate mixed with procaine. In addition, he recommends a very rigid diet, consisting only of brown rice, raw fruit, and raw and cooked vegetables. Whitaker claims that even severe cases of high blood pressure can be brought substantially under control on this strict diet along with the magnesium injections. This is a radical program, so never attempt it without a doctor's supervision.

Rice

In his book, *The Nature Doctor*, Dr. H. Vogel states that eating daily servings of whole grain rice can reduce blood pressure. Rice is a low-fat, high-fiber food that also promotes weight loss, and even if Vogel is wrong, rice is good for you.

Coleus

A member of the mint family, Coleus grows in India. It's cultivated in the United States as an ornamental plant. The root has been used for medicinal purposes and as a condiment for salads.

Coleus has been used for hundreds of years in Hindu and Ayurvedic traditional medicine because it's the source of a unique compound called forskolin.

Forskolin has been shown to have an antispasmodic affect on smooth muscles, which are the type of muscles found in the walls of the blood vessels. Using coleus lowers blood pressure, and improves the contraction of the heart muscle. This chemical has also been shown to be effective in treatment of glaucoma, and has the ability to prevent asthma attacks in some people.

Hawthorne

Hawthorne *(Cretaegus oxycantha)* leaves, berries and blossoms contain many biologically active compounds called flavonoids. These compounds are responsible for the red and blue color of berries, and also cause the red and blue color of cherries, grapes and many flowers. Flavonoids are highly concentrated in hawthorne berries.

Hawthorne extracts are effective in lowering blood pressure, reducing angina attacks, lowering serum cholesterol levels, and preventing the deposit of cholesterol in the arterial walls. Hawthorne is widely used in Europe and Asia for its antihypertensive activity.

Hawthorne appears to improve the blood supply to the heart by dilating the coronary arteries. It improves the metabolic processes of the heart, which results in an increase in the force of contractions of the heart muscle, and eliminates some types of rhythm disturbances by inhibiting an enzyme in the body called angiotensin converting enzyme (ACE). Hawthorne's ability to dilate coronary arteries has been repeatedly demonstrated in experimental studies. This effect appears to come from the relaxation of smooth muscle in the blood vessels.

Recently, several substances in hawthorne have been shown to inhibit ACE in a similar way to catapril, a drug that is used to treat high blood pressure.

In order for hawthorne to work effectively, it must be taken at least two weeks before adequate tissue concentrations are achieved. The dosage of hawthorne depends on the type of preparation and the source of the material. Check with a qualified herbalist for proper dosage.

Garlic

The *Journal of Longevity Research* recommends garlic *(Allium sativum)* as an effective treatment for high blood pressure. Although many doctors debate the usefulness of garlic, several studies show that the regular use of garlic supplements can lower blood pressure. It appears that the benefits are temporary, and the supplements must be used continuously to be of benefit.

Celery

Celery *(Apium graveolens)* has been used as a folk remedy for lowering blood pressure for many generations. Although celery contains large amounts of sodium, it also appears to contain substances which lower blood pressure

Researcher William J. Elliott has identified a chemical called 3-n-butyl phthalide which he suggests is responsible for celery's pressure lowering effect. The chemical acts by lowering stress hormones in the body.

Nutritionists recommend eating two stalks of celery every day. Studies show that rats who consumed the equivalent of four stalks of celery a day lowered their blood pressure an average of 13 percent.

Black Cohosh

Cohosh *(Cimicifuga racemosa* or *Actaea racemosa)* is known to act similarly to estrogen, and is sometimes used as a natural estrogen therapy.

It has long been recommended by herbalists as having positive effects on high blood pressure. After an extensive search, I was unable to find any scientific studies to verify that this herb is useful as a therapy to lower blood pressure.

Actein, a chemical found in black cohosh, seems to be the substance that has a hypotensive effect. One study revealed that it lowered blood pressure in rabbits and cats but not in dogs. So if you are a dog, you're out of luck.

There is evidence however, that overdoses of the herb may cause a depressed heart rate in susceptible individuals, even at relatively low doses.

Because of this it's recommended that anyone with heart disease not use black cohosh and that patients taking medications to control high blood pressure should be cautioned about black cohosh because of the potential for an additive hypotensive effect.

Cayenne Pepper

Cayenne *(Capsicum annum)* has been shown to reduce cholesterol and blood pressure. It is available in capsule form in health food stores. Contrary to what many believe, for the majority of us, cayenne pepper does not irritate the stomach.

Apple Cider Vinegar

Apple cider vinegar and honey is a well known folk remedy for high blood pressure. The best way to take it is by diluting two tablespoons of vinegar into a glass of water and sip it during a meal. You can add honey to improve the taste. You can also add vinegar to the diet in salad dressings and in cooking. This remedy is said to reduce blood pressure up to 20 percent.

Valerian Root

Valerian *(Valeriana officinalis)* root causes a tranquilizing effect on the brain and the nervous system. It is an important herb for lowering stress, which is a cause of high blood pressure.

Chervil

Chervil *(Anthriscus cerefolium)* is native to the Caucasus Mountains, south Russia and western Asia, and is also grown in the United States. It's an herb that has been used for years to lower blood pressure, although I could find no scientific studies that prove its effectiveness (There are several studies that do find it to be an effective antioxidant.) The leaves and flowers are the parts of the plant that are utilized for this purpose.

Chives

Chives *(Allium schoenoprasum)* are a member of the onion family, and like garlic, can help lower blood pressure. They contain the sulfur-rich oil found in garlic, but in smaller quantities. It is best to use chives along with other herbs for this purpose.

Serpentwood

Also called Indian snakeroot, serpentwood *(Rauwolfia serpentina)* is an herb that has been used for many years to lower blood pressure. It has been used in India for more than four thousand years. Grown in India, Thailand, and other parts of Asia, South America, and Africa, there are more than 100 known species of this plant.

Reserpine, a chemical found in the roots, is responsible for most of the plant's therapeutic effects.

The prescription drug reserpine is used in conventional medicine to treat high blood pressure You should be aware that the drug reduces the level of catecholamines within the brain and has been linked to memory problems, Parkinson's-like symptoms, and depression.

Other Methods of Lowering Blood Pressure

Exercise

The first and most important non-drug therapy for high blood pressure is exercise. Exercise can be a very effective treatment for moderately high blood pressure, but it takes time to see the effects. In some cases it takes up to a year, but most people see results within three months.

To reduce blood pressure effectively, the exercise must be aerobic, that is, it must be exercise that raises the pulse to your target heart rate for at least a half an hour. To establish your target heart rate, subtract your age from 220, and multiply the result by 85 percent.

Aerobic exercise doesn't have to be grueling. A brisk walk for 30 or 40 minutes, three or four times a week, is effective. At that rate, it will take four to six months to lower blood pressure.

Although aerobic exercise is very good for lowering blood pressure, isometric exercises like weight lifting, are not good. Weight lifting can actually cause blood pressure to skyrocket. If you have high blood pressure, talk to your doctor before beginning a weight lifting program.

Stress Reduction

Years of research have shown that stress reduction training such as meditation, self-hypnosis and breathing techniques, can lower the tension in the body, and also lower blood pressure.

Exercise also lowers stress and tension in the body and therefore has a doubly good effect. If you think that stress may be causing your high blood pressure, one of the ways to find out is to take your blood pressure several times a day during different situations. Identify any pattern in your blood pressure related to stress. For example, if you take your blood pressure right after a stressful situation, is it significantly higher? If so, begin a stress reduction program.

Although most stress reduction seminars focus primarily on relaxation methods, the most effective method of stress management is coping skills, that is, learning effective communication skills and effective problem-solving skills. Gaining these skills makes life considerably easier.

Pets

Getting a pet can significantly lower blood pressure. While pets are very effective for this, it has been shown that even taking care of plants can lower blood pressure. Living with plants or pets involves bonding, commitment, and emotional gratification, which in turn reduce stress.

In one study, 92 people who had suffered a heart attack were discharged from a coronary care unit in the hospital, and monitored frequently. Thirty-nine of them owned pets, and fifty three did not. One year later, the mortality rate of the people with no pets was 28 percent, while the mortality rate of the people with pets was only six percent. Get a pet.

Human Touch

It has also been found that physical touch lowers blood pressure. Caressing, holding, loving, massaging and stroking, significantly lowers blood pressure in people. So, if you can't get a pet, get married.

Social Support

It's very clear from scientific research that people with many friends and a large social support network have less stress in their life, less problems, and lower blood pressure than people who don't have the support.

Happiness

It's also been shown that people who are happy have lower blood pressure than people who are worried and anxious. This is hard evidence that you should put some fun in your life.

Research has also shown the longer that people live together, the more likely it is that their blood pressure will become the same. This suggests that if your blood pressure is high, there is a good chance that your spouse's blood pressure is high also. Monitor your blood pressure together. Apparently happy people have a positive effect on each other, while unhappy people have a negative effect.

Chapter Fourteen

A Whack on the Head

Magnum enters the darkened room with his gun drawn. He knows that there are two armed men in the room, and his next move could be his last.

As he inches around a packing crate, a sinister figure appears above him. Suddenly without warning, the villain hits him with the butt of his gun, knocking him unconscious. Magnum falls to the floor in a heap.

Several minutes later, he awakens to find himself a prisoner. Slowly coming back to consciousness, he unexpectedly jumps up, tackles the villain, and overpowers him.

We've all watched scenes like this hundreds of times on television. Villains and heroes alike are constantly getting smacked on the head with guns, and are knocked out by a punch in the nose. They recover within minutes and go on about their business with no ill effects.

But things don't happen that way in the real world. A blow to the head that causes a loss of consciousness can inflict one of several types of serious injury.

Being knocked unconscious can cause a closed head injury. This condition is caused by the bruising or tearing of delicate brain tissue. The brain is a jelly-like substance that is suspended in a bath of spinal fluid. It is protected by rubbery membranes called the meninges. Minor bumps on the head do not usually cause any damage. But getting hit hard enough to cause a loss of consciousness can cause serious injury to the brain's delicate tissues.

A concussion is a temporary loss of consciousness occurring after a blow to the head. The impact of the blow causes the semi-liquid brain tissue to slosh about inside the skull, causing it to bruise. Like any bruise, the injured tissue then swells. When the brain becomes bruised and swollen, brain function can be disrupted for weeks after the injury. This can cause loss of memory, and sometimes permanent brain damage.

Most concussions are caused by traffic accidents, but they can also occur from falls, or from being hit on the head by any object.

Immediately after a concussion, the victim may experience confusion, memory loss, vomiting, and blurred vision. The longer the person is unconscious, the more severe the symptoms tend to be.

As soon as possible after a person has experienced a loss of consciousness, she should see a doctor to rule out skull fracture, brain injury, or bleeding inside the lining of the brain called *subdural hematoma.* Subdural bleeding is a serious condition that requires immediate medical attention.

Weeks after a head injury, the person may experience headaches, dizziness, changes in behavior, drowsiness, and memory loss.

About one-third of the people who experience a concussion will exhibit post concussion syndrome. This syndrome includes chronic memory loss, dizziness, and changes in behavior that can last over a year. Because most knocks on the head are soon forgotten, the person usually does not connect the symptoms with the accident.

Repeated concussions, such as those experienced by boxers, can cause permanent brain damage, including a condition called *punch drunk syndrome.* One study revealed that 87 percent of former boxers showed evidence of brain damage. We also know that a significant number of those suffering from dementia have a history of head injury.

Elderly people often fall or bump their head, and later forget that the incident happened. In a younger person, these bumps may be unimportant. But the brains of elderly people are sometimes smaller, and slosh about inside the skull more easily. The decreased amount of neurons in the elderly brain makes minor damage more serious. Even minor bumps on the head in the elderly, such as a bump on the head from a cabinet door, can cause subdural hematoma. So any bump on the head should be checked out by a doctor.

Two fairly recent studies — one in the Dutch city of Rotterdam involving many volunteers 55 years and older, and the other taken from U.S. military records of head trauma victims — seem to have settled concerns about minor head injuries as a cause of Alzheimer's disease in older patients. According to the findings, minor head injury (loss of consciousness of less than 30 minutes) appears to have no significant association with the development of Alzheimer's disease. Moderate to severe head injury may, on the other hand, be a contributor to memory loss progression. This is why it is so important that victims of head injuries should always be examined by a physician.

Chapter Fifteen

Depression and Memory

Depression is the most common mental disorder in our nation. In fact, one out of two hospital beds in this country is occupied by someone suffering from depression. Worldwide, depression is considered as one in the eight major ailments plaguing people.

What is less recognized is the fact that depression is also one of the most frequent and under-diagnosed causes of memory problems. Depression has a profound effect on the ability to think, reason and remember. In fact, the symptoms of depression can be so severe that it's often difficult to tell whether a person is suffering from depression or dementia. Because of this, several diagnostic tests have been developed to ferret out the differences between these two memory destroying disorders.

A growing body of evidence shows that in many cases, a decline in the power of memory may be due not simply to inevitable age-related neurological changes, but, at least in part, to psychological depression. Depression appears to correlate with an increased risk for developing Alzheimer's disease and other senile dementias — along with a poor prognosis for recovery from stroke or heart attack.

Untreated depression increases the level of a group of chemicals called glucocorticoids. Over time, these chemicals can cause permanent damage to the hippocampus, that part of the brain that stores memory.

Each year, hundreds of people seek help from physicians and psychologists for memory complaints, when what they are actually suffering from is depression. If you feel that you are having memory problems, you should have a neuropsychological examination to discover if your problem is, in fact, depression.

A recent screening of 67 persons over 55 with memory problems, conducted at the Medical College of Wisconsin Memory Disorders Clinic and Marquette University School of Nursing, illustrates this problem. Of the 43 percent of subjects who said they were "worried" about their memory, only 14 percent registered in the lower range for memory based on standardized tests. Of that 14 percent, all but one person scored high on the depression scale. From this study and others, science has learned that memory loss may be tied to anxiety and depression. When treated, the memory issues go away.

The Wisconsin study was also an effort to find individuals with true early memory impairment — people who are fully functioning but in most cases remain unaware that they have memory problems. As we discussed earlier, previous studies have shown that individuals with true early memory impairment develop Alzheimer's at a rate of roughly 15 percent per year. However, in this study, none of the persons screened fell into this group.

The Wisconsin study reaffirmed a fact that science has long established: Depression destroys memory faster than age. Conversely, withdrawal from participation in challenging mental activity may lead to depression.

This is why depression often follows hard on the heels of retirement. The lesson to be drawn from this is simple. Since happiness and mental acuity are if anything faster friends than forgetfulness and aging, the best way to be happy is to keep yourself intellectually busy.

Treating depression can reduce memory complaints. One recent study, conducted by Finnish researchers, involved 174 adults with major depression. At the start of the study, the depressed patients performed poorly on several neuropsychological tests of memory, including the ability to repeat short stories or lists from memory. For the next six months, the patients were given treatment for their depression, including medication and/or therapy. At the end of this period, patients whose depression had been reduced also reported fewer memory problems. Their performance on the memory tests also improved.

How Depression Effects Memory

Depression interferes with memory in several ways.

First, depressed people become focused on internal events. These may be memories about tragic losses, or about real and imagined transgressions. Often the focus is on physical symptoms such as body aches and pains.

Even when memory is working well, only a few of our daily experiences will become permanently stored in our brains. Unusual or important events will be transferred from working memory into short-term memory — the bin where we store memories for minutes or hours. The rest will disappear within minutes.

In depression, an internal preoccupation prevents the person from attending to the outside world. Therefore, the depressed person may be too inattentive and unfocused to store daily events in short-term memory. It is not that the person has forgotten, but that the memory was never stored in the first place. Because the activities and accomplishments of the day are not stored, life seems empty and pointless.

Second, there is a selective bias in the memories of the depressed. At Kansas State University, Charles Thompson has spent 15 years researching episodic and involuntary memory. Thompson has found that in non-depressed people, negative emotions fade faster than positive ones. But in depressed people the positive memories fade faster.

This same pattern holds true in the case of involuntary memory, that is, memories that are triggered by eternal cues such as sight or smell. We all tend to remember happy events when we are happy and sad events when we are sad. But depressed people have four times the number of negatively cued memories than the non-depressed.

Dr. Norman Rosenthal, the man who discovered seasonal affective disorder, agrees that depressed people tend to recall mostly the negative, unhappy experiences. This can appear to family and friends as a loss of memory. It also reinforces the person's drab and negative view of life, fueling the depression.

Third, depression actually disrupts the level of brain activity in the afflicted person, so that memory and thought processing are impaired. People suffering from depression often are sometimes said to exhibit poverty of thought, which is the inability to process thought at all. This type of impairment suggests a loss of coordination between working, short-term, and long-term memory. Studies show that brain-cell activity in the frontal lobes — located in the front of the brain, behind the forehead — is often reduced in depressed people.

Fourth, depression has also been linked to decreased levels of chemicals in the brain, called neurotransmitters. The neurotransmitters involved in depression include serotonin, melatonin, dopamine, adrenaline, and noradrenaline, substances which also play an important role in memory. It is believed that antidepressant drugs work by raising the levels of these chemicals.

Fifth, depression is accompanied by feelings of helplessness and hopelessness. This leads the sufferer to ignore any input from the outside world. They just don't care if they remember anything.

Memory is but one of a set of executive functions of the brain that are impaired by depression. In addition to becoming forgetful, a person suffering from major depression may have trouble initiating tasks, making decisions, planning future actions, organizing thoughts.

Depression also interferes with prioritization. When shown film clips of neutral, moderately disturbing, and very disturbing incidents, non-depressed individuals were able to decsribe the amount of emotional reaction to the clips. Depressed people however showed an all or nothing response, that is, there was no response to the neutral clip, but an extreme response to both the moderate and severe clips. This all-or-nothing mode of thinking causes the person to become over-whelmed by any emotional demand on them, and consequently, they shut down. This may be in part because of abnormal emotional reactions to the world around them. Research suggests depressed people in prolonged elaborative processing of emotional information become stuck on certain events in their life.

The amygdala is the part of the brain that tags memories with emotion. In a recent study, people who had never been depressed showed activity in the amygdala in response to both negative and positive stimuli, which decayed within 10 seconds. Depressed individuals, however, showed prolonged amygdala responses to negative words that lasted throughout the following non-emotional processing trials (about 25 seconds later). These findings suggest that depression prolongs the response to negative events, and may interfere with subsequent events.

Another part of the brain affected in depression is the *right anterior cingulate gyrus,* a part of the brain that processes emotion. In a study done using the Hamilton Depression Rating Scale as a measure of depression, an inverse relationship was found between blood flow to the cingulate and the severity of the depression.

Brain scans revealed that the depressed group had significant perfusion reduction over the left frontal lobe and the right cingulate gyrus. The right anterior cingulate gyrus showed the most significant reduction in activity.

The importance of this study is that the authors concluded that the same type of brain damage can account for primary depression and depression associated with Alzheimer's.

Pain and Depression

New evidence suggests that chronic pain may bring on depression and impair executive function. According to pain researcher Marshall Devor, pain signals originate at the site of injury but soon disrupt the entire nervous system. In chronic pain, spinal cord neurons become hypersensitive and start sending pain signals to the brain even in response to weak stimuli. For this reason people with arthritis, cancer and diabetes sometimes experience widespread pain from even the lightest touch.

A. Vania Apkarian, a bioelectrical engineer and physiologist at Northwestern University, compared the overall volume and regional gray matter density in patients who had chronic back pain with those features in non-suffering control subjects.

He found that the average amount of atrophy was greater in those with lower back pain than in normal subjects. Functional brain imaging studies indicated the damage was in prefrontal cortex and cingulate gyrus — areas involved in mood and decision making.

He then asked 26 people who had suffered lower back pain for more than one year to play a gambling card game called the Iowa Gambling Task. The game involves selecting cards from decks with different potential cash payouts and penalties. People without pain did well in this task, but those with pain did poorly. They seemed to make their decisions carelessly. The amount of pain they expressed was related to the choices they made. This led Apkarian to posit that these people may be making poor choices on their daily life. This was thought to be a result of frontal lobe damage as a result of the pain, which interferes with executive function.

Causes of Depression

Although depression is most often caused by loss, isolation, or biochemical imbalances in the brain, it can also be triggered by nutritional deficiencies or excesses; prescription, over-the-counter, and illegal drugs; alcohol, caffeine and nicotine; hypoglycemia; aspartame (Nutrasweet); and hormonal imbalances. In fact, research suggests that almost any chronic nutritional deficiency or imbalance can trigger depression.

Several medications, especially blood pressure medications, are known culprits. Yet even though this is common knowledge, many doctors are unaware of how often their patients are suffering from drug-induced depression.

Harvard researcher Dr. Jerry Avorn and his colleagues looked at how often antidepressants were prescribed to people taking beta-blockers such as Inderal, Lopressor, and Corgard.

Examining the medical records of 143,253 patients, they found that 23 percent (almost one out of four) of those taking beta-blockers were also taking antidepressants.

This study revealed that doctors often give patients additional prescriptions to overcome side effects of another medication without realizing that the problems could be solved by eliminating the first medication. For this reason, ask your doctor if any medication you are taking might cause depression.

Other Causes of Depression.

In addition to medication problems, depression can also be brought on by allergies and environmental toxins. For example, solvents like those used in paints, furniture making, and boat building have been reported to evoke depression, confusion, and memory loss in many people.

Another cause is chronic exposure to heavy metals. When this is a suspected source of the problem, hair analysis is an accurate and cost effective method of detecting heavy metals, and should be used to aid the diagnosis.

Depression is often one of the first signs of thyroid disease. Even subtle decreases in thyroid hormone can induce depression. For this reason, depressed patients should be routinely screened for hyperthyroidism, particularly if they complain of fatigue. Like the thyroid gland, dysfunction of the adrenal gland has been associated with depression, so adrenal function should also be checked.

In a few cases, chronic vitamin C deficiency has been shown to cause hypochondriasis and depression. In contrast, high levels of vitamin C seem to have a positive effect on multiple functions of the brain.

Folic acid and B12 levels are low in a large proportion of patients suffering from various emotional problems, especially depression. But although B12 deficiency is common in depression, measuring levels of B12 in the blood is not useful. B12 deficiency may not become apparent until long after serum levels have been greatly reduced, and depression has begun.

Folic acid deficiency is the most common nutritional deficiency in the world. In studies of people with depression, as many as 30 percent were shown to be deficient in folic acid. This deficiency is especially prevalent in the elderly. In one study, 67 percent of the patients admitted to a geropsychiatric hospital were folate deficient. Folic acid deficiency can cause chronic forgetfulness, insomnia, apathy, depression, and dementia-like symptoms.

Niacin (vitamin B3) deficiency and biotin deficiency can also bring on depression and memory problems, as well as cause emotional instability, while a pantothenic acid (vitamin B5) and pyridoxine (vitamin B6) deficiency can cause restlessness, irritability, and depression.

Thiamin (vitamin B1) deficiency is very common among alcoholics, and can lead to a condition called Korsakoff's psychosis, which causes profound memory loss, as well as depression, apathy, anxiety and irritability. B1 deficiency in the brain results in a condition called metabolic acidosis, which upsets the neurotransmitter balance.

Illness and Depression

Depression has been called the common cold of psychopathology. Indeed, like the common cold, all of the sources of depression may be elusive and remain a challenge to your doctor. You can help him to help you if you understand and report to him any of the symptoms listed in the seven causes described below:

1. A depressing event can cause a physical illness. Both may be effects from a single cause. Data about the increased rate of physical illnesses among the widowed and those in areas of high unemployment show a rise in circulatory disorders, neoplasms, infections, and other physical illnesses under depressing circumstances.

2. A physical illness can cause a depression. This seems particularly likely in a person who experiences an extreme disability or a fatal prognosis.

3. Physical illness and depression can occur at the same time with no clear cause-effect relationship. Those geneticists who are most convinced that heredity causes depression might see this as a likely possibility.

4. Physical illness can serve as a communication of a need for nurturance or of relief from responsibilities in persons whose self-image does not permit awareness of a "psychiatric" condition in themselves. In such cases depression may not be at the level of awareness, and certainly it would not be verbalized.

5. Physical illness can cause a depression through metabolic, endocrine and other physiologic changes which lead to feelings of reduced vitality.

6. As we indicated earlier, medications used for physical illnesses may cause depressions.

7. The cause-effect relationship between substance abuse and depression is perhaps the most unclear of the seven types described here. Low personal self-esteem, loss, and loneliness contributing to substance abuse, and substance abuse that lowers self-esteem, loss, and loneliness are symptoms of depression.

Prescription Drugs Can Produce Depression

With the increased medical care available to the American population, many patients move from physician to physician and keep taking or compounding the prescriptions given by each. The list of drugs that singly or in combination may produce depression is long. Anxiety may often appear as the cause of depression, but may mask an underlying depression. Another factor is that patients with a previous history of depression are most likely to have repeat episodes precipitated by drugs.

Particularly prone to precipitate depression are those drugs that act on the central nervous system, including anti-emetics, sedatives, and tranquilizers.

New on the scene within the past two decades is the widespread use of "recreational" drugs, those obtained from the street in varying compositions, dosages, and effects. Often increased dosages are required to alleviate what may or may not be true depressive symptoms. "Letdown" from these drugs when they are withdrawn, even for short periods, may be mistaken for a depressive syndrome. Users frequently speak of depression when, in reality, the physiologic response of combinations, or abstinence, might be producing the "depression." Even with the plethora of drugs, legal or illegal, which singly or in combination can contribute to depression, there are several groups that stand out in particular. Most have a depressive effect on the central nervous system.

Drugs that Cause Depression

- Digitalis
- Clonidine
- Levodopa
- Antipsychotics
- Propranolol
- Reserpine

- Methyldopate
- Barbiturates
- Benzodiazepines
- Steroids
- Cimetidine
- Gaunethidine

Post-Surgical Depression

Post-surgical patients who suffer depression are often viewed as responding psychologically to an insult to their bodies. Most doctors who recognize the symptoms will prescribe an electrolyte study done to determine if there is an electrolyte imbalance.

Hormonal Disorders

Closely akin to, and inter-related with the electrolyte disorders, are the hormonal disorders. Again, a myriad of symptoms may be produced, but depression is one of the most common. Hormone associated depression is discussed in a forthcoming chapter.

Adrenal Cortex Dysfunction

Addison's Disease affects the majority of its victims with depression. Frequently, patients are treated for apathy before anorexia, sufficient weight loss, and other symptomatologies occur that lead to an Addison diagnosis. Cushing's syndrome is associated with an even higher incidence of depression and it, too, usually presents its diagnostic features after depressive symptoms have already occurred.

Hyperinsulinism

This pancreatic disorder often is exhibited by overeating, a sign not often associated with depression. Usually, other psychiatric symptoms are observed first, but depression can and does occur with this disorder.

Parathyroidism

Hypoparathyroidism has long been associated with a host of psychiatric disorders, depression being one of the less common. Hyperparathyroidism is a more common cause of depression and is usually seen in this disorder as a cyclic phenomenon.

Thyroid Disorder

Contrary to the usual hyperactivity seen in hyperthyroidism earlier in life, thyroid conditions in later life may include depression. The condition is usually combined with various anxiety symptoms. Hypothyroidism is usually associated with myxedema but less severe states may produce anxiety and/or depression.

Menopause

Affecting both men and women, menopause is one of the most common endocrine disorders. While frequently associated with psychological "losses," correct hormone therapy often alleviates the psychiatric symptomatology, including depression.

Treatment of Depression

Treatment of depression begins by eliminating possible environmental toxins and nutritional imbalances. Once this is done, cognitive therapy is very helpful. If therapy alone does not relieve the symptoms, adding natural antidepressants or prescription antidepressant medication improve outcomes.

Natural Antidepressants

Many people today are opting to use natural remedies instead of prescription drugs.These substances can be very effective. However, the assumption is often made that because something is natural, it must be safer. this is not the case. Be aware that anyone may have an adverse reaction to anything. tell your doctor what you are taking, and do not mix herbs with other medications. The combination can be harmful.

Below are some of the most popular natural antidepressants on the market today.

PEA

Phenylalanine is an amino acid found in food. It is transformed in the body to a chemical called phenylethylamine, or PEA. PEA is also found in high concentrations in chocolate. This compound has amphetamine like properties.

Low urinary PEA levels are found in depressed patients, and because of this, it's been suggested that PEA is a natural antidepressant.

Taking supplements of the amino acid phenylalanine is said to increase PEA production. But direct phenylethylamine replacement is also effective against depression, and has been shown to have long-term effects in combating it.

Dr. Hector Sabelli at Rush University in Chicago reported that twelve out of fourteen patients successfully treated with PEA and selegiline (also known as deprenyl) remained free of symptoms for twenty to fifty weeks after treatment ceased. The patients continued to experience therapeutic benefits and reported no adverse side effects from the treatment. The results of this study suggest that lowered levels of PEA play a role in depression in a significant number of patients, and that PEA treatment works for relieving depressive symptoms.

EPA

In the last few years, eicosapentaenoic acid (EPA), a component of fish oil, has become recognized as an effective antidepressant. A case study published in 2001 describes adding EPA to conventional antidepressant treatment of a treatment-resistant severely depressed and suicidal male. This person had a seven-year history of severe, unremitting depressive symptoms. Within one month of adding EPA to his treatment there was a dramatic and sustained clinical improvement in all the symptoms of depression, including a cessation of previously severe suicidal ideation.

SAMe

A substance called S-Adenosyl-methionine (SAMe) has been shown to be an effective antidepressant. Its effect is comparable to the tricyclic antidepressants, and several studies have proven it to be safe and effective. Improvement is usually noted within four to seven days, and no side effects have been reported. In a 2002 study the antidepressive efficacy of 1600mg. SAMe given orally was comparable with that of 150mg. imipramine, but SAMe was significantly better tolerated.

Biopterin

A vitamin-like compound called tetrahydrobiopterin (also called biopterin and BH4) has been found to be a useful antidepressant. In the body, biopterin plays a crucial role in the manufacture of the numerous neurotransmitters mentioned previously.

It's been found that patients with recurrent depressions have reduced tetrahydro-biopterin synthesis, and these patients respond well to supplementation of this substance. Although this chemical is not available yet in the United States, its production can be stimulated by taking folic acid, vitamin B12, and Vitamin C. It's possible, therefore, to increase vitamin levels and stimulate BH4 formation.

Biopterin also plays a part in other neurological diseases, such as Parkinson's disease, and autism. New research suggests that biopterin also plays a role in Alzheimer's. A 1986 study measured biopterin, the cerebrospinal fluid, and plasma of 30 patients with Alzheimer's disease and in 19 healthy controls. The biopterin concentration in Alzheimer's patients was significantly less than in age-matched controls, suggesting that a central biopterin deficiency exists in Alzheimer's disease.

Vitamin B12 supplementation combined with 5-Methyltetrahydrofolate are thought to be required for the biosynthesis of tetrahydrobiopterin. It is posited by researchers that dementia patients could benefit by administration of 5-methyltetrahydrofolate.

St. John's Wort

St. John's wort *(Hypericum perforatum)* has been a popular antidepressant in Europe for many years. The leaves and flowers of St. John's Wort contain a variety of natural antidepressant substances including, hypericin, pseudohypericin and hyperforin. Recently researchers have found that the herb works like an SSRI (a class of antidepressant medication) and a weak MAO inhibitor. Numerous studies have confirmed that St. John's Wort does possess antidepressive effects in cases of mild to moderate depression. It does not seem to help severe depression.

Resources

Effective treatment of depression is often all that's needed to correct long-standing memory problems. For more information about depression, contact the following organizations:

National Foundation for Depressive Illness, Inc
P.O. Box 2257 \
New York, NY 10116
800-239-1265
http://www.depression.org/

National Alliance for the Mentally Ill (NAMI)
Colonial Place Three
2107 Wilson Blvd.
Suite 300
Arlington, VA 22201-3042
800-950-NAMI (6264)
http://www.nami.org/

National Mental Health Association
2001 N. Beauregard Street, 12th Floor
Alexandria, VA 22311
800-969-NMHA
http://www.nmha.org/

Obsessive-Compulsive Foundation, Inc.
676 State Street
New Haven, CT 06511
203-401-2070
http://www.ocfoundation.org/

Anxiety Disorders Association of America
8730 Georgia Avenue, Suite 600
Silver Spring, MD 20910
240-485-1001
http://www.adaa.org/

Depression and Bipolar Support Alliance
730 N. Franklin Street, Suite 501,
Chicago, IL 60610-7224
800-826-3632
http://www.dbsalliance.org/

National Alliance for Research on Schizophrenia and Depression
(NARSAD)
60 Cutter Mill Road
Suite 404
Great Neck, NY 11021
800-829-8289
http://www.narsad.org/

Symptoms of Depression

Thinking

- Negative self-evaluations
- Negative expectations
- Negative interpretation of events
- Memory loss
- Confusion
- Impaired attention span
- A focus on past mistakes
- All or nothing thinking
- Unwanted thoughts
- Poverty of thought
- Hopelessness
- Helplessness
- The wish to be dead
- Suicidal thoughts
- The conviction of being a burden

Emotions

- Ambivalence
- No sense of humor
- Feeling inadequate
- Chronic apathy
- Sadness
- Guilt
- Powerlessness
- Emotions are dulled
- No motivation

Symbolic

- Destructive fantasies
- Nightmares
- Bothersome images
- Punishment from God

Behavior

- A change in activity level
- Aggression
- Destructive acts
- Crying spells
- Suicide attempts
- Slowed speech
- Substance abuse
- Impulsiveness
- Violation of personal values
- Agitation
- Perfectionism

Relationships

- A "victim" relational style
- Extreme dependency
- High reactivity
- Social isolation
- Avoidance
- Approval seeking
- Martyrdom
- Passive-aggressive behavior
- Boundary problems
- Hypercritical
- Poor communication skills

Physical

- Multiple physical complaints
- Sleep problems
- Appetite changes
- Weight changes
- Change in sex-drive

Geriatric Depression Scale

Based on contributions from depression experts in the health care field, this Geriatric Depression Scale is quite useful in providing an inventory of personal emotions that may help in the diagnosis of depression. Choose the best answer for how you felt over the past week:

1. Are you basically satisfied with your life? Yes/No
2. Have you dropped many of your activities and interests? Yes/No
3. Do you feel that your life is empty? Yes/No
4. Do you often get bored? Yes/No
5. Are you in good spirits most of the time? Yes/No
6. Are you afraid that something bad is going to happen to you? Yes/No
7. Do you feel happy most of the time? Yes/No
8. Do you often feel helpless? Yes/No
9. Do you prefer to stay at home, rather than going out and doing things? Yes/No
10. Do you feel that you have more problems with memory than most? Yes/No
11. Do you think it is wonderful to be alive now? Yes/No
12. Do you feel pretty worthless the way you are now? Yes/No
13. Do you feel full of energy? Yes/No
14. Do you feel that your situation is hopeless? Yes/No
15. Do you think that most people are better off than you are? Yes/No

If most of your answers to this questionnaire are yes, it might be a good idea to make an appointment with your doctor and show him the results of this test.

Chapter Sixteen

Hormones and Memory

Hormones are molecules that regulate the complex balance of the many systems in the body. They are secreted into the body through an intricate system of organs called ductless glands. Because hormones work in concert with one another, and they control the major metabolic functions, almost any hormonal imbalance has the potential to upset normal memory function.

Thyrotoxicosis

Thyrotoxicosis is a syndrome that occurs as a result of excess thyroid hormone. This can result from the body manufacturing too much hormone, or when the hormone is taken as a medication. A person with this syndrome feels tense, excitable, and emotionally unstable. They may have temper tantrums, crying spells, and episodes of euphoria.

People with this syndrome have feelings of constant physical fatigue, but they also have a need to remain active. Impaired attention, concentration, and memory are common symptoms. Other common complaints include heart palpitations, shortness of breath, muscle weakness and insomnia. This condition is often confused with an anxiety disorder, especially in women.

Hypothyroidism

Thyroid hormones stimulate and alter the structure of the hippocampus, the area primarily responsible for learning and memory. They also modulate enzymes that regulate the metabolic rate of brain cells.

Hypothyroidism is a condition resulting from inadequate production of hormones in the thyroid gland itself, or from impaired peripheral conversion of the thyroid hormone thyroxine (T4) into triiodothyronine (T3) in the kidney or the liver.

Symptoms of this disorder include cold hands and feet, menstrual problems, dry skin, thinning hair, low energy, slowness of mental processes, depression, slow speech, and impaired recent memory.

In Stockholm, Sweden researchers at the Karolinska Institute found that levels of thyroid stimulating hormone (TSH) correlate with episodic memory performance in healthy men and women over the age of 75. They posited that TSH may participate in the memory storage process.

This is important to know, because memory loss may be the only symptom of thyroid insufficiency, and may occur without physical signs of thyroid imbalance. In a 1997 study, a group of female patients with goiter reported that memory loss was the only cognitive symptom of sub-clinical hypothyroidism. The problem was effectively alleviated with thyroid hormone treatment.

More importantly, even sub-clinical thyroid imbalances can affect mental ability. Evidence indicates that as levels of thyroid hormone thyroxin decrease, cognitive function generally declines.

Dr. Broda Barnes in his book, *Hypothyroidism: the Unsuspected Illness,* lists forty-seven symptoms that he feels are related to low thyroid. According to Barnes, body temperature below 97.8 degrees is one indication of hypothyroidism.

Fortunately, in most cases memory loss from thyroid imbalance can be effectively treated by supplementing the body with synthetic thyroid hormone.

Hypoparathyroidism

The parathyroid gland is located in the neck. It regulates immune function. Hypoparathyroidism is a malfunction of this gland. Most people with this disorder are women over fifty who have been ill for a prolonged period of time.

Hypoparathyroidism is characterized by weakness, muscle cramps, abnormal sensations such as tingling, burning and numbness of the hands (called paresthesias), headaches, and uncontrollable cramping muscle movements of the wrists and feet.

More than half of the people with parathyroid problems develop psychiatric symptoms. The symptoms usually begin as irritability and a lack of initiative. The disorder then progresses into depression, marked by the loss of interest in eating, social withdrawal, and memory problems.

In one study of fifty-four patients with hypoparathyroidism, thirty-six had mood disorders, twelve had memory problems, and five had psychotic episodes. Thirty-seven percent of the patients showed personality changes. All of these problems disappeared when the disorder was treated.

Malfunction of the parathyroid causes hypocalcemia, a deficiency of calcium. Hypoparathyroidism is treated with calcium and ergocalciferol and dihydrotachysterol (forms of vitamin D). Supplementing the diet with 1500mg. of calcium a day helps.

Addison's Disease

Addison's disease is an adrenocortical hormone deficiency due to damage to the outer layer of the adrenal gland (the adrenal cortex). This damage can be caused by the immune system attacking the gland, or by tuberculosis, hemorrhage, cancer, or infection.

The disease leads to decreased levels of chemicals called corticosteroids (which include aldosterone, cortisol, and adrenal androgens). The mental symptoms caused by this problem include apathy, fatigue, lack of initiative, depression, episodes of amnesia, and memory loss.

Replacement therapy with corticosteroids reduce the symptoms of the disease. Usually a combination of glucocorticoids (cortisone or hydrocortisone) and mineralocorticoids (fludrocortisone) are given. However, there is no cure, and these drugs must be continued for life. Although this is necessary therapy, long term use of cortisone can cause cognitive problems.

Cortisone

Cortisone is an important hormone that regulates biochemical systems such as sugar, fat and protein metabolism. Dr. Harvey Cushing of Johns Hopkins University discovered the syndrome that bears his name, Cushing's Syndrome. It is caused by too much cortisone.

Common mental symptoms of Cushing's syndrome include depression, emotional instability, manic behavior, and memory loss. People with Cushing's syndrome are often exposed to elevated levels of endogenous cortisone for years. The size of the hippocampus increases in these people after cortisone is lowered to normal levels. When this is successful, the patients show improvement in memory and thinking.

The hormone is used to treat many illnesses, including asthma, arthritis, and lupus. This treatment is not without side effects, however. Prolonged treatment with cortisone can cause depression, hallucinations, delusions and dementia. Elderly people may experience mental symptoms even with small doses of this hormone.

Withdrawal from cortisone can also cause memory and mental impairment. Never stop taking this drug without a doctor's supervision.

Birth Control Pills

Birth control pills work by altering the hormone balance in the body. It has been claimed that up to 50 percent of women on the pill have some type of mental or cognitive symptoms as a result of the medication. The most common side effect is depression, which impairs memory.

Many of the side effects of oral contraceptives can be corrected by using vitamin B6 supplementation. But the use of oral contraceptives also causes other nutritional deficiencies, including folate, zinc, and vitamin B2, B12, B6, and C. At the same time iron, copper and vitamin A levels are often increased. These findings suggest decreased liver metabolism of these essential nutrients.

Estrogen

Many studies have shown that estrogen replacement therapy can improve memory and reduce symptoms in elderly women suffering from Alzheimer's disease.

Estrogen appears to be beneficial in several regions of the brain. It may raise levels of certain brain chemicals (neurotransmitters) such as acetylcholine (implicated in memory), serotonin (implicated in mood), noradrenaline (implicated in mood and other autonomic functions), and dopamine (implicated in motor coordination and pleasure).

The results of several studies suggest that estrogen could reduce the risk for Alzheimer's by up to 50 percent although other studies did not find this benefit.

However. the Women's Health Initiative Memory Study (WHIS) found that estrogen plus progestin therapy actually increases older women's risk for dementia. Furthermore, estrogen plus progestin did not protect against mild cognitive impairment. Thus, estrogen plus progestin should not be prescribed with the expectation that it will enhance brain performance in postmenopausal women.

On the heels of the WHIS results, researchers made the dramatic announcement that one section of the WHIS would be stopped immediately because women taking Prempro™ hormone replacement therapy had a twenty-five percent increase in the normal incidence level of breast cancer, or an average of eight extra cases per 10,000 women.

Now, as the dust raised by the announcement settles, many scientists have expressed concern that this one study, which tested only one drug formulation, has unnecessarily — and predictably — sullied the public's perception of hormone replacement therapy and that many women will suffer because of this misconception.

These researchers all say that the study has done a great disservice to American women. The negative effects it showed can likely be avoided by choosing a more natural drug and a more natural dosing schedule that would mimic the hormone cycle experienced in a woman's pre-menopause years. But with the high profile failure of this study, the researchers fear that many women will mistakenly think the concept of hormone replacement therapy is dangerous and will shun any such treatments — even ones that could help their cognitive ability, as well as their bones, heart and general health.

The strength of these researchers' conviction is based on scientific data indicating that both estrogen and progesterone are necessary for optimal brain function, including neuron survival, memory and cognition.

Women readers who have doubts or question about the use of hormone therapy are advised to consult with their physicians for advice on treatment.

One way around some of the problems of these hormones might be isoflavones. Isoflavones are a form of phytoestrogens — plant based compounds that have a weak estrogenic activity in the body. Isoflavones are found in chick peas and legumes, but soy has the most concentrated amount. These substances do not seem to carry the risks associated with hormone replacement therapy.

In a recent study 56 women aged 55 to 74 years who were in good health, were postmenopausal at least two years, and were not using estrogen replacement therapy, took two pills per day, each containing 55mg. of soy-extracted isoflavones. Women assigned to placebo took two identical-appearing pills per day containing inert ingredients.

The women in the treatment group did consistently better on tests of cognition and memory, both compared with their own baseline scores and with the placebo group. The results indicate that isoflavone supplementation improves cognitive function and verbal memory in postmenopausal women.

Another possible solution appears in the October 22nd issue of *The Journal of Neuroscience*. Researchers report that they have discovered a compound that offers the benefits of estrogen replacement but lacks the side effects and risks.

In collaboration with an organic chemist at the University of California, scientists at the Oregon Health Science University (OHSU) developed a substance called a *selective estrogen receptor modulator.* Called STX, this new drug may be a safe alternative to estrogen treatment.

This chemical acts like estrogen in the central nervous system, but not in other tissues, which means it has none of the cancer-causing effects of estrogen

STX appears to act by stimulating a novel estrogen receptor, located in the cell membrane in brain cells that activates proteins involved in rapid cell signaling. In this way, it avoids the uterus and breasts, whose growth is stimulated by estrogen through a different pathway, leading to increased cancer risk.

Women that don't have hormone replacement therapy have been known to have more cognitive impairment in terms of loss of memory, and a higher incidence of Alzheimer's disease. In animal studies, it's been shown that estrogen can reduce neuronal cell death from stroke. The new signaling pathway unveiled by the research team demonstrates the hormone's importance to the brain in protecting itself from cell death caused by disease and the aging process.

Peter Kohler, M.D., an endocrinologist and president of OHSU, said the discovery of STX could lead to improvements in the quality of life for tens of thousands of women suffering from the uncomfortable symptoms of menopause.

Testosterone

A study published in the November 2002 issue of *The Journal of Clinical Endocrinology & Metabolism* measured the testosterone levels of 407 men, ages 50 and older, who participated in the Baltimore Longitudinal Study of Aging.

In men, testosterone is produced in the testes, the reproductive glands that also produce sperm. As men age, their testes often produce somewhat less testosterone than they did during adolescence and early adulthood when production of the hormone peaks. According to the Baltimore study data, 68 percent of men over 70 have significantly low levels of free testosterone.

The investigators then correlated free and total testosterone levels — measured over an average of 10 years — with the men's performances on memory and other cognitive tests. It was found that older men with higher levels of testosterone circulating in their bloodstreams have better visual and verbal recall than their peers.

According to investigators, the findings suggest that the hormone could be used to protect against memory decline and cognitive skills in later life.

In the body, testosterone tends to bind with sex hormone binding globulin (SHBG). But some testosterone remains freely circulating in the bloodstream. Unlike the SHBG-bound form of the hormone, free testosterone can circulate into the brain and affect nerve cells. Only free testosterone was significantly associated with higher scores on verbal and visual memory tests, such as recalling word lists and drawing a recently seen image.

Testosterone replacement therapy is available now, and is becoming quite popular. However, currently it is not considered advisable because long-term effects of hormone supplementation are unknown. Some clinicians believe that testosterone replacement increases the risk of prostate cancer, the second leading cause of cancer death among men. In addition, other studies suggest that supplementation might trigger excessive red blood cell production in some men. This side effect can thicken blood and increase the risk of stroke.

Pregnenolone

Pregnenolone is the raw material, for the production of all human steroid hormones, including DHEA, progesterone, estrogen, testosterone, cortisol and aldosterone.

When it was first discovered in the 1930s, researchers thought it was an inert substance, because when they gave it to healthy young animals, it had no effect. But by the 1940s, human studies had demonstrated that it improved performance of ordinary physical and mental tasks.

One action of pregnenolone is to counter damage caused by cortisol, the natural stress hormone, released by the adrenal glands. As noted elsewhere in this book cortisol at higher levels can damage the brain. Blocking this process may be one of the main reasons for the known memory-enhancing effect of pregnenolone.

Recent studies indicate that it may also work in part through its impact on N-methyl-D-aspartate (NMDA) receptors in the brain. It also blocks the inhibitory amino acids glycine and GABA, helping to balance excitation and inhibition in the central nervous system. There is evidence that pregnenolone may actually cause hippocampal neurogenesis, the growth of new brain cells.

The body's own production of pregnenolone is reduced with aging, stress, depression, hypothyroidism and toxin exposure. Pregnenolone is generally safe and effective at doses of 50mg. to 200mg. per day. Do not use pregnenolone instead of medically prescribed steroids, and always tell your doctor what you are doing.

Much of the research on this substance has been done by Raymond Peat, Ph.D. For more information contact Raymond Peat, P.O. Box 5764, Eugene, OR 97405. To subscribe to his newsletter go to http://www.efn.org/~raypeat/

DHEA

DHEA (Dehydroepiandrosterone) is a naturally occurring molecule in the human body. In the body DHEA is converted into as many as twenty different steroid hormones. Numerous animal studies have shown DHEA and its sulfate form, DHEA-S, protect the brain from neuronal damage and enhance memory function.

In humans, low DHEA-S is found in elderly men with organic brain syndrome and in Alzheimer's disease in both men and women.

DHEA appears to improve retention of information previously learned. Several studies have shown that the drug increases memory retention in mice.

However a review of clinical studies shows DHEA has not been effective in improving memory and cognition in healthy humans. This may be because DHEA-S affects brain function through its balancing effect on the adrenal hormone cortisol. Many brain researchers agree. They feel that DHEA is important because it is necessary for proper production of many other hormones, and because it decreases with age. The average 70 year old has only one-fifth the level of DHEA he had at twenty. DHEA-S, functions as an anti-glucocorticoid, and can block some of the damaging effects of cortisol in the processes that mediate learning and memory.

There is some evidence that DHEA may increase the risk of prostate cancer. Because of this, some memory researchers feel that men should always take saw palmetto with DHEA in order to decrease this risk. No studies have been done on the long term effects of taking DHEA. For this reason, it should be used with caution.

DHEA is available by prescription and by mail order. Recommended dosage ranges from 25mg. to 100mg. per day.

ACTH

The pituitary hormones adrenocorticotrophic hormone (ACTH) and melanocyte-stimulating hormone (MSH), when combined as ACTH/MSH, show potential as a memory-enhancing drug. Injections of this hormone combination seem to boost the power of concentration, and may be useful in treating certain types of mental retardation. The drug is also being tested on Alzheimer's victims and patients with senility. But the drug is still experimental and has potentially dangerous side effects.

ACTH receptors are abundant in much of the brain, especially the limbic system which participates in learning and emotional regulation. The hippocampus, which helps store memory, does not contain ACTH receptors. But the septum which is known to pace the activity of the hippocampus, has ample ACTH receptors. Elevated levels of activity in the septum are associated with faster learning. So ACTH could alter learning rate by affecting septal modulation of hippocampal activity.

Vasopressin

Vasopressin, (VP) a naturally occurring substance in the brain, is also known as an antidiuretic hormone. It is manufactured in the posterior pituitary gland, which is located at the base of the brain. The hormone is used by the body to regulate blood pressure and urine volume, but it has also been shown to have an important effect on memory.

In several interesting studies, scientists found that vasopressin could restore memory in amnesia victims, sometimes within minutes after their taking it. Other studies showed improved learning in men aged 50 to 60.

Researchers now believe that vasopressin should be considered a neurotransmitter. VP and its receptors are present in brain regions known to be involved in memory function, and can significantly enhance the growth of neurons involved in memory function. VP content in brain increases over time during the active phase of remembering. VP metabolites appear to improve both consolidation and retrieval of memory.

Researcher Brinton Diaz at the Rudolf Magnus Institute for Neurosciences, is enthusiastic about the benefits of vasopressin and states, "We stand on the threshold of a new era in our research as we begin our studies of the role VP and its receptors play in the cerebral cortex. Thus far, results of these studies are quite exciting and promise to yield fascinating insights into the complexities of VP action in the most highly developed region of the mammalian brain, the cerebral cortex, the site of abstract reasoning, judgment, complex analysis and the repository of those memories that last a lifetime."

Cocaine releases vasopressin, but soon depletes the brain's supply of it. This is why people who go on two- or three-day cocaine binges often become psychotic. Nicotine, alcohol, and marijuana inhibit the release of vasopressin, resulting in memory impairment.

Most physicians are familiar with vasopressin only as a substance used for treating frequent urination associated with diabetes. Therefore, if you want a prescription for memory improvement, you should provide your doctor with the research papers on the use of the drug for memory improvement.

Large doses of vasopressin (several hundred International Units) can increase blood pressure, and therefore it should be used with careful supervision. This hormone is available by prescription under the brand name Pressyn and Diapid, and comes in the form of a nasal spray.

The recommended dose for Diapid is 16 International Units per day. As a nasal spray, use one spray in each nostril 3 to 4 times per day, which is equivalent to 12-16 U.S.P. units.

Melatonin

Melatonin is a naturally occurring hormone that is produced by the pineal gland. Melatonin production declines with age.

In the 1980s, scientists began to look at the possibility that melatonin could be used to adjust the body's biological clock. A study of patients suffering from dementia found night-time levels of melatonin significantly reduced in proportion to the severity of their mental impairment.

In young animals and humans the twenty four hour cycle of melatonin is very robust. However, the cycle frequently deteriorates during aging and is totally abolished in patients with neurological diseases such as Alzheimer's.

Some researchers suggest that melatonin actually protects against Alzheimer's disease, by preventing the loss of memory function from oxidative damage of the mitochondria in the most active brain neurons. According to this theory, sub-optimal levels of melatonin actually set in motion the degenerative triggers of global brain atrophy.

Melatonin is a highly efficient free-radical scavenger, especially of hydroxyl radicals. Dementia due to premature aging in patients with

Down's syndrome, and accelerated aging in patients with Alzheimer's disease may be caused by exposure to hydroxyl radicals.

Amyloid beta protein plays a central role in the progression of Alzheimer's disease. Melatonin has been found to protect neurons against amyloid beta toxicity. The benefit of melatonin is that, unlike conventional anti-oxidants and available anti-amyloid compounds, melatonin crosses the blood-brain barrier, is relatively devoid of toxicity, and could become a potent therapeutic agent in preventing Alzheimer's disease.

Results from several therapeutic trials of melatonin in Alzheimer's disease patients have demonstrated improved function, improved sleep, and a significant slowing of the progression of the disease.

High doses of melatonin (over 200mg. per day) can worsen depression and insomnia, but doses of 3 to 30mg. a day usually show no side effects. Melatonin should not be taken by patients with myelo-cytic leukemia or multiple myeloma.

Many of the claims made about melatonin are overblown and unsubstantiated, but melatonin can be used to relieve insomnia, to alleviate depression, and to reduce free radical damage in the body. It can also be taken to reset the body's clock to minimize jet lag.

Dosage and timing are important when using this substance, and use should be supervised by a physician.

A test for hormone levels is available from Aeron Labs. Measuring baseline levels of these hormones via saliva is a non-invasive way to monitor the impact of dietary, herbal, supplemental and pharmaceutical interventions.

This test will tell you your levels of Estrone, Estradiol, Estriol, Progesterone, Testosterone, DHEA, Cortisol, Melatonin and Adrenal Function. Your doctor's signature is required to obtain testing. Contact Aeron Life Cycles, 1933 Davis Street, Suite 310, San Leadro, CA 94577 Phone: 800-631-7900 Web: http://www.aeron.com/

Chapter Seventeen

Medications and Memory

Although most people don't realize it, many over-the-counter medications interfere with memory. Yet few if any of these medications indicate memory impairment as a side effect.

Prescription medications also grossly interfere with memory. But most doctors don't mention that the drug they are prescribing may have this effect.

Most people take any medication their doctor recommends without question. The majority of the people I work with don't know the names of the medicines they are taking, or why they are taking them. They are seldom aware of the potential side effects and therefore if they develop memory problems, they do not ponder the possibility that the symptoms may be caused by medication.

To further complicate matters, physicians are often unaware of the potential side effects of the medications they prescribe. It is not unusual for a patient to complain of side effects after taking a drug only to be told, "That medication doesn't do that."

In his book, *The People's Pharmacy,* Joe Graeden claims that many people diagnosed as memory impaired are actually displaying the toxic effects of over medication. He calls this problem the "spaced-out Grandma syndrome."

Over-medication is a very common problem. One woman who came to see me was taking seventeen prescription medications! These drugs had been given to her by several doctors for various ailments she had suffered over a period of years, but it seemed that no one had ever asked her if she was taking any other medication. Furthermore, none of the doctors told her when to stop taking the medication, so she continued to take pills for ailments that had disappeared long ago.

The average number of prescription drugs given to people over sixty years old is fifteen per year! Although elderly people (those over 65) comprise 12 percent of the population, they take 30 percent of all prescribed medications. Two-thirds of this population is taking at least one prescription drug. Thirty-seven percent are taking at least five drugs. Another 20 percent are taking seven or more medications at once.

Loss of brain cells and the lower amounts of neurotransmitters in the older brain amplify the effects of many medications, and doses that may be safe for younger people are often toxic for the aged. Decreased liver and kidney function also increase the risk of toxicity. But that's only part of the problem. About one-third of elderly people make serious mistakes in taking their medication, either forgetting to take it, or forgetting that they have taken it, and therefore overdose. About 12 percent of people taking prescription drugs are using medications that were actually prescribed for someone else. For all of these reasons, medications should be taken with care, and closely monitored.

It is estimated that almost 200,000 people in this country are currently suffering from medication-induced memory loss.

Drugs that Can Cause Memory Problems

- Antidepressants
- Antihistamines
- Antipsychotics
- Atropine
- Barbiturates
- Benzodiazepines
- Blood Pressure medication
- Bromides
- Clonidine
- Digitalis
- Dilantin
- Disulfiram
- Eye drops for glaucoma
- Glutethimide
- Haloperidol (Haldol)
- Lithium Carbonate
- Mephenytoin
- Methyldopa
- Misolene
- Phenytoin
- Propranolol
- Reserpine
- Scopolamine
- Serpasil

Sleeping Pills

Sleeping pills can cause confusion and memory loss. People who use sleeping pills regularly often complain that their memory is bad. Most sleeping pills contain ingredients that interfere with REM sleep, the part of sleep in which dreaming occurs. When dreaming is disrupted, long-term memory storage is impaired. One of the more popular sleeping medications, Halcion, is known to cause confusion and amnesia.

Sleeping pills are meant to be used once in a while. If they are used more than three consecutive weeks, they become ineffective, because the body adjusts to them. Even though the pills no longer work, the user becomes dependent on them, and begins to believe that he cannot sleep without them. Unfortunately, the only effect the pills have is impairing memory. If you have been taking sleeping pills for any length of time, do not stop without consulting your doctor. Sudden withdrawal from these medications can have serious consequences.

Stimulant Drugs

Stimulant drugs such as cocaine and amphetamine cause damage to tiny blood vessels in the brain (called capillaries) and decrease the supply of nutrients and oxygen. They also deplete the brain of the neurotransmitter dopamine, which is necessary for decoding sensory input. If these drugs are used frequently, psychosis and permanent brain damage can occur.

Tranquilizers

The most common treatment of anxiety is the use of tranquilizing drugs. Each year, thousands of people are given Valium and Xanax to reduce symptoms of anxiety. But not only are these drugs ineffective as a treatment, they are highly addictive. Once a person becomes addicted to tranquilizers, it is extremely difficult to get them off the drugs. Tranquilizing drugs are sedating, and interfere with memory in many ways.

If you are suffering from anxiousness, anxiety, or panic attacks, seek help from a psychologist trained in treating these disorders without medication.

Caffeine

Americans consume about one-third of the caffeine in the world. The average American consumes 150-225mg. of caffeine a day. The compound is a hidden ingredient in many beverages like coffee, tea, cola, over-the-counter drugs, and many stimulants and analgesics. A typical cup of coffee contains from 50 to 150mg. of caffeine. A cup of tea contains 50mg., and a 12-ounce cola contains about 35mg. Some people consume an excess of 7,500mg. per day.

Addiction to caffeine is sometimes called caffeinism. When a person becomes addicted to caffeine, she needs it to function normally. If she stops using it, she suffers from fatigue, depression, and severe headaches. Excessive caffeine intake has been shown to increase the degree of mental illness in psychiatric patients, but extreme amounts of caffeine may worsen the effects of both mental and physical illness in everyone.

Caffeine stimulates the central nervous system by blocking the action of a substance called adenosine. Caffeine can trigger phobias and panic attacks. It can also cause sleep disturbances. As mentioned before, sleep disturbances impair memory storage. In sensitive individuals, one cup of coffee in the morning can disrupt sleep patterns that night. Regular coffee drinkers do not build up a tolerance for the stressful affects of caffeine.

Despite all of caffeine's potential negative effects, the 2002 Canadian Study of Health and Aging showed coffee consumption reduced the risk of dementia. Research published in the *European Journal of Neurology,* compared 54 Alzheimer's patients with 54 healthy people of the same age. At least three cups of coffee a day reduced the risk of developing Alzheimer's disease by as much as 60 percent.

The study found that elderly people with no signs of the brain disease, had consumed an average of three to four cups a day since the age of 25, while those with the illness drank, on average, just one cup of coffee each day.

Scientists posit that it is the caffeine in coffee that protects against Alzheimer's. Previous experiments on mice have targeted caffeine as a potential treatment for the disease. However, this is the first study to show the link in humans.

According to an article posted on the United Kingdom's Alzheimer's Society website there are three effects of caffeine that might enable it to protect against dementia:

First, it can stimulate brain cells to take in choline, the precursor to acetylcholine, a neurotransmitter that is reduced in dementia.

Second, as mentioned above, caffeine interferes with the action of the neurotransmitter adenosine. It has been suggested that might be beneficial in Alzheimer's disease, as it would increase brain activity.

Third, chemicals related to caffeine seem to be able to damp down the activity of 'housekeeping' cells in the brain, called glia. One such chemical, propentofylline, has been shown to be a powerful antioxidant. It is the first drug to have sought an approval in Europe for use in vascular dementia. A recent review of the literature on propentofylline concluded that it might benefit cognition, but there is not enough data at this time to confirm its usefulness.

Marijuana

Although marijuana is considered to be a relatively harmless drug, there is mounting evidence that long-term use interferes with the ability to form new memories.

The brain transmits information from cell to cell by chemicals called neurotransmitters. These molecules jump from one cell to another across a small space between cells called a synapse. Some studies suggest that long-term use of marijuana impairs memory by increasing the distance between synapses, making it difficult for the neurotransmitters to reach the next cell.

There is also some evidence that marijuana decreases brain levels of acetylcholine, the neurotransmitter necessary for memory transfer from short- to long-term memory. This problem is believed to occur because the active ingredient in marijuana, tetrahydrocannabinol (THC), damages the hippocampus, a brain area responsible for memory transfer.

In laboratory experiments, rats given THC show the same reduced ability to perform tasks requiring short-term memory as other rats showed after nerve cells in their hippocampus were deliberately destroyed. THC dosed rats had the most difficulty performing tasks during the times when the drug was interfering most with the functioning of cells in the hippocampus.

Rats exposed to THC every day for 8 months (approximately 30 percent of their lifespan), when examined at 11 to 12 months of age, showed brain cell loss equivalent to unexposed animals twice their age. In humans this damage is thought to be reversible.

Tagamet

Tagamet (cimetidine) is a popular drug used to reduce excess stomach acid. Although it was once available only by prescription, it has been declassified, and is now available over the counter. Tagamet has been shown to cause trouble with memory and concentration, promote irritability, and in a few cases, cause severe headaches.

These effects are thought to be caused by the drug robbing the body of iron. Impairing acid secretion in the stomach, the main effect of the drug, blocks the absorption of ionic iron (the form of iron found in vegetables). This drug should not be taken by those using cyclic anti-depressants, as it interferes with their effectiveness.

Questions to Ask Your Doctor about Medications

- Why do I need to take this drug?
- How does it work?
- How long will I have to take it?
- What are the side effects of this drug?
- Can this drug effect my memory in any way?
- What are the effects of taking this drug for more than a year?
- Will this drug interact with any of the other drugs I am taking?
- What will happen if I stop taking this drug?

Mineral Oil

This commonly used laxative prevents the absorption of the fat soluble vitamins C, E, A, D, and K — by creating a physical barrier between food and the intestinal wall. People who use mineral oil regularly are preventing nutrients from entering their bodies by coating their intestines with oil. Use mineral oil sparingly. A high-fiber diet is a much more effective way to eliminate constipation.

Blood Pressure Medication

Several types of blood pressure medication can cause depression and memory problems. A commonly prescribed diuretic, Dyazide, depletes the body of folic acid. Folic acid deficiency is associated with both mental and emotional disturbance.

A physician placed on an experimental diet deficient in folic acid reported that after four months he suffered from sleeplessness and forgetfulness. These symptoms disappeared two days after the vitamin was reintroduced to his diet.

A three-to-five month supply of folic acid is stored in the human liver. Folic acid functions as a co-enzyme in the manufacture of the neurotransmitters norepinephrine and serotonin.

Diuretic drugs also deplete the body of potassium. Low potassium can cause the brain's arteries to clamp down, impairing the blood flow. This contributes to clot formation and stroke. If you are taking Dyazide, make sure you are taking potassium supplements.

Two other blood pressure medications, Inderal (propranolol) and Aldomet (methyldopa), are known to significantly impair verbal memory. There is some evidence that methyldopa might impair the body's ability to manufacture the substance co-enzyme Q10.

Sugar

Refined sugar accelerates the aging process. Although glucose is present in and around every cell in the body, an excess causes premature aging.

Glucose enters the blood stream from the small intestine. Some is used as fuel by the cells, and the rest is stored in the liver in the form of glycogen until it is needed later. In a healthy body, glucose level is kept constant by the hormone insulin. Cells getting too much glucose, as happens in people with diabetes, form proteins mixed with glucose called advanced glycosylation end products (AGE). These particles stick like glue to other molecules and cause cross linking. Cross linking leads to age-related problems such as cataracts, atherosclerosis, and dementia. Eating candy bars and other high sugar food on a regular basis overloads the blood with sugar and sets off this process.

Researchers Cerami, Brownlee, and Ulrich have developed a drug called aminoguanidine which inhibits the formation of AGE's. Recent research on this substance suggests it impairs the formation of beta amyloid — one of the primary causes of Alzheimer's Disease. Another new drug, tenilsetam, is also an AGE inhibitor and has improved cognitive function in Alzheimer's patients.

Belladonna

Belladonna *(Atropa belladona)* means "pretty woman" in Italian. The drug is so named because a drop of it in each eye causes the pupils to dilate, enhancing beauty. Belladonna has been used for many centuries, usually in its naturally occurring form in the plant deadly nightshade. Although the drug is not used as commonly as it was a century ago, currently belladonna is used to relieve symptoms of irritable bowel or spastic colon.

This drug has many side effects, one of which is interference with memory. These memory problems are caused by one of belladonna's active ingredients — scopolamine.

Scopolamine

Scopolamine originates from the plant henbane *(Hyoscyamus niger)*. This drug has been known for years to cause memory problems. Women used to be given large doses of scopolamine because it was thought to relieve the discomfort of childbirth. What it was actually doing was completely wiping out the memory of the birth! Doctors used to call this twilight sleep.

Scopolamine interferes with memory by blocking receptors in the hippocampus, the part of the brain used in transferring new material into long-term memory. Scopolamine is so effective in preventing memory that it is routinely used in memory experiments.

Scopolamine is an ingredient in several over-the-counter drugs, and is the active ingredient in some sleeping pills. Many people use patches containing scopolamine to relieve the symptoms of seasickness. If you are taking this drug, be aware that it prevents the learning of new material. Read the labels on sleeping and seasick pills before you take them.

Chapter Eighteen

Neurotoxins and Memory

A neurotoxin is any substance that causes damage or malfunction in the nervous system. Every day millions of people are exposed to hundreds of these powerful chemicals. The chemicals include cosmetics, food additives, pesticides, drugs, and common solvents. Acute exposure to neurotoxic chemicals causes nausea, dizziness, weakness, and blurred vision.

But subtle symptoms caused by chronic exposure — such as irritability, fatigue, confusion and memory loss — often go unnoticed. In addition, the chronic effects of neurotoxins do not show up on traditional medical tests, so doctors tell the sufferer that there is really nothing wrong with them, that what they are feeling is "stress."

In October 1989, the United States Government Subcommittee on Investigations and Oversight held hearings to explore the effects of neurotoxins in the environment. They concluded that neurotoxic reaction was one of the top ten causes of illness in the country.

As of this writing, the government has identified 850 neurotoxic chemicals in our environment, of which only 167 have regulatory standards imposed on their use.

Virtually any toxic chemical is capable of producing psychological symptoms, even substances that have never been investigated. For example, the role that bacterial byproducts play in brain disorders hasn't been investigated, but it's likely that they have an effect on brain chemistry.

Can you imagine how surprised the president and founder of Commonweal, health and environmental research institute in Marin County, California must have been when he volunteered to give blood and urine samples to medical researchers and discovered that his body was polluted with 101 industrial toxins and penetrated by elevated levels of arsenic and mercury? Scientists call such contamination, a person's "body burden." Michael Lerner was one of nine people — who live and work in the San Francisco Bay Area — who were tested for 210 chemicals commonly found in consumer products and industrial pollution. Mt. Sinai School of Medicine in New York, the Environmental Working Group of Oakland and Washington, and Commonweal collaborated on this innovative study of the body burden.

Why is this information important to you? Because researchers have revealed that on average, each person in the U.S. has 50 or more chemicals in their tissues that are linked to cancer, considered toxic to the brain and nervous system or known to interfere with the hormone and reproductive systems.

Lerner was astounded. In an article written about him by Ruth Rosen, he said, "Being tested yourself brings the body burden home in a very personal way." For years, he has lived with a condition that causes a hand tremor. Now he suspects why. "Mercury and arsenic both cause tremor, so I've stopped eating all fish that have high mercury levels."

Lerner's wife, Sharyle Patton — co-director of the Collaborative on Health and Environment — also participated in the study. To her surprise, the residents of their suburban area had as many toxins as people who have lived in cities. In fact she had the highest levels of dioxins and PCBs — both highly toxic substances — of anyone in the test group. "What we learned," says Patton, "is that we all live in the same chemical neighborhood.'

Lerner, who has devoted his life to promoting the health of people and the planet, hopes that such bio-monitoring tests will become routine and affordable. "Body burden tests," he says, "are the thermometer that gives us our body's chemical fever. In a prudent world no household would be without a chemical thermometer in the medicine cabinet.'

But individual tests only provide information; they don't reduce our contamination. "The truth is," Lerner says, "we are unwilling participants in a huge chemical experiment, which would never be permitted by the FDA if these chemicals came to us as drugs. But because these chemicals enter our bodies from industrial and agricultural sources, they are not subject to testing that would ensure our safety."

The medical researchers' report called for "the reform of the Toxics Substance Control Act, under which chemical companies may put new compounds on the market without any studies of their effect on people or the environment."

According to the story, another person, "Andrea Martin, founder and former executive director of the San Francisco's Breast Cancer fund, strongly supports the recommendation. Martin is a breast cancer survivor who climbed Mount Fuji in 2000 with 500 breast cancer survivors and supporters. More recently, she underwent surgery to remove a brain tumor unrelated to breast cancer.

Martin, who also gave samples to the Body Burden project, was stunned by the results. "I was completely blown away." Her body indicated the presence of 95 toxins, 59 of which were carcinogens.

Martin has never worked with or near chemicals. But she now wonders whether her formative years may have turned her into a self-described "walking toxic waste site." When she grew up in Memphis, she and her friends loved to get splashed by the streams of insecticide sprayed by trucks that roamed the neighborhood. Later, she indulged a passion for water skiing — in lakes clouded by chemical pollutants.

Where did I get all these PCBs and dioxins?' she asks. "I'll probably never know." In fact, no one is sure how industrial and synthetic chemical residues — even long-banned pesticides such as DDT — end up in our bodies. But scientists suspect that chemicals first pollute the air, soil, food and water, then climb through the food chain and finally accumulate in our blood, fat, mother's milk, semen and urine.

Martin was asked if she regretted being a volunteer in the Body Burden Project. "At first, I was really angry," she said, "but I believe knowledge is power. We're starting to learn that pollution isn't only in the air, soil and water, it's also in us." She also wonders whether her chemical body burden has caused her cancers. "We'll never know," she said, "because right now chemical companies don't have to prove the safety of their products and no government agency has ever studied the health risks that can be caused by chemical toxins."

That may change. Not too long ago the Centers for Disease Control also issued its second report card on the body burden of chemicals carried by Americans. Using data from 2,500 anonymous donors, the CDC provided further evidence that chemical residues have polluted the bodies of most of us. Although no one yet knows what amount of trace chemicals are harmful for human health, scientists and environmental health activists worry about the cumulative assault on our health.

We are living in a chemical stew and lobbyists for the chemical industry resist further regulation. As the conflict for more regulation grows more heated, individuals are warned to be more alert for neuro-toxins that can harm their health.

Aluminum

As you will learn in the following pages, aluminum is suspect in the list of chemicals that may be harmful to the mind and body.

For example, the incidence of Alzheimer's disease is more prevalent in a region in Italy where levels of aluminum in the drinking water supply are the highest, according to new research presented at the Experimental Biology Conference in San Diego. Theories linking aluminum with Alzheimer's have circulated for years, but the researchers said they were surprised to find higher death rates from Alzheimer's in a region where drinking water aluminum exceeded environmental standards.

The researchers also noted that when the type of aluminum molecule found in the drinking water was added to cell cultures, it hastened cell death, and when it was added to cell cultures containing beta-amyloid (the protein linked to Alzheimer's plaques), the combination killed off more brain cells. It should be noted, however, the average low exposure to aluminum probably does not create an imminent hazard to the average person.

From the website of the National Institute of Environmental Health Sciences, (http://www.niehs.nih.gov/ or http://www.neihs.nih gov/external/faq/alum.htm), a question has been posed which reflects the anxiety of many Americans about aluminum contamination:

Question: I have heard that aluminum may be involved in the development of Alzheimer's disease. Does use of aluminum cookware and drinking from aluminum beverage cans place me at greater risk for developing this disease?

Answer: Aluminum is one of the most abundant elements found in the environment. Therefore, human exposure to this metal is common and unavoidable. However, intake is relatively low because this element is highly insoluble in many of its naturally occurring forms. The significance of environmental contact with aluminum is further diminished by the fact that less than one percent of that taken into the body orally is absorbed from the gastrointestinal tract.

The average human intake is estimated to be between 30 and 50mg. per day. This intake comes primarily from foods, drinking water, and pharmaceuticals. Based on the maximum levels reported in drinking water, less than 1/4 of the total intake comes from water. Some common food additives contain aluminum. Due to certain additives, processed cheese and cornbread are two major contributors to high aluminum exposures in the American diet.

With regard to pharmaceuticals, some common over-the-counter medications such as antacids and buffered aspirin contain enough aluminum to increase the daily intake significantly.

Over the last few years, there has been concern about the exposures resulting from leaching of aluminum from cookware and beverage cans. However, as a general rule, this contributes a relatively small amount to the total daily intake. Aluminum beverage cans are usually coated with a polymer to minimize such leaching. Leaching from aluminum cookware becomes potentially significant only when cooking highly basic or acidic foods. For example, in one study, tomato sauce cooked in aluminum pans was found to accumulate 3–6mg. aluminum per 100g. serving.

Certain aluminum compounds have been found to be an important component of the neurological damage characteristics of Alzheimer's disease. Much research over the last decade has focused on the role of aluminum in the development of this disease. At this point, its role is still not clearly defined. Since Alzheimer's disease is a chronic disease which may take a long time to develop, long-term exposure is the most important measure of intake. Long-term exposure is easiest to estimate for drinking water exposures. Epidemiological studies attempting to link Alzheimer's disease with exposures in drinking water have been inconclusive and contradictory. Thus the significance of increased aluminum intake with regard to onset of Alzheimer's disease has not been determined.

It should be added that aluminum has been found in high concentrations in the brains of people with Alzheimer's disease. At this time, researchers are uncertain about aluminum's exact role in Alzheimer's. It is not known whether aluminum is one of the causes of it, or if the disease allows aluminum to accumulate in the brain. Until all the evidence is in, it is a good idea to avoid any products containing aluminum. Autopsies done on Alzheimer's victims show that bundles of debris in the brain called neuritic plaques, one of the hallmarks of the disease, contain a tiny core of aluminum.

Dr. Daniel Perl claims that aluminum inhaled through the nose can enter the brain through the olfactory nerves, which are linked to the sense of smell. Biochemist Eugene Roberts agrees, stating that inhaled aluminum is absorbed directly into the olfactory lobes. The most common source of inhaled aluminum is in spray deodorants, but aluminum is also present in the air in most urban areas.

Two acids contained in fruit, citric acid and malic acid, have been shown to increase excretion of aluminum in animals. Malic acid works best in eliminating aluminum from brain tissue. This substance is found in wine, apples, cherries, and other fruits.

Mercury

Quicksilver is a fascinating element. It is the only metal that occurs naturally as a liquid. While the metal itself is shiny, slippery, and elusive, its ability to poison the nervous system is clear and concrete.

More commonly known today as mercury, quicksilver is a highly neurotoxic chemical that has been poisoning people for centuries. Although mercury damages all types of human tissue, it is extremely toxic to the central nervous system. People with mercury poisoning display many of the symptoms of Alzheimer's disease. Lewis Carroll's "Mad Hatter" represented people who suffered from erethism, a disease caused by exposure to mercury — a chemical used in hat making.

In 1972, five thousand people died in Iraq from eating grain that was treated with a fungicide containing methyl mercury. The grain was seed corn that was treated with the fungicide, and was not meant to be eaten. However, the local people could not read the warning labels, and made bread from the contaminated seeds. Hospitals reported that 6,530 people showed symptoms of mercury poisoning.

The Chisso Factory in Minimata, Japan, used mercury as an ingredient for manufacturing vinyl chloride to make floor tiles. Between 1932 and 1968, they dumped about 100 tons of mercury into the local bay. This toxic waste was absorbed by the fish, which were then eaten by the townspeople. People in Minimata would often serve fish at every meal. By 1982, there were 1,773 reported cases of mercury poisoning in the town, which caused severe brain damage in most of its victims. Four hundred and fifty-six people died from the toxin. This poisoning was so rampant that the disorder resulting from it came to be known as Minimata disease.

There is a growing body of evidence that suggests dental fillings can be a potent source of mercury poisoning. Dental fillings are a mixture of mercury, silver, copper, zinc, and tin. Some researchers feel that these toxic metals leach into the body and cause nerve damage.

Germany and Sweden have banned the use of mercury in dental fillings. The majority of dentists to whom I have talked are convinced that the fillings are perfectly safe, and the American Dental Association states unequivocally that dental fillings pose no threat. But despite the dental association's position, there are a growing number of dentists in this and other countries who feel that mercury fillings do have a subtle yet harmful effect on mental functioning.

The U.S. government has decided that mercury is a health threat. In 1990, the Environmental Protection Agency banned the use of mercury in latex house paint. Then, in 1988, the agency defined discarded dental amalgam as hazardous waste. It does seem odd that this substance would be considered hazardous waste when it is outside of your mouth, but perfectly safe when it's inside.

For more information about the possible toxicity of fillings, see the book, *Chronic Mercury Toxicity* by H. L. Queen, and the book *Beating Alzheimer's,* by Tom Warren. Warren claims that removing his mercury fillings (along with changes in diet and lifestyle) helped him recover from Alzheimer's, but I don't put much stock in his book. It's poorly documented and somewhat hysterical.

Lead

Lead is one of the most common neurotoxins in our world today. Lead poisoning causes irreversible brain damage. For centuries people have been exposed to lead poisoning. Records from ancient Rome show that many people were poisoned by lead found in wine casks.

Lead is especially toxic to the growing brains of children. There is a clear and direct correlation between low I.Q. and childhood exposure to lead. Children often ingest lead by eating paint that is peeling from walls.

Though paint containing lead was banned in 1978, toxic lead is found in a multitude of places in our modern environment. In fact, it is believed that because of modern mining and manufacturing, lead levels in our environment are 500 times higher than they were in prehistoric times.

Food in lead soldered cans can be toxic. Within five days of opening a lead soldered can, canned juices accumulate five times the amount of lead considered safe. Until 1995 lead soldered cans accounted for 14 percent of the lead ingestion in this country, but that year the U.S. canning industry voluntarily stopped the use of lead solder to seal food cans.

Even so, lead-soldered cans still find their way into the U.S. from foreign countries. The FDA estimates that up to 10 percent of food imported each year is still packaged in lead-soldered cans.

Be sure to check to see if the can you're opening contains lead solder. You should be able to see a silver-gray metallic bead of solder along the seam. These cans will also have small dents along the seam from the soldering process. Lead-free cans either have a thin, sharply defined blue-black paint line along the seam from wire welding, or have no seam.

The FDA has discovered that coffee and tea urns in many fast food restaurants are a potent source of lead. Some older urns contain as many as 680 parts per billion (ppb), which is thirteen times the federal safety standard of 50 ppb. The EPA feels that the safety standard is too high, and wants the safe level of lead lowered to 10 ppb. daily

Researchers in Australia have found similar problems with their coffee urns. A study conducted in 1995 in Perth showed that 67 percent of the samples of water collected from water boilers, urns, coffee and cappuccino machines from restaurants, offices, workplaces and schools contained excessive levels of lead. They concluded that the probable sources of the contamination were the brass components in contact with hot water

Drinking hot acidic beverages such as tea and coffee from lead-glazed ceramic cups or mugs is another source of lead contamination.

High-quality crystal has always contained lead. Joseph Graziano, Ph.D., and Conrad Blum, M.D., conducted an experiment on lead crystal. They poured port wine into crystal containers containing between 24 and 33 percent lead oxide. After four months, the lead content of the port was 65 times greater! The lead in the crystal containers began to leach into the wine in as little as 20 minutes, and the lead level tripled in four hours. Crystal baby bottles leach lead also, and should not be used.

Many older buildings are plumbed with lead soldered pipes, and much of ingested lead comes from drinking water from these pipes. If you would like to test your water for lead, contact the American Council of Independent Laboratories, 1629 K Street, NW, Suite 400, Washington, DC 20006-1633. Phone: 202-887-5872. Web: http://www.acil.org/. They can provide a contact in your area.

Before it was banned in 1972, gasoline containing tetra ethyl lead was responsible for pouring 220 million pounds of lead into our atmosphere. Over three billion pounds of lead were released into the air by manufacturing. Although it has been many years since lead was eliminated from gasoline, the lead particles settled into the soil where they still remain.

A group headed by Rufus Chaney from the U.S. Department of Agriculture developed a test that assesses lead levels in the soil. It is called the Chaney-Mielke soil test. Chaney found lead levels of 5,000 parts per million in the soil of many Maryland gardens. Normal soil should contain about 15 to 40 parts per million. Soil containing more than 500 parts per million is defined as toxic waste by the Environmental Protection Agency. It is believed that the soil in many larger cities is contaminated with lead from many years of accumulation of paint and gasoline particles.

Mr. Chaney tells me that if you would like to test the soil in your area, contact your local County Agricultural agent. For information on Chaney's work go to the Environmental Quality Laboratory, Agricultural Research Service; United States Department of

Agriculture, 10300 Baltimore Avenue, BARC-West, Building 007, Room 224, Beltsville, MD 20705. Phone: 301-504-6511. Web: http://www.ars.usda.gov/is/pr/2000/000622.htm

In the human body, a blood level of lead above 10 micrograms (mcg.) per 100 milliliters of blood is considered dangerous. People showing levels above 60 mcg. are said to have lead poisoning.

The most accurate test for lead levels in the body is hair analysis, except in cases of acute lead poisoning, where body fluid analysis is better.

For information on hair analysis for lead, contact Doctor's Data Inc, P.O. Box 111, West Chicago, IL 60186. Phone: 800-3233-2784. Web: http://www.doctorsdata.com/

Also contact the Leek Corporation, 219 Virginia Place, Costa Mesa, CA 92627. Phone: 714-548-5595. (no website)

Dr. Richard Leek is one of the leading experts in accurate hair analysis.

The most effective treatment to eliminate lead from the body is chelation therapy (discussed earlier). A drug called succimer (brand named Chemet, and pronounced key-met) which also reduces lead levels, is available from Ovation Pharmaceuticals, Four Parkway North, Deerfield, IL 60015 Phone: 847-282-1000 Web: http://www.ovationpharma.com/

Although this drug is used primarily for lead poisoning in children, it has been shown to be effective in adults also.

In an online article from the *Austin Chronicle* about lead contamination, James Heffley, Ph.D. cautions, "If you use herbal products, be aware that several products from other countries contain significant amounts of lead. Azarcon, also known as alarzon, Maria Luisa, liga, Greta, coral, or rueda, is a Mexican treatment for colic-like illness that is 90 percent lead. Pay-loo-ah, an Indochinese remedy for fever can also contain as much as 90 percent lead. It is truly tragic that these remedies are often used in children, who are much more susceptible to lead poisoning than adults."

Tin

Tin has no known biological function and is toxic to humans. Elevated tin levels have been found in patients with Alzheimer's disease. In laboratory experiments, organic tin compounds given to animals produce a syndrome similar to Alzheimer's disease. It is thought that these compounds disrupt fat metabolism in dementia. This is a relatively new finding, and researchers are studying the implications of exposure to tin.

Some tin containing compounds appear in polyvinyl chloride (PVC) products such as shower curtains, vinyl flooring, and vinyl wallpaper. These compounds also accumulate in fish and in plants, as well as in animals higher up the food chain.

Glutamate

Scientists at Massachusetts General Hospital found that brains of Alzheimer's victims have deformed glutamate containing neurons. Memantine, the new Alzheimer's medication, acts by modulating levels of glutamate in the brain.

Monosodium glutamate (MSG) and aspartame (Nutrasweet) contain glutamate, and some experts assert that these substances should be avoided. However, a document issued in August 31, 1995 by the U. S. Food and Drug Administration states, "No evidence exists to suggest that dietary MSG or glutamate contributes to Alzheimer's disease, Huntington's chorea, amyotrophic lateral sclerosis, AIDS dementia complex, or any other long-term or chronic diseases."

But the report also states. "An unknown percentage of the population may react to MSG and develop *MSG symptom complex*" which includes symptoms of anxiety, weakness and drowsiness. The report also acknowledges that there are anecdotal reports that a small percentage of people may have severe toxic reactions to MSG, but this has not been proven scientifically.

As with many controversies, the truth may lie somewhere in the middle. This substance may be safe for some and toxic for others. My advice, don't gamble with toxins.

Nutrasweet

Despite its approval by the FDA, Nutrasweet, or aspartame, has not been proven to be safe. Since 1983, aspartame has been used in carbonated beverages. It's composed of two amino acids: aspartic acid and phenylalanine, and metabolizes into methanol, a neurotoxin.

Aspartame can significantly affect mood and behavior. In animals, at levels comparable to those of human consumption, aspartame increases central nervous system tyrosine and phenylalanine levels while decreasing the levels of tryptophan. Tryptophan is an amino acid needed to manufacture the neurotransmitter serotonin. Low levels of serotonin are found in people suffering from depression (Prozac is an antidepressant drug that works by increasing brain serotonin levels). Evidence suggests that continued use of aspartame results in decreased serotonin levels, which can lead to depression.

Aspartame is made by joining two protein components, aspartic acid and phenylalanine, with 10 percent methanol. The methanol portion of Aspartame could also have significant effects on the brain. Methanol is quite toxic, and the amount of methanol in one gram of Nutrasweet is 100mg. The affect of long-term intake of toxic doses of methanol has yet to be determined. Methanol is widely found in fruits, vegetables and other plant foods, and this is the basis of the safety statement the manufacturers of Nutrasweet post on their website.

"Methanol is a natural and harmless breakdown product of many commonly consumed foods and is part of the normal diet. The methanol produced during the digestion of aspartame is identical to that which is obtained in much larger amounts from many fruits, vegetables and their juices. In fact, a glass of tomato juice provides 6 times as much methanol as an equal amount of beverage sweetened with aspartame."

The recommended EPA limit of methanol consumption is 7.8mg./day. A person consuming 70mg. of Nutrasweet per day is consuming 10 times the Environmental Protection Agency's recommended daily limit for consumption of methanol.

Dozens of studies have been done on the safety of aspartame. At the time of this writing, the jury is still out. It does seem interesting, however, that many of the studies that show the dangers of asprtame are done outside of the United States. Since there are a number of natural sweeteners on the market (including stevia), I would avoid nutrasweet until the dust settles.

Smoking

Smoking affects behavior through the actions of carbon monoxide and nicotine. Smoking also causes low vitamin C levels and elevated levels of blood fats and adrenal corticosteroids. At levels typical of those of cigarette smokers, nicotine causes an altered pattern of brain waves (as measured by an EEG).

Smoking has been shown to produce a significant rise in growth hormone, cortisol, antidiuretic hormone, norepinephrine, epinephrine and glycerol in the plasma. It increases blood pressure and pulse rate, while it decreases skeletal muscle tone, deep tension reflexes, and decreases skin temperature.

Processed tobacco contains cadmium, a heavy metal ten times more toxic than lead, which causes free radical damage. Smoke also carries with it small amounts of radioactive isotopes, which also promotes free radical damage.

These problems are compounded by the fact that cigarette smoking is associated with increased sugar and caffeine consumption. The effect of this combination is reactive hypoglycemia, which can lead to both depression and memory problems. There is no question that smoking is harmful. Stop now.

Alcohol

It's been said that some drink to remember while others drink to forget. But the odds are that forgetting is the more likely result.

Alcohol is metabolized in the body into a chemical called acetaldehyde, which then creates free radicals. Acetaldehyde is a close relative of formaldehyde (embalming fluid) which causes cross linkage of connective tissue. This is the same chemical reaction that is used in tanning hides and browning food.

Chronic alcoholism is a major cause of memory and mental disorders. Chronic alcohol intake destroys brain cells.

There is mounting evidence that alcohol literally shrinks the brain. High blood levels of homocysteine are associated with alcoholism, and cause hippocampal atrophy.

In the brain homocysteine acts as an excitatory amino acid which increases the vulnerability of neuron cells oxidative injury. High levels of plasma homocysteine showed a significant correlation shrinkage of the hippocampus

If the damage is continuous over a period of time, a condition known as Korsakoff's psychosis results. The main symptom of this disorder is severe memory loss. People with Korsakoff's have amnesia for past and present events. They attempt to cover up their memory loss by making things up, a process known as *confabulation.* Constant drinking results in many nutritional deficiencies including shortages of vitamin A, B-complex, vitamins E and C, magnesium, selenium and zinc. Many experts feel that adding vitamins to beer would help prevent this disease.

Alcohol can impair memory performance up to fourteen hours after ingesting it. Studies show that in general, heavy drinkers do worse on memory tasks than light drinkers.

Recent research has linked alcohol to several types of brain damage. Rats given alcohol show damage to the hippocampus, the part of the brain responsible for memory storage. There is also evidence that alcohol damages the cerebellum, the part of the brain responsible for fine motor movement and balance. Some heavy drinkers of Italian Chianti suffer damage to the corpus callosum, the connection between the brain's hemispheres.

Long-term memory is not impaired while a person is drinking. Drunk people still remember who they are and details about their life. But things experienced while a person is drunk are not remembered later on when they are sober. About two-thirds of alcoholics experience complete "blackouts," a total loss of memory for events that occur while the individual is drunk.

Although it is clear that long-term heavy drinking damages the brain, new findings suggest that even moderate drinking can be harmful. In 2004, brain researcher Jingzhong Ding and his colleagues evaluated 1,909 patients, ages 55 and older. Using magnetic resonance imaging, (MRIs), they measured the size of the patients' ventricles and sulci: parts of the brain containing only cerebrospinal fluid. Increased ventricular and sulcal size means brain atrophy.

The findings showed that both areas grew larger the more people drank. A study found low to moderate drinking may cause a loss of brain tissue in some middle-age people. In fact, each alcoholic drink per week was associated with greater ventricular size.

There is also mounting evidence that a person's overall nutritional status has an effect on alcohol consumption, that is, proper nutrition may prevent alcoholism. In a study done on nutrition and drinking, people placed on a diet high in raw foods began to spontaneously avoid alcohol and smoking. Alcoholics placed on the same diet had a much higher abstinence rate than subjects in the control group.

Thirty two people with high blood pressure were fed 62 percent of their calories in the form of raw foods for six months. As a result of the change in diet, 80 percent of the people in the study spontaneously stopped using alcohol and tobacco!

In another study, rats fed a junk-food diet continuously increased alcohol consumption, while another group fed a highly nutritious diet showed no escalation. Interestingly, when the rats were given caffeine, both groups increased alcohol consumption. This is something every AA chapter should consider. Rats made deficient in B vitamins chose alcohol over water, while their preference was reversed when they were given B vitamins.

The amino acid L-glutamine has been shown to reduce the craving for alcohol. Evening Primrose Oil, an extract of the primrose *(Pemptjera boemmos)*, which contains high levels of gamma linoleic acid, also reduces the craving for alcohol, by preventing tolerance to the drug.

The nutrients DL-carnitine, catechin, gamma linoleic acid, glutathione and panthetine all appear to protect the liver from damage by alcohol. But taking these supplements does not replace the need to minimize alcohol intake.

The precursors of prostaglandin E1 may lessen alcohol withdrawal symptoms, while nicotinic acid and pantethine have the ability to reduce acetaldehyde, a toxic chemical formed by the metabolic breakdown of alcohol.

In addition to the above effects of drinking, chronic alcohol consumption causes destruction of the liver, leading to a condition called cirrhosis. Even very early liver failure results in inability of the body to store vitamin A. This is true even when serum levels are normal. Vitamin A and zinc deficiencies cause night blindness, impaired immune function, and loss of taste and smell, which can lead to loss of the desire to eat. This loss of desire to eat then results in many nutritional deficiencies.

When damage occurs, the liver can no longer metabolize nutrients or eliminate toxins from the body. Liver disease leads to the failure of protein synthesis, reduced zinc, and decreased ability to store vitamin B6 and vitamin A.

Still another reason to avoid alcohol is that chronic consumption causes nutritional problems because of gastritis, an irritation of the lining of the stomach and intestines which causes anorexia and vomiting. Irritation of the small intestine leads to chronic diarrhea, resulting in electrolyte imbalances and the failure to absorb nutrients. All of the body's systems then malfunction, including memory systems.

The increase in stomach acid that occurs when drinking may cause increased insulin release, which leads to reactive hypoglycemia, a temporary drop in blood sugar.

Nutritional researchers have discovered a link between nicotinic acid (a form of vitamin B3) and alcohol addiction. When alcohol is broken down in the body, it is converted into the chemical acetaldehyde. In the brain, this chemical combines with the neurotransmitter dopamine to form a substance known as tetrahydropapoveroline. *Tetrahydropapoveroline* is a morphine like substance that may be a contributing cause for alcohol addiction. Nicotinic acid interferes in the production of tetrahydropapoveroline, and therefore reduces the craving for alcohol. The recommended dose is 500mg. a day.

Vitamin B12 is essential for normal memory functioning. However, the liver content of B12 in alcoholics has been found to be low, even though blood levels of the vitamin were high. This and other studies suggest that B12 levels may be low in tissues even though they appear normal in blood tests. In fact, several studies show that serum B12 levels are actually higher in alcoholics even though their brain and tissue levels are significantly low. This occurs because the damaged liver cannot absorb and metabolize the B12.

There are several groups and organizations that specialize in the treatment of alcoholism through nutrition. Joan Larson has developed a program which is available in her book, *Seven Weeks to Sobriety*. The book can be ordered from Bio-Recovery, Inc., 3255 Hennipin Avenue South, Minneapolis, MN 55408, Phone: 800-247-6237.

Other information can be obtained from California Recovery Systems, Mill Valley, CA, Phone: 415-383-3611, and Lakeside-Milam Recovery Centers, Seattle, WA, Phone: 206-241-0890, Web: http://www.lakesidemilam.com.

Mold

Molds produce poisonous gases known as mycotoxins. When these mold toxins become airborne, they can stick to clothing or skin or become trapped in mucus membranes from breathing. Exposure to mold is known to lead to abnormal natural killer cell activity which disrupts the immune system. It can cause a wide range of neurological symptoms, such as severe headaches, fatigue, irritation to the nose and throat, persistent cold-like symptoms, and significant memory loss. Toxic molds such as *stachybotrys* cause mental problems similar to Alzheimer's disease, and toxic mold victims may be misdiagnosed as demented. Because of the epidemic rise of mold in this country in the past few years, many companies now offer mold inspection and elimination services. If you are having memory problems or the other symptoms listed above, you should talk to a mold expert.

Chapter Nineteen

Free Radicals and Antioxidants

The car came out of nowhere. The young boy was thrown from his bike and knocked unconscious. When the paramedics arrived, they immediately put an oxygen mask over his face.

Oxygen is absolutely essential to life. Paramedics are quick to give injured people oxygen because the brain can survive only a few moments without it. Oxygen does its work in the body by combining with other molecules through a process called oxidation. This is the same reaction that causes iron to rust.

But even though oxygen is essential to life, it is also involved in chemical processes that can damage the body. Certain chemical reactions in the body create a chemical called singlet state oxygen, which can cause damage to cells.

The human body is composed of millions of complex molecules. Molecules in the body are said to be stable when the electrons attached to them exist in pairs. When one of these electrons is missing, as is the case with singlet state oxygen, the resulting molecule is called a free radical.

Free radicals are highly reactive molecules in the body that rapidly combine with other molecules. The missing electron allows a free radical to react with any substance in its vicinity. Free radicals quickly steal electrons from other molecules, and damage the molecules in the process. Free radicals create abnormally functioning cells that die or mutate into cancerous tissue.

Furthermore, when a free radical steals an electron, it starts a chain reaction that creates thousands of other free radicals. DNA and RNA, which are the molecules that make up our genes, are very vulnerable to free radical damage.

Free radicals come from inside and outside of the body. For example, white blood cells in the body generate thousands of free radicals that help destroy invading germs, while sunlight, X-rays, radiation, and environmental pollutants are external sources of free radicals. The harmful effects of radiation (X-rays, ultraviolet rays, and gamma rays) occur because photons of radiation knock electrons out of orbit, creating free radicals in the body.

In addition to attack by environmental factors, lifestyle plays an important role in free radical production. Smoking creates a large amount of free radicals, and high levels of stress can induce this type of damage.

Fat is also a contributor. The average human can consume 20 percent of calories in the form of fat without upsetting the body's free radical protection system. But the average American now consumes over 40 percent of his or her calories from fat. High fat diets produce millions of free radicals, and are a major cause of cancer.

Research in senility, dementia and stroke incriminates free radicals as a major cause of nerve damage. In fact, Alzheimer's and other dementias are thought by some researchers to be largely the result of free radical damage.

Antioxidants

Antioxidants are substances that seek out and neutralize free radicals by combining with them. For this reason, these compounds are also called free radical scavengers. They gobble up free radicals, and prevent damage to the body.

Catecholamines are important chemicals that transmit information from one neuron to another. They produce free radicals when the catecholamines are broken down after use.

In a healthy brain, these free radicals are removed by the free radical scavengers. But if the nervous system's free radical defense system is impaired, the receptors on the neurons can be damaged. This damage may lead to Parkinson's disease, and possibly some types of schizophrenia.

Proper amounts of oxygen in the body help to prevent free radicals. Exercise increases oxygen uptake, resulting in adequate oxygenation of capillary beds, the tiny blood vessels that feed oxygen to cells. Other ways to reduce free radical damage include reducing the amount of animal fat in the diet, and avoiding nitrites, toxic chemicals that are found in bacon and other prepared meats.

Vitamins and Nutrients

The antioxidants that are especially important in slowing brain aging include vitamin E, vitamin C (both the water and fat soluble types), beta carotene, selenium and melatonin. These substances are discussed elsewhere in this book, but several other interesting antioxidants are explored here. However, you will be interested to know that the ingredients in tea are the strongest antioxidants in the world, 25 times more effective than vitamin E and 200 times more effective than vitamin C.

While examining the effects of fruits and vegetables on reducing brain damage, Tuft's researchers found that a diet rich in blueberry extract improved short term memory loss and also reversed loss of balance and coordination in older rats.

In the *Journal of Neuroscience,* the researches reported that rats consuming an extract of blueberries, strawberries and spinach every day showed measurable improvements in short-term memory. The rats that received the fruit and vegetable extracts learned faster than the other rats, and their motor skills also improved, but only the blueberry extract improved balance and coordination. A previous study had shown that compared to other fruits or vegetables, blueberries have the highest antioxidant level. This was the first study to show that fruits and vegetables actually reverse nerve cell damage.

Other studies have shown that antioxidant nutrients which include vitamins C, E, and the vitamin A family of carotenoids, plus several minerals, notably selenium — help prevent the brain cell damage that causes Alzheimer's disease.

Treatment with antioxidant vitamin E and the antioxidant drug selegiline significantly slow the progression of the disease. Antioxidants also help prevent heart disease, stroke, cancer, and other degenerative, age-related conditions.

Scientists have created a list of fruits and vegetables which they rate in terms of Oxygen Radical Absorbance Capacity (ORAC). The following is a list of vegetable and fruits with assigned ORAC units per 100 grams:

Prunes	5,770	Plums	949
Raisins	2,830	Alfalfa sprouts	930
Blueberries	2,400	Broccoli florets	890
Blackberries	2,036	Beets	840
Kale	1,770	Oranges	750
Strawberries	1,540	Red grapes	739
Spinach	1,260	Red peppers	710
Raspberries	1,220	Cherries	670
Brussels sprouts	980		

All these fruits and vegetables are richly colored: red, purple, blue, orange, or deep green. This is no coincidence: The antioxidants in these foods are most concentrated in the pigments that give them their color.

Bioflavinoids

Albert Szent-Gyorgyi, the man who first synthesized vitamin C, discovered that an impurity in his preparation had the ability to stop bleeding. The "impurity" turned out to be a family of chemicals called bioflavinoids. *Bioflavinoids* are not classified as vitamins, because they are not considered to be essential for life. However, they play important roles in health and well-being. They are powerful antioxidants, and they protect the liver from damage from environmental toxins.

Most importantly for our purposes, they prevent capillary damage and therefore significantly reduce the risk of stroke. Good sources of these chemicals are apples, the white part of citrus fruits, tea and onions.

Glutathione and Cysteine

Glutathione is a substance produced in the body that acts as a powerful antioxidant. The level of glutathione in the blood is proportional to the amount of cysteine in the body, so more cysteine means more glutathione. In addition, cysteine possesses the ability to eliminate heavy metals from the body.

Pronathocyanidins (PAC)

One of the most potent antioxidants found in nature is a class of bioflavinoids called *proanthocyanadins* (PAC). Until recently the high cost of extracting these chemicals has kept many people from using them. But there are now inexpensive processes which can extract proanthocyanadins from grape seeds and from pine bark.

Some nutritionists claim that proanthocyanadins are the most effective natural antioxidants yet discovered.

The makers of grape seed extract claim that it contains 95 percent proanthocyanadins and is less expensive than pycnogenol, the substance that is extracted from pine. Still another source of proanthocyanadins is European bilberry.

It was Professor J. Masquelier who first patented the pine bark extract in 1951. He also patented grape seed extract in 1986. But the original source of PACs was actually from peanuts, discovered by him in 1948.

Proanthocyanadins are rapidly absorbed and distributed throughout the body within minutes of ingestion. They readily cross the blood-brain barrier to provide immediate antioxidant activity to the central nervous system.

These substances are claimed to have antioxidant properties 50 times greater than vitamin E, and 20 times greater than vitamin C. They restore the antioxidant status of oxidized vitamin C, and help transport vitamin C into cells.

Proanthocyanadins are also said to increase the elasticity and flexibility of collagen, which helps restore the connective tissue underlying the skin to a more youthful structure. They also act as a smooth muscle relaxant in the blood vessels.

A single 100 milligram dose of PAC increases capillary resistance by 140 percent. This means that it strengthens the walls of the capillaries. This same treatment has been shown to reduce cholesterol by 30 percent. Dr. Richard Passwater in his book *Supernutrition*, claims these substances are effective in treating senility.

Green Tea

In numerous studies, green tea has been shown to reduce the incidence of cancer, heart disease, stroke, hypertension and infections. The active components of green tea are substances called polyphenols.

Dr. Brian Leibowitz in the *Journal of Optimal Health,* states "… polyphenols are a remarkable group of naturally occurring nontoxic molecules which hold tremendous promise for the prevention and treatment of a variety of diseases including allergy, asthma, inflammation, cancer, infectious diseases, diabetic cataracts, alcoholic hepatitis and other liver diseases, and cardiovascular disease."

Alpha-lipoic acid

Alpha-lipoic acid (often called ALA) is a compound which is naturally produced in the body. When discovered it was initially classified as a vitamin, but it is now known to be a potent antioxidant. In fact, it is many times more potent than vitamins C and E, and there is evidence that it may help recycle C and E.

One of the properties that makes alpha-lipoic acid so effective is that it is both water and fat-soluble. This allows it to reach areas of the body tissues composed mainly of fat (as in nerve tissue and brain cells) as well as those containing high levels of water (such as the cardiovascular system).

Intravenous forms of alpha-lipoic acid are administered in hospitals to treat cases of acute mushroom poisoning and for other cases of acute poisoning that affect the liver.

Several animal studies show that ALA may protect the brain from oxidative damage, improve long-term memory, and reduce the risk of dementing illnesses. It also appears to minimize brain cell damage occurring after a stroke. However, human clinical trials are few.

In a 2001 study done in Hannover, Germany, 600mg. alpha-lipoic acid was given daily to nine patients with Alzheimer's and related dementias (all of whom were receiving treatment with acetylcholinesterase inhibitors). Over an observation period of approximately a year ALA treatment led to a stabilization of cognitive functions in the study group, demonstrated by constant scores in two neuropsychological tests. Patients with Alzheimer's disease would normally have experienced a constant decline in test scores over the course of a year. This however was not a double blind, controlled study.

So, despite the growing body of evidence that ALA may stave off dementia, the scarcity of randomized double-blind placebo-controlled trials has led the Cochrane review to suggest that until data from trials become available for analysis, ALA cannot be recommended for people with dementia.

Even so, it would appear that evidence of ALA's value may be found in its effect on diabetics. Because of its effect on glucose metabolism, alpha-lipoic acid may improve the glucose-lowering action of insulin (the hormone that regulates blood sugar).

Diabetic neuropathy is a serious complication in patients with diabetes. Clinically, alpha lipoic acid is marketed in Germany as Thioctacid®, which has been used for decades in Europe to counter neuropathy in people with diabetes (both types 1 and 2).

For example in a clinical trial, 328 people with diabetic neuropathy received 100mg., 600mg. or 1,200mg. a day of alpha-lipoic acid for three weeks. Participants who took 600mg. daily had the greatest reduction in pain and numbness. And in a separate study, blood sugar levels dropped in 74 people with type 2 diabetes who took 600mg. or more of alpha-lipoic acid daily. Alpha-lipoic acid is also thought to be of value in the approximately 25 percent of people with diabetes who risk sudden death from nerve-related heart damage. In one study, improved heart function was observed in people at risk for this complication who took 800mg. of alpha-lipoic acid daily for only four months.

ALA is thought to work by increasing blood flow in capillaries. This is significant in light of the finding that diabetics are at much higher risk for dementia.

Dietary sources of alpha-lipoic acid include yeast, spinach, broccoli, potatoes, liver, and kidneys, but the richest food source is red meat.

Milk Thistle Extract

Milk thistle extract contains 85.6 percent of a substance called silymarin, an antioxidant that is said to have a beneficial effect on liver function. *Silymarin* protects and enhances liver function through its ability to stimulate liver protein synthesis and deters liver damage from such factors as free radicals, poisons and pollutants.

Barley and Wheat Grass Juice

Organic barley and wheat grass juice are rich in natural vitamin C, betacarotene, potassium, magnesium and calcium.

Barley juice has also been used successfully to treat arthritis. Its exact mechanism of action is not known. However, life extension doctor Julian Whitaker, in his newsletter *Health And Healing,* states that he has added dried barley and wheat grass juice to his recommended list of everyday supplements. Whitaker says that he has observed significant improvements in arthritis patients who consume barley and wheat grass juice powders.

Wheat grass juice comes only from wheat sprouts, and therefore, has no wheat allergens. Wheat grass functions as a blood purifier and as a cleansing agent for cells because of the abundant amount of chlorophyll it contains.

These juices are also thought to stimulate the production of superoxide dismutase (SOD), a powerful free radical scavenger.

Superoxide dismutase is the fifth most prevalent molecule in the human body. According to Dr. Richard Cutler of the National Institute on Aging, the life span of man is directly proportional to SOD content. In youth, the liver produces 1700 units of SOD per gram of body weight each day, but by age 80, the production of SOD drops to less than 50 units per gram.

Gerontological researchers have for years been looking for an effective method for increasing SOD levels. Wheat sprouts, along with barley and wheat grass juices contain abundant amounts of SOD and other antioxidant enzymes. These natural antioxidant enzymes have also been shown to alleviate the symptoms of chronic arthritis.

Peter R. Rothschild, M.D., Ph.D., has found that when large amounts of SOD are taken orally, much of it survives all the way to the bloodstream within one hour of consumption. Dr. Rothschild demonstrated that SOD can be absorbed by bonding with lecithin to form an emulsified "liposome" that is assimilated through the small veins in the small intestine.

If Rothschild is correct, and the SOD found in barley and wheat grass juice actually does survive into the blood stream in this form, it would be one of the most effective anti-aging substances known.

Royal Jelly and Bee Pollen

Royal jelly and bee pollen are loaded with antioxidant vitamins. There is also a high concentration of pantothenic acid in these substances. Royal jelly is thought to contribute to the longevity of the queen bee, who far outlives all the other bees in a hive. Bee pollen contains high amounts of SOD and is a powerful source of vitamins, minerals and coenzymes.

EDTA

Chelation therapy uses a drug known as EDTA, which is a chemical that some believe can reduce the production of free radicals as much as a millionfold. It binds ionic metal catalysts making them chemically inert and removes them from the body. Be aware that orthodox medicine believes chelation has no medical value.

Hyperbaric Oxygen Therapy

Hyperbaric oxygen therapy (HBO) is a controversial treatment that is claimed to stop free radical damage due to brain injury. For the greatest effectiveness the treatment should begin within thirty minutes of injury to the brain, but proponents claim that it helps even months after the injury.

Lack of oxygen, which results from an impaired blood supply, increases free radical reactions. Oxygen, in properly controlled doses, is an excellent free radical scavenger.

The therapy consists of intermittent exposures of 100 percent oxygen at up to twice normal atmospheric pressure. This is said to interrupt free radical damage. Hyperbaric oxygen raises oxygen tension to normal levels in damaged tissues. It also stimulates an increase of free radical scavenging enzymes such as superoxide dismutase (SOD).

Rebound dilation of blood vessels occurs following HBO which improves blood flow to affected organs. HBO also kills disease causing organisms such as anaerobic bacteria, and stimulates the growth of new blood vessels.

HBO protects the fatty sheaths surrounding nerve tracts in the brain and spinal column from free radical damage, relieving symptoms of stroke, senility and multiple sclerosis. It is most effective in the early stages of these conditions.

This treatment must be done carefully, as too much oxygen is just as damaging as too little. For more information on hyperbaric oxygen therapy, contact the The Brain Therapeutics Medical Clinic, 26381 Crown Valley Pkwy #130 Mission Viejo, CA 92691 Phone: 800-300-1063, Web: http://www.strokedoctor.com/

Chapter Twenty

Drugs that Improve Memory

Not too long ago in *The Scientist,* Eugene Russo published a perceptive article that promises a brighter future for middle-aged persons and older individuals who are concerned about losing memory.

"Cognition — memory, perception, and attention," said Russo, "is a prerequisite to success, an essential for a normal life. When it becomes impaired through illness or accident, a person's life is turned upside down. Existing memory enhancement drugs treat maladies that rob memory, but they are relatively ineffective and have significant side effects. Some researchers, realizing the huge market that an aging, memory-slipping population can generate, are working to modify some drugs currently on the market and to generate others that improve memory, sharpen perception, and focus attention.

"A new generation of enhancers," Russo continued, "is promising to be more specific and more powerful. Companies such as Memory Pharmaceuticals and NeuroLogic are seeking to uncover compounds that will alleviate an array of diseases by targeting the basic molecular underpinnings of memory formation. Researchers have shown that aged rodent models can demonstrate memory deficits, specifically within pathways involved in long-term memory consolidation, which may be akin to that in humans. Theoretically, the animals provide a good way to test compounds that restore the ability to form new memories. Nobel laureate Eric Kandel, who helped illustrate how changes in synaptic function underlie learning and memory, cofounded

Memory Parmaceuticals in 1998. Its mission: generate treatments for chronic learning and memory deficits associated with conditions like Parkinson disease, vascular dementia, and Alzheimer's disease."

The result of the research that's been going on has produced a new class of drugs that improve or enhance memory. Some of these drugs improve memory problems caused by age and illness. Others can actually improve memory in normal, healthy people. These drugs are called *nootropics*, a term which comes from the Greek words *noos* (mind) and *tropein* (toward). In the popular press they are called smart drugs.

Modafinil and Adrafinil

Modafinil (Provigil®) and Adrafinil, (Olmifon®) developed by Lafon Laboratories, are marketed as agents that improve alertness. Modafinil is a more recently developed analogue of Adrafinil. The company states that these substances will not prevent a person from sleeping if they want to, but while awake they will report greater alertness.

A study conducted over a period three years discovered that Modafinil reduced drowsiness in 83 percent of hypersomniac patients and 71 percent of narcoleptics. Modafinil did not produce side effects, disturb night sleep, or promote drug dependence.

These two substances selectively stimulate adrenergic neuron receptors in the brain thought to be involved in regulating normal wakefulness and general alertness towards the external environment. They stimulate the postsynaptic sites that are receptors for norepinephrine, a neurotransmitter used by the brain to regulate alertness, attention, memory, and learning.

These functions of norepinephrine are a recent discovery. Researcher Michael Jouvet states that this system is responsible for "improvement in the signal over background noise ratio" and selects significant stimuli to form a true interface between the outside world and the central nervous system.

This central noradrenergic system deteriorates with age which causes motor and cognitive function to slow down. This slowing is seen in Alzheimer's, Parkinson's disease, and depression. Adrafinil and Modafinil, with their pure and specific noradrenergic enhancement improve brain function in these disorders.

After about fifteen days of use there is an increase in energy, and after about three months, intellectual function is enhanced.

Centrophenoxine

Centrophenoxine (Lucidril) is used throughout Europe to reverse the aging process. First synthesized in 1958, it has been shown to increase mental stamina in humans.

It is a compound of two chemicals — dimethylaminoethanol (DMAE) and parachlorphenoxyacetic acid (PCPA). PCPA is a type of plant growth hormone called auxin.

The main dietary source of DMAE is fish, which could be the origin of the idea that fish is brain food. Clinical trials with centrophenoxine in geriatric patients with impaired memory and cognition showed improvement after several weeks of treatment

Like Hydergine, it appears to remove and prevent further accumulation of a substance called lipofuscin in brain cells. This drug has also been found to reduce the symptoms of tardive dyskinesia, a movement disorder caused by antipsychotic medication, by 6 percent. It is also a potent enemy of hydroxyl radicals, the most dangerous of free radicals.

Lucidril is available in 500mg. tablets. The recommended dose is from 1,000 to 3,000mg. per day. Increased alertness and a sense of stimulation occur soon after ingestion.

DMAE

DMAE (Dimethylaminoethanol) was once marketed as the prescription drug Deaner, and was used to treat hyperactivity. It is a building block of the neurotransmitter acetylcholine. It is also an antioxidant free radical scavenger.

DMAE is found naturally in sardines and anchovies. In capsule form the recommended dosage is from 250 to 1,000mg. per day, which is usually taken in the morning. Every person must establish his or her own effective dose level. It usually takes several weeks to experience the effects. DMAE does have side effects, and can produce insomnia, headaches, muscle tension and depression. I personally have used DMAE and find that it makes me anxious and depressed, but other people report good results with it.

DMAE is a precursor to choline and acetylcholine. However, DMAE has been shown to cross the blood-brain barrier faster than choline. It is likely that all the benefits of centrophenoxine may be obtained more inexpensively from DMAE.

Hydergine

Hydergine is the first drug ever to have a positive effect on people with Alzheimer's disease. Hydergine is one of a family of drugs called hydrogenated ergot alkaloids.

Ergot is a fungus that grows on rye. Practitioners of folk medicine often used ergot to lower blood pressure in mothers during childbirth. It was this effect on blood pressure that led the Sandoz Company to research the family of chemicals found in ergot. From this research came Hydergine. Hydergine is actually the brand name used by the Sandoz Company. Other brand names of Hydergine are Deapril-ST and Circanol.

Hydergine affects brain function in several ways. It normalizes systolic blood pressure, lowers cholesterol, reduces dizziness, and decreases ringing in the ears (tinnitus). The drug also acts as a central nervous system stimulant, increases the brain's capacity to use oxygen, boosts the blood supply to the brain, enhances metabolism in brain cells, and improves memory and learning. There is evidence that Hydergine also slows the accumulation of the age pigment lipofuscin in brain cells.

One of the most important effects of Hydergine is that it protects brain cells from damage from oxygen starvation. It also inhibits damage from free radicals.

Even though Hydergine has been shown to exhibit all of the above effects, it is used in the United States only to treat senility and poor blood circulation to the brain (which is responsible for many of the symptoms of senility).

In their book, *Life Extension,* biochemical researchers Durk Pearson and Sandy Shaw state that many people fail to get results from Hydergine because they do not take it long enough. The drug usually begins to work within six months, but may take as long as two years before the benefits are experienced.

Hydergine may work by imitating the action of a chemical in the body called nerve growth factor (NGF). NGF has been shown to increase the growth of dendrites, the tiny branches at the end of nerve cells that enable one neuron to communicate with another. These connections are where memory and learning take place.

In Europe, the approved dose is 9mg. But at the present time in the United States the FDA has limited the approved dosage to 3mg., even though there are no negative side effects from higher doses. Studies show that patients receiving higher doses of the drug actually show more improvement. Hydergine is useful, but it is not a miracle drug. Most people show slight to moderate improvement on the drug, and it works best on people with mild mental deterioration.

In 2003 *The Cochrane Review* found Hydergine to show significant treatment effects, but because of the small number of studies they analyzed they state that, "uncertainty remains regarding Hydergine's efficacy in dementia."

Too large an initial dose of Hydergine can cause nausea, headache, or gastrointestinal upset. A large overdose of Hydergine may in fact cause amnesia like symptoms.

Piracetam

Piracetam was the first medicine to be called nootropic. It enhances cognition and mental performance, but not mood or behavior.

Marketed since 1972, it is registered in eighty-six countries under a variety of names. This drug appears to enhance dopamine and acetylcholine levels. This substance is not marketed in the U.S. because the patent has expired.

Piracetam is a central nervous system stimulant which appears to have no side effects and no contraindications. It is similar in molecular structure to the amino acid pyroglutamate. It appears to selectively affect the cerebral hemispheres. It affects the cells of the cortex by stimulating the production of ATP (an energy producing chemical found in all cells), which increases the rate of metabolism and energy level of brain cells. It also appears to increase protein synthesis in the brain, and protects the brain from oxygen starvation.

Piracetam enhances learning and memory. In 1976, researchers Dimond and Bowers found that a group of students using 4.8 grams of Piracetam daily had a significant improvement in memory for verbal material. Piracetam somehow facilitates the transfer of information between the two halves of the brain, and for this reason has been used in the treatment of dyslexia. This substance also prevents memory loss from physical injury to the brain. There is also evidence that Piracetam can minimize the damage from stroke. The recommended dosage is from 2,400 to 4,800mg. daily, divided into three equal doses.

Dr. Raymond Bartus has shown that Piracetam works much more effectively in enhancing learning and memory when combined with a cholinergic compound such as centrophenoxine.

L059

LO59 is a Piracetam derivative now called Levetiracetam (trade name Keppra). It is marketed as an anticonvulsant. Thomas Crook, Ph.D., of the Memory Assessment Clinic in Bethesda, Maryland states that this drug is particularly effective with age-associated memory impairment. It is most useful in people over 50 who have memory problems with no signs of disease. This substance may slow progression of Alzheimer's disease. It is ten times more potent than Piracetam. Despite its potential I was unable to find any published studies on this chemical's memory enhancement properties.

L-DOPA

The neurotransmitter dopamine affects sex drive, movement, the immune system, and mood. There is evidence that schizophrenia may be caused by disruption of the neurotransmitter activity of dopamine. Parkinson's disease is caused by damage to dopamine-producing cells in the brain.

The prescription drug L-DOPA helps the brain manufacture dopamine. It's been known to increase cognition and memory in both Parkinson's and Alzheimer's patients. This drug has also been shown to increase the life span of lab animals by as much as 50 percent. Like many of the substances that improve brain function, it is also an antioxidant.

Vinpocetine

Vinpocetine is a derivative of vincamine, an extract of the periwinkle *(Vinca major or Vinca minor)*. Marketed in Europe under the brand name Cavinton, vinpocetine enhances memory in several ways. It enhances the capillary blood flow in the brain, ATP production, and utilization of glucose and oxygen in the brain. This drug is used for treatment of cerebral circulatory disorders, dizziness and other inner ear problems, and headaches.

In a study done in Hungary, 62 percent of patients with various neurological disorders showed clinical improvement when given vinpocetine. In another study, subjects showed improvement in short-term memory within an hour of taking the drug.

Clonidine

Initially this drug showed promise in improvement in memory of patients with Korsakoff's psychosis, a brain disease caused by alcohol abuse, and in schizophrenics. Although this does appear to be true, studies show that it impairs attention and memory in people with Alzheimer's, and causes impulsivity and inattention in other subjects. It's quite possible that the mechanism which improves memory in Korsakoff's and schizophrenia has something to do with the interaction of the drug with a severely damaged brain. At present the literature on this medication is contradictory, and this is probably not a good drug for cognitive enhancement in normal people.

Deprenyl

Deprenyl, is also known under the brand names, Jumex, Eldepryl, Movergan, and Selegiline. It is actually closely related in structure to phenylethylamine (PEA), a substance found in chocolate which has been said to have antidepressant qualities, and which is discussed elsewhere in this book. Deprenyl inhibits an important chemical called B-type monoamine oxidase (MAO-B), an enzyme found in the glial cells of the brain. This enzyme's activity significantly increases with age, and is linked to depression.

At this time, Deprenyl is the only MAO-B inhibitor in clinical use, and it's the only MAO inhibitor that can be given without dietary restrictions. (Other MAO inhibitors require that you eliminate tyramine from your diet. This substance is found in cheese and wine.) Other MAO-B inhibitors that are in various stages of development include lazabemide and mofegiline, which are differentiated from selegiline by their greater specificity for MAO-B and the absence of active metabolites.

Deprenyl also enhances superoxide dismutase (SOD). This effect is unrelated to its effect on MAO-B and the inhibitory effects of the drug on neurotransmitter uptake.

Deprenyl is widely used in treating Parkinson's disease, and appears to improve symptoms in people with Alzheimer's disease. It is the only drug known to affect a part of the brain called the substantial nigra which seems to play a part in the ability to control movement. Researchers believe that the drug is also useful in treating Alzheimer's and in enhancing memory.

Phosphatidylserine

Studies suggest that phosphatidylserine increases memory by increasing glucose metabolism and increasing the number of neuro-transmitter sites. This molecule is found on the surface of every brain cell membrane. In one U.S. double-blind trial on mildly impaired aged subjects, phosphatidylserine statistically improved the learning and recall of names and faces, telephone numbers, and misplaced objects, as well as paragraph recall and the ability to concentrate.

A recent study done in Germany showed that this substance improved brain function in people with early signs of Alzheimer's.

In 1991, Italian researchers found memory improvement in seventy Alzheimer's patients given the drug for three months. Another study done by the National Institute of Mental Health showed memory improvement in 150 people suffering from age associated memory impairment. It was said to be most effective when used in people who are just beginning to show signs of the disorder.

The effect of this drug can last up to a month after it is given. It has also been shown to relieve depression

On May 13, 2003, in response to a request that the substance be advertised as improving cognition, the FDA issued a statement that, "Very limited and preliminary scientific research suggests that phos-phatidylserine may reduce the risk of dementia in the elderly. FDA concludes that there is little scientific evidence supporting this claim."

On the other hand, memory researcher Thomas Crook states that memory enhancing drugs are, "By and large a bunch of nonsense." Yet

Crook concedes that of all the substances researched, "phosphatidylserine stands out. I'm not sure I can fully explain it. Phosphatidylserine may do a lot for a 55- to 75-year-old suffering from Age Associated Memory Impairment"

Quinones

For several years, research scientist Paul Gallop has been studying a family of molecules called quinones. Quinones are found in many fruits and vegetables, but they are also found in human cerebrospinal fluid. It's not clear whether quinones originate from the food we eat or if they are manufactured in the body.

Quinones are involved in connective tissue growth and brain metabolism. There is evidence that quinones protect against aging problems such as liver damage, cataracts, stroke, dementia, and memory impairment. Quinone may also protect tissues from free radical damage.

A quinone called Idebinone seems to protect brain cells from damage from loss of blood supply, as in stroke. The drug delayed the onset of amnesia in rats whose blood supply was reduced from 60ml./sec to 130ml./sec.

When given seven days in a row after the blood supply was reduced, Idebinone significantly improved learning capabilities in the rats.

In human studies, Idebinone was given to seven elderly individuals for two months. Their scores on the dementia rating scale improved as much as five points.

Researchers think that quinones may retard the slowing of cerebral energy metabolism that accompanies aging. Studies show that Idebinone prevents damage to brain cell mitochondria, where fuel is converted to energy.

There is evidence that heavy alcohol consumption reduces quinone levels. In one study, thirty alcoholic patients had half the blood quinone levels of non drinking people.

Idebinone is closely related to co-enzyme Q10, a nutrient that is found in high concentrations in the human heart. In the body, CoQ10 plays an important role in creating ATP (Adenosine triphosphate) which is the body's main source of energy. Although CoQ10 does some remarkable things, it has been shown in some studies to create free radicals. Idebinone does not.

Idebinone is a potent antioxidant, and in animal studies, has been shown to reduce brain damage from strokes. It also protects brain cells from oxygen starvation (a condition called hypoxia).

One human study suggests that Idebinone increased the levels of serotonin (a neurotransmitter involved in mood and memory) in dementia patients.

Idebinone is now marketed under the brand name Avan. It is considered to be a cerebral metabolism enhancer effective for combating intellectual impairment in patients with dementia and Alzheimer's disease.

Aspirin and other NSAIDS

Recently 210 Alzheimer's patients in the Johns Hopkins Alzheimer's Disease Research Center were compared to patients taking nonsteroidal anti-inflammatory drugs (NSAIDs) or aspirin on a daily basis. The patients were tested on clinical, cognitive, and psychiatric measures.

The patients taking NSAIDs performed better on three commonly used tests for mental functioning: the Mini-Mental Status Examination, the Boston Naming Test, and the delayed condition of the Benton Visual Retention Test. At the end of one year the people taking NSAIDs had less mental decline than the non-NSAID group in measures of verbal fluency, spatial recognition, and orientation.

These results suggest that NSAIDs play a protective role in Alzheimer's disease, and may delay both its onset and its progression.

Lithium

Lithium, a drug that has been used in the treatment of various neurological symptoms, is now regarded as possibly crucial as a blocker of an enzyme critical to formation of Alzheimer's plaques and tangles in the brain. By blocking the enzyme, lithium stems the accumulation of beta amyloid, which forms Alzheimer's plaques, scientists funded by the National Institutes of Health (NIH) reported in the May 22, 2003 issue of *Nature*. Inhibiting the enzyme, glycogen gynthase kinase-3 alpha (GSK-3 alpha), also blocks formation of neurofibrillary tangles by the tau protein.

Since certain non-steroidal anti-inflammatory drugs (NSAIDs — see above) similarly reduce beta amyloid levels, but via a slightly different mechanism, the researchers suggest that combination therapy with lithium and NSAIDs could have an enhanced effect in reducing amyloid peptide accumulation.

Lithium also protects neurons from stimuli that trigger programmed neuronal cell death in Alzheimer's disease. Pending development of new medications that target the enzyme, the researchers suggest that lithium "might be considered for the prevention of Alzheimer's disease, especially in younger patients with an inherited tendency for Alzheimer's disease or Down's syndrome." The new findings have spurred interest in whether patients taking lithium for bipolar disorder might have a lower incidence of Alzheimer's disease, Klein noted.

Semax

From Russia come reports of a product called Semax (heptapeptid) which is said to slow the progression in early stage Alzheimer's disease, and to minimize the symptoms.

Semax is synthesized from seven natural amino acids: methionine, glutamine, histidine, phenylanine, prolil, glycine and proline. It is actually an analogue of corticotrophin fragment (ACTH 4-7) but has no hormone activity.

Developed in Russia by the Russian Academy of Science, Institute of Molecular Genetics in accordance with the Guidelines of the Russian Food and Drug Administration, the substance received Approval in 1996 by the Ministry of Public Health and Medical Industry Russian Federation.

The developers claim this substance has no contraindications, no known toxicity, and no side effects. The drug is administered in nasal drops. Patients put 2 to 3 drops in each nostril at 2 minute intervals between drops for maximum absorption.

In the heart and kidneys it decomposes after a very short period of time but the substance stays in the brain in very small quantities for at least 20 hours.

In clinical trials, 80 percent of patients with cerebro-vascular disorders taking Semax exhibited a significant improvement in cognitive capacity and audio-verbal memory, and moderate improvement of sleep and mood. The mechanism of action is thought to be changes in cell membranes of the limbic system leading to increased production of cyclic AMP and increasing acetylcholinesterase and dopamine activity.

For Alzheimer's disease 3 drops, 4 times a day, are recommended in both nostrils for 6 weeks.

Cypin

A protein called cypin is involved in learning and memory. Cypin appears to be crucial for the growth of fine filaments between nerve cells, which could explain how new memories are formed. A study in the journal *Nature Neuroscience* found that in the brain, cypin acts as an enzyme, shaping neurons by the process of branching. Cypin was first identified in humans in 1999, but this study found the chemical to be an active enzyme — a molecule that speeds up biological reactions. Bonnie Firestein of Rutgers State University is investigating this protein, and believes that memory-enhancing drugs that mimic the protein's natural effect could soon be developed.

Cerebrolysin

Cerebrolysin is a drug with the ability to reduce amyloid in the brain and improve synaptic plasticity in Alzheimer's disease. It also promotes synaptic regeneration. The drug is composed of low molecular weight peptides and a mixture of free amino acids.

Dr. Xiao Shifu of the Shanghai Mental Health Center in China compared the effects of cerebrolysin to that of a placebo in 157 patients with mild to moderate Alzheimer's disease. The drug was given intravenously five days a week for four weeks. The findings showed that mental function improved significantly in the patients taking the drug.

This drug is believed to mimic a naturally occurring growth factor in the body. It is manufactured by Ebewe Pharmaceuticals, Ltd., of Austria, and is approved for marketing in 28 countries.

Although not all cognitive enhancing drugs are available in the U.S., they can be purchased from many sources. The Cognitive Enhancement Research Institute (CERI) publishes *Smart Life News,* and is a great source of current information on memory improving drugs and where to purchase them. For more information contact The Cognitive Enhancement Research Institute, P. O. Box 4029, Menlo Park, CA, 94026. Phone: 650-321-CERI (650-321-2374) Web: http://www.ceri.com/

Their website has an extensive list of drug resources.

Chapter Twenty-One

Vitamins and Memory

Vitamins play a crucial role in keeping your mind healthy and functioning properly. Because there are so many vitamin supplements offered on the market, it is important that you know the truth about how vitamins work.

Many of the so called brain boosting supplements on the market today fail to provide adequate amounts of the nutrients and do not deliver the protection and extra brain power they advertise. Not only are the dosages too low, but the concoctions contain ingredients that you may not need. As a rule, avoid products that offer you super brain power and eternal youth. These products are snake oil, not nutrition.

Researchers, Karin Johnson, Marie Bernard and Karen Funderburg, at the University of Oklahoma College of Medicine have confirmed that proper vitamin nutrition is essential for all people — but especially for older people — because they are at higher risk for deficiencies. The researchers recommend that all older adults take one multivitamin a day.

While I highly recommend that everyone take a high potency multivitamin every day, science has established beyond any reasonable doubt that additional supplements are needed for maximum brain protection.

But before you run out and buy everything described in this chapter, do your homework. Look at labels for potency and heed medication warnings. Understand that vitamins, while helpful, can interact with medications you are taking and, like prescription medications, they can also cause side-effects and adverse reactions.

Because of this, when you decide to start taking these supplements, start low and go slow. Add only one vitamin at a time to your diet. In this way, if you have an adverse reaction you will know what is causing it.

Always tell your doctors what supplements you are are taking so they can advise you of potential problems. They don't have to believe in what you are doing, but they should know what you're doing.

Vitamin E

Lipofuscin occurs primarily in postmitotic cells (cells that do not divide). These cells include heart muscle and liver cells, but also nerve and brain cells. In non-replicating cells, lipofuscin increases with age. Because of this, lipofuscin is considered a valid marker of cellular aging and has come to be known as 'age pigment.'

Lipofuscin accumulation in a brain cell disrupts the cell's activity, and can eventually lead to the death of the cell. Some of the drugs in this book, such as Hydergine and Centrophenoxine, remove lipofuscin. Vitamin E has also been shown to reduce the accumulation of the pigment. However, at the time of this writing there is still controversy over the importance of slowing lipofuscin accumulation.

Two studies mentioned in the June 26, 2002 issue of *Journal of the American Medical Association* suggest that vitamin E, in its natural form (from nuts, and leafy green vegetables) reduces the risk of Alzheimer's disease.

This was further confirmed when scientists at the Rush Institute for Healthy Aging studied the dietary habits of 815 Chicago area residents — all at least 65 years old and free of clinical signs of dementia. They found that those who consumed the most vitamin E from their diets were 70 percent less likely to develop Alzheimer's disease than those who consumed the smallest amount. Vitamin E from supplements did not have the same effect. This may be because alpha tocopherol, which is found in most supplements, is not as effective as gamma tocopherol which is found in foods. Unexpectedly, this association was observed only among individuals without the APOE E4 gene.

David Schubert, Ph.D., at the Salk Institute for Biological Studies in San Diego claims that exposing brain cells to vitamin E in the laboratory protects them from the effects of a stroke. The vitamin's protective effect comes from its ability to limit the number of cells damaged by glutamic acid. Schubert has also shown that bathing brain cells in vitamin E protects them from a toxic protein found in amyloid plaques — the plaques that cause Alzheimer's disease.

In addition, Dr. Marguerite Kay, in the *Proceedings of the National Academy of Sciences,* has reported that vitamin E protects both the immune and nervous systems.

The difficulty with using vitamin E for these purposes is that it doesn't easily cross the blood-brain barrier, a natural protective mechanism that protects the brain from toxins. Because of this, Schubert and his colleagues are attempting to attach vitamin E to steroid-like molecules so that it readily crosses this barrier. Although it's too early to conclude that vitamin E can actually ward off Alzheimer's, Dr. Schubert believes that there is enough evidence to warrant taking the vitamin.

Vitamin E is actually a group of related chemicals called tocopherols. As mentioned above alpha tocopheral is the type usually sold in stores, but gamma tocopherol is actually the most useful to the body. You can now purchase gamma tocopherol in many nutrition outlets. Research has shown that natural vitamin E is, in fact, more active than synthetic forms. The effective dosage is 400 IU a day, and should not exceed 800 IU a day.

Beta-Carotene

Beta-carotene (also called provitamin A) is a food substance that is turned into vitamin A by an enzyme in your body. It is also an antioxidant and free radical scavenger. Beta-carotene is preferable to vitamin A because it is less toxic. The adult daily supplement range for beta-carotene is from 10,000 to 50,000 International Units a day. Beta-carotene sources include green leafy vegetables, seaweed, asparagus, carrots and sweet potatoes.

Folic Acid

Folic acid functions as a coenzyme in the manufacture of norepinephrine and serotonin — two important brain neurotransmitters. It's not surprising then that research suggests that a deficiency in folic acid is associated with mental and emotional disturbance. In a recent study, a physician placed on a diet deficient in folic acid reported that after four months he suffered from sleeplessness and forgetfulness. These symptoms disappeared two days after supplementation with folic acid.

High homocystine has long been known to be a risk factor for cardiovascular disease and Alzheimer's disease. But as mentioned earlier, new research suggests that high homocystine may also increase the risk of brain atrophy — shrinking of the brain. Researchers found that people with extensive brain atrophy were more likely to have high homocystine levels. Interestingly, in this study, homocystine levels did not appear to have any effect upon how well participants scored in mental ability tests.

In combination with vitamin B12, folic acid can lower the levels of homocystine in the blood, making it a vitally important nutrient for optimal brain health.

Folic acid supplements can correct anemia associated with vitamin B12 deficiency. Unfortunately, folic acid may mask the symptoms of vitamin B12 deficiency without correcting the deficits in the nervous system that are caused by it. Permanent nerve damage can occur if vitamin B12 deficiency is not treated.

Most people today do not get enough folic acid in ther diet. This is because the major sources of folic acid are whole grains and green leafy vegetables like spinach and turnip greens — not our favorite foods in this country. A study of teenagers revealed that up to 85

Drugs that interfere with Folic Acid Absorption

- Antacids
- Anti-inflammatories
- Anticonvulsants
- Aspirin
- Azulfidine

- Birth control pills
- Anti cholesterol drugs
- Diuretics
- Gold shots
- Methotrexate

percent of them got less than one third of the minimum daily requirement of folic acid in their diets.

Several recent studies have suggested that folate supplementation should be considered in all elderly people, especially those with elevated plasma homocystine levels and cardiovascular disease, and individuals who have neuropsychiatric disorders

B Vitamins and Brain Function

Vitamin B1 (Thiamin)

A study by Dr. Ruth Flynn Farrel at the Presbyterian Children's home in Lynchberg, VA. showed that B1 improved brain function. She noticed that the recovery of an accident victim suffering from aphasia (the inability to speak) was speeded up by the addition of vitamin B1 in his diet. Based on this observation, she decided to add vitamin B1 supplements to the diets of three retarded children who could not talk. Once placed on the B1 supplements, two of the children learned to speak.

Impressed by these results, Dr. Farrel then did a double-blind study with two groups of children matched in mental ability. The group given two milligrams of B1 scored from 7 to 87 percent higher than the group given a placebo.

Researcher Bruno Mind found that a stimulated nerve cell gives off eighty times the amount of B1 than a cell at rest. This suggests that the more mental activity you engage in, the more of this vitamin you need. B1 is also an antioxidant, and protects the brain against the harmful effects of smoking.

Chronic alcoholics often suffer from a memory disorder called Korsakoff's psychosis, caused in part by a deficiency of vitamin B1. People with this disease have severe memory problems, and often make up stories to fill the gaps in their memory, an activity called confabulation. B1 supplements are routinely given to these people, with the result of improvement in cognition.

The vitamin can also be useful in those with Alzheimer's. When Dr. John Blass, director of the Dementia Research Service at the Burke

Medical Research Institute, gave people with Alzheimer's symptoms 1,000mg. of thiamin three times a day for three months, their memory improved slightly. In another study researchers found that participants improved when they took 5,000mg. of thiamin per day.

Vitamin B2 (Riboflavin)

Riboflavin is important to myelin, the fatty substance that insulates nerve cells. Alcoholics and people who use oral contraceptives are often deficient in this substance. A deficiency of riboflavin can result in nervous disorders, degeneration of the myelin sheaths, edema and photophobia. Dietary sources of riboflavin are meats, nonfat milk and oysters.

Vitamin B3 (Niacin, Niacinamide)

Niacin plays a part in the metabolism of protein, carbohydrates and fats. It also has the ability to improve circulation and nervous system function. Although we get most of our niacin from our diet, if needed, the body can convert tryptophan into niacin.

Niacin deficiency can cause depression, fatigue, and short-term memory problems. This vitamin has also been used as a tranquilizer and to treat schizophrenia. Another use has been to increase blood circulation, by way of its ability to dilate blood vessels.

A 1985 study published in the journal *Psychopharmacology* has shown that 141mg. of niacin per day improved memory from 10 to 40 percent in 96 healthy subjects between the ages of 35 and 85.

The National Heart, Lung and Blood Institute feels that niacin is the preferred way to lower cholesterol levels. Niacin has been found to reduce total cholesterol, triglycerides, and LDL (bad) cholesterol levels while simultaneously increasing HDL (good) cholesterol. It is the most effective drug available for raising HDL cholesterol levels.

Niacin is available as a nutritional supplement as either niacin (nicotinic acid) or niacinamide (nicotinamide). Each form has different applications. The nicotinic acid form is the cholesterol reducer.

Side effects include hot flashes (sometimes called niacin flush), nausea, indigestion, and increased blood sugar. Sustained-release niacin, popular because it causes less niacin flush has been shown to be toxic to the liver and should only be used under the supervision of a health care professional.

This is not a small problem. A recent study published in the *Journal of the American Medical Association* strongly recommended that sustained-release niacin be restricted from use because 78 percent of patients stopped using it because of side effects. Fifty two percent developed liver damage. If you take niacin on a regular basis, regardless of the form of niacin you use, monitoring your liver enzymes every 3-months is recommended.

In 2003 the Food and Drug Administration approved a new prescription medication called Advicor that combines sustained release niacin (to increase good cholesterol) and lovastatin (to lower bad cholesterol).

Natural sources of niacin include fish, chicken, cheese, broccoli, carrots and Brewer's yeast

In Russia a popular drug called Picamilon is made from binding niacin to gamma aminobutyric acid (GABA), a neurotransmitter in the brain which causes calmness. Valium, Xanax and other tranquilizers act by increasing GABA.

Picamilon is purportedly the only drug known to increase calmness without causing drowsiness. The substance also acts as a potent vasodilator, which lowers blood pressure while increasing blood flow in the brain. People taking this drug report a feeling of calmness, alertness, and sharper thinking. It also has antioxidant properties. This substance is now available in the United states and is sold by many nutrition retailers.

Vitamin B5 (Pantothenic acid)

Pantothenic acid is required for the conversion of choline and lecithin into the neurotransmitter acetylcholine. It is also involved in the cell's energy cycle, called the citric acid cycle, and acts as a metabolic stimulant.

In the last decade several studies suggest that lack of this nutrient may play a part in a serious condition similar to Reye's syndrome — a severe neurological disease which includes liver failure, hypoglycemia, coma, and often death. In one study three dementia patients developed fatal, acute encephalopathy while receiving calcium hopantenate, a drug that eliminates pantothenic acid activity. The level of pantothenic acid examined in one patient was lowered significantly. Evidence obtained indicated that, ironically, calcium hopantenate was once touted as the first of "cerebral activators" and was a popular treatment for dementia. It is now known to be toxic. More than 47 victims including 11 fatal cases have been reported.

The Reye-like syndrome was thought to be caused by the calcium hopantenate, possibly due to the artificial induction of pantothenic acid deficiency.

Vitamin B6 (Pyridoxine)

Lack of B6 can cause convulsions, but an excess can cause peripheral nerve damage. An adequate amount is needed to manufacture the neurotransmitter noradrenaline. The requirement for this vitamin can be from 5 to 400mg. per day.

Vitamin B6 enters the body from the small intestine and plays a role as cofactor in most enzymes that support amino acid metabolism. It controls the absorption, metabolism and conversion of amino acids into neurotransmitters. The manufacture of the neurotransmitters, serotonin, dopamine and adrenaline are all dependent on Vitamin B6. Studies show that 50 percent of depressed patients show a B6 deficiency. As depression is an imbalance of neurotransmitters, this makes sense.

Never use more than 100 milligrams of Vitamin B6 for long periods of time because it can cause headaches, loss of balance, and nerve damage. Food sources include pork, whole grains, wheat germ, potatoes, beans, and bananas

---

Symptoms of Low Vitamin B-6
- Depression
- Difficulty recalling dreams
- Insomnia
- Learning difficulties
- Mental stress
- Nervousness
- Premenstrual tension

Symptoms of High Vitamin B-6
- Excessive dreaming
- Destruction of the sensory nerves causing a loss of feeling.

Chapter Twenty-Two

Two Vitamins Essential to Memory

Vitamin B12

Of all vitamins, B12 is the most essential to memory. It is needed for the manufacture of RNA, which is involved in the memory storage process, and participates in many metabolic processes that regulate brain function. One such function is the conversion of homocystine into methionine. B12 along with folic acid, therefore, can reduce homocystine level. Homocystine, you may recall is a risk factor for cardiovascular disease.

Low B12 has also been implicated in multiple sclerosis, neural tube defects, myelin protein deficiency, depression, panic attacks, mood swings, and optic and peripheral neuropathy. People with B12 deficiencies often feel tired, inattentive, and forgetful. But significant deficits in the vitamin may cause confusion, dementia, and even psychosis.

B12 deficiency is very common, especially in people over 50, because at this age many of us begin to show a significant drop in a compound called *intrinsic factor.* Intrinsic factor is a protein produced by glands in the stomach lining, which is necessary for intestinal absorption of vitamin B12. If your intrinsic factor is low, B12 taken by mouth will be not be absorbed.

Vegetarians are also at high risk of B12 deficiency because B12 is only found in animal products.

Since B12 is so essential to human memory it is sometimes tested in people with neurological symptoms. The Schilling test is the most common vitamin B12 deficiency test.

There are several diseases known to affect the body's uptake of vitamin B12. The Schilling test checks to see if the B12 deficiency is caused by low levels of a compound called intrinsic factor, which must combine with B12 before the vitamin can be absorbed. In the first part of the Schilling the person takes a capsule that contains a small amount of radioactive vitamin B12. One hour later he or she is given an injection of non-radioactive B12. Urine from the patient is then collected for the next 24 hours. In the nuclear medicine laboratory the urine is checked for radioactive B12. If the vitamin was absorbed it will be detected in the urine.

If the first part of the Schilling test shows that the B12 was not absorbed, the patient returns for the second part of the test some days later. In the second part of the test the person again takes B12 but also takes a capsule containing intrinsic factor. If there is now radioactive B12 in the urine and there was none in the first study, it means that the intrinsic factor deficiency is likely to be the cause of the B12 deficiency.

A shortcoming of this test is that while a positive Schilling test clinches the diagnosis, a normal Schilling test does not rule out cobalamin deficiency. This means the results of a Schilling test may be normal in patients with symptoms of deficiency. Blood tests are not definitive either. Serum levels of B12 are normal in over 30 percent of patients with vitamin B12 deficiency.

For this reason researchers E. Steve Roach and Thomas McLean at the University of Texas suggest that, "The possibility of vitamin B12 deficiency should be considered in all patients with nervous system disorders, even in those who do not have anemia. If treatment is started early, most of the neurologic deficits will resolve."

Japanese researchers discovered that brain cells are damaged and destroyed every day by the excessive release of glutamate. They are using a form of vitamin B12 called methylcobalamin to treat neurological disease caused by excess glutamate release (a phenomenon called excitotoxicity).

Vitamin B12 is actually a group of cobalamin-containing compounds. Methylcobalamin is the neurologically active form of vitamin B12. The liver does not convert regular vitamin B12 (cyanocobalamin) into adequate amounts of methylcobalamin to prevent or correct most neurological defects.

At the low price, this vitamin B12 analog represents one of the better valued anti-aging supplements available. You can buy methylcobalamin tablets at most nutrition stores. Mythylcobalamin tablets are sublingual, meaning they are placed under the tongue. Healthy people only need one tablet per day, whereas those with neurologic impairment should take 20 to 80 milligrams a day in the form of 5 milligram lozenges. Published studies show that this natural B12 metabolite is safe even when administered in large doses. You cannot overdose on B12 and there are no known side effects.

New research demonstrates that methylcobalamin has additional benefits that extend beyond the brain and nerves. Methylcobalamin may also be an effective treatment for dementia, psychosis and manic depressive illness, as well as certain sleep disorders, HIV infection, cancer and immune impairment. Specifically, methylcobalamin has been shown to increase the numbers of certain immune T-cells and enhance natural killer cell activity. This vitamin B12 analog may also protect against the side effects caused by certain drugs, hemodialysis and nitrous oxide anesthesia.

Japanese researchers have been using intravenous injections of methylcobalamin for the treatment of Alzheimer's.

When vitamin B12 levels were measured and compared to the level of intellectual function scores in ten patients, methylcobalamin significantly improved intellectual function, memory, emotional functions, and communication. These improvements remained constant as long as the B12 levels in the cerebrospinal fluid were maintained. Further improvements in communication occurred when high B12 levels were maintained for a longer period of time.

Other researchers claim that one out of three people showing signs of cognitive decline will improve when given B12 supplements.

Ask your doctor about using the vitamin B12 analog. Copy this information and the B12 reference section in this book and take it with you when you see your doctor. Most doctors appreciate seeing research.

Vitamin C

The human brain is literally bathed in vitamin C. Human cerebrospinal fluid contains 100 times the concentration of vitamin C than any other body fluids. It is kept in this high concentration by a biological vitamin C pump.

Vitamin C is a natural chelating agent, thereby protecting us against pollution and poisoning of heavy metals such as mercury, lead and cadmium. Not only does it protect us from the lead in automobile exhaust, it also protects us from carbon monoxide.

It is also a highly effective antioxidant. Even in small amounts vitamin C can protect indispensable molecules in the body, such as proteins, lipids (fats), carbohydrates, and nucleic acids (DNA and RNA) from damage by free radicals. Vitamin C may also be able to regenerate other antioxidants such as vitamin E.

The blood brain barrier forms a protective shield between the blood and brain tissue, screening any chemical that can be potentially toxic. But this barrier can be a drawback, as it also blocks the transport of substances to it that could benefit brain function. One such substance is vitamin C.

But researchers David Agus and David Golde at Memorial Sloan-Kettering Cancer Center believe that they have discovered how to get vitamin C past the blood brain barrier. The investigators reported their findings in an issue of the *Journal of Clinical Investigation.*

Previous research by Dr. David Golde, physician-in-chief of Memorial Hospital, established that substance known as glucose transporter molecules were responsible for transporting vitamin C into cells.

In order for this to occur vitamin C, which is normally used in the body as ascorbic acid, is converted into another form called dehydroascorbic acid.

This allows it to be transported into the cell. Once inside the cell it is converted back to ascorbic acid. Agus and Golde posited that vitamin C could also cross the blood brain barrier using glucose transporters. Using mice as subjects they found this to be true. The researchers are now exploring ways to help this conversion take place in humans.

Vitamin C may also help people with hypertension (high blood pressure). This effect was reported in the *Lancet,* an international medical journal published in Britain. In the study, researchers from the Boston University Medical School and Oregon State University studied the effect of daily doses of vitamin C on the blood pressure of 39 people averaging about 48 years of age with high blood pressure.

The study subjects took vitamin C pills for one month, after which their blood pressure and vitamin C blood levels were measured. As expected, vitamin C supplementation significantly increased the vitamin's blood levels compared to initial levels. In addition, there was a significant decrease in the systolic pressure of subjects taking vitamin C. Those who received vitamin C also had a small decrease in their diastolic blood pressure, but this decrease was not statistically significant. Importantly, the greater the change in the blood level of vitamin C, the greater the decrease in blood pressure.

Another connection between vitamin C and brain health is a fascinating study of the arctic ground squirrel at the Institute of Arctic Biology. According to researcher Kelly Drew, the squirrel is providing information that may benefit human stroke victims.

Strokes occur when a clot or ruptured vessel interrupts blood flow to the brain. Without blood there is no oxygen supply and, starved for oxygen, brain cells die by the millions. Drew likens hibernating ground squirrels to human stroke victims.

She discovered that in the deepest stage of hibernation, a ground squirrel's body temperature may fall below 32 degrees Fahrenheit (freezing temperature). The waking heart rate for a ground squirrel is about 200 beats per minute, but during hibernation the squirrel's heart may slow to an amazing two beats per minute.

Such a drastically reduced blood supply should be expected to cause significant brain damage, but it doesn't. Drew believes that ground squirrels use several methods to prevent the expected destruction. Because the squirrels get so cold while hibernating, their blood doesn't clot and their white blood cells become inactive. But most importantly, their blood contains very high levels of vitamin C.

In fact, Drew found that a hibernating ground squirrel's blood has four times the amount of ascorbic acid than it contains when they are not hibernating. When the ground squirrel stirs from the deepest stages of hibernation, the vitamin C content of their blood quickly returns to normal.

She is now trying to find out if the vitamin C-rich blood of hibernating squirrels is what protects the brain. If this turns out to be true, this method could be applied to humans.

A stroke causes immediate destruction of brain cells, but because of the glutamate cascade (described in the stroke section of this book), cell death can continue for as long as a week after the stroke.

Drew's findings suggest that an intravenous injection of ascorbic acid, given soon after a stoke, might significantly decrease this damage. She believes that with this treatment, symptoms could actually improve rather than decline in the first week after the stroke.

Another piece of good news about vitamin C was reported by *Reuters Health Service*. Taking vitamin C and vitamin E supplements, the story asserted, may help protect memory and mental decline as you age.

In this study, elderly men who took vitamin E and C supplements at least once a week, over a number of years, were protected from dementia and actually showed improvements in cognitive function.

Although a protective effect was seen for vascular dementia and mixed dementia in men who took both vitamins, the supplements did not appear to prevent dementia due to Alzheimer's disease.

The authors noted that men who took both vitamin E and C supplements together for many years tested higher than those who did not, suggesting that long-term use is required to sustain cognitive function in late life.

These results suggest that vitamin E and C supplements may protect against vascular dementia and may improve cognitive function in late life.

A study done in England suggested that many geriatric patients suffered mental confusion due to a vitamin C deficiency.

Other research showed that students with high vitamin C levels scored higher on an I.Q. test than those with low levels.

Jeffrey Bland reported a study in which students with high serum vitamin C levels had I.Q.s almost five points higher than those with low serum levels. When both groups were given vitamin C (a glass of orange juice daily for six months), the high I.Q. group showed minimal improvement while the low group increased their I.Q. by 3.54 points. Children with developmental disorders showed a rise in I.Q. of up to twenty points when given the vitamin.

There is a fat soluble form of vitamin C called ascorbyl palmitate. In this fat soluble form, vitamin C is more able to enter the fatty parts of the brain and prevent free radical damage. I have tried this form of the vitamin, and found that it made me nervous and jumpy, but others have reported that they tolerate it well.

A new form of vitamin C, called Ester C, has recently shown promise in preventing and reversing cardiovascular disease. Some researchers claim it can reduce arterial plaque by 50 percent. This type of vitamin C is readily absorbed into all body tissues. It is available in most health food stores.

Vitamin C reinforces the immune system. It is absolutely necessary for the formation and maintenance of collagen, the primary substance of skin and connective tissues, which hold our bodies together. Vitamin C fights stress and extra amounts are needed in times of stress and in periods of cold weather. It is necessary for healthy liver and adrenal gland function.

Recent studies suggests that vitamin C may also help patients with congestive heart failure (CHF). This condition occurs when the heart can no longer pump enough blood to supply the needs of the brain and body.

Caused by factors such as narrowed arteries or high blood pressure, CHF, some scientists believe may also be caused by apoptosis — the death of cells on the inner lining of blood vessels. Investigation by German researchers confirmed that vitamin C taken by volunteers reduced the levels of particles in the blood that indicate apoptosis.

Because CHF causes the heart to work inefficiently, patients often experience heart weakening, exhaustion and shortness of breath upon exertion. CHF is generally treated with a proper diet, rest and modified daily activity.

Vitamin C also plays an important role in the synthesis of the neurotransmitter, norepinephrine. Neurotransmitters are critical to brain function and are known to affect mood. In addition, vitamin C is required for the synthesis of carnitine, a small molecule that is essential for the transport of fat to cellular organelles called mitochondria, for conversion to energy.

Research also suggests that vitamin C is involved in the metabolism of cholesterol to bile acids, which may have implications for blood cholesterol levels. In seven out of 12 studies which examined large numbers of people over a number of years (3 to 20), a significant relationship between higher levels of vitamin C intake and a lower risk of cardiovascular diseases was found.

The ability of blood vessels to relax or dilate is compromised in individuals with atherosclerosis. The damage to the heart muscle caused by a heart attack and damage to the brain caused by a stroke is related, in part, to the inability of blood vessels to dilate enough to allow blood flow to the affected areas. The pain of angina pectoris is also related to insufficient dilation of the coronary arteries. Treatment with vitamin C has consistently resulted in improved dilation of blood vessels in individuals with atherosclerosis as well as those with angina pectoris, congestive heart failure, high cholesterol, and high blood pressure. The blood vessel dilation has been demonstrated at a dose of 500mg. of vitamin C daily.

Individuals with high blood pressure studies have demonstrated a blood pressure lowering effect of vitamin C supplementation. One recent study of people with high blood pressure found that a daily supplement of 500mg. of vitamin C resulted in an average drop in systolic blood pressure of 9 percent after 4 weeks. Because the findings regarding vitamin C and high blood pressure have not yet been replicated in larger studies it is important for individuals with significantly high blood pressure to continue current therapy (medication, lifestyle changes, etc.) in consultation with their health care provider.

Although most animals manufacture vitamin C in their bodies, humans lack an enzyme necessary for its manufacture. Therefore, all of our vitamin C comes from our diet. And because the vitamin is water soluble, it is not stored in the body, and must be replaced every day.

Recommended daily amounts: (RDA) for vitamin C in the U. S. was recently revised upward from 60mg. daily for men and women. The RDA continues to be based primarily on the prevention of deficiency, rather than the prevention of chronic disease and the promotion of optimum health. Nutritionists often recommend 500mg a day.

The RDA for smokers is higher than for non-smokers, because smokers are under increased oxidative stress from the toxins in cigarette smoke and generally have lower blood levels of vitamin C. If you are taking barbiturates, tetracycline, aspirin, cortisone, antacids or estrogen on a regular basis, you need even more vitamin C. Stress and illness also increase the need for this vitamin.

The latest RDA established a maximum dose limit for vitamin C: 2,000 milligrams daily was recommended in order to prevent most adults from experiencing diarrhea and gastrointestinal disturbances. Such symptoms are not generally serious, and resolve with discontinuation or reduction of the dose.

A number of possible problems with very large doses of vitamin C have been suggested, mainly based on in vitro experiments or isolated case reports, including: genetic mutations, birth defects, cancer, atherosclerosis, kidney stones, "rebound scurvy", increased oxidative stress, excess iron absorption, vitamin B12 deficiency, and erosion of dental enamel. However, none of these adverse health effects have been confirmed, and there is no reliable scientific evidence that large amounts of vitamin C (up to 10 grams/day in adults) are toxic or detrimental to health.

A number of drugs are known to lower vitamin C levels, requiring an increase in its intake. Estrogen-containing contraceptives (birth control pills) are known to lower vitamin C levels in plasma and white blood cells. Aspirin can lower vitamin C levels if taken frequently. For example, two aspirin tablets taken every six hours for a week has been reported to lower white blood cell vitamin C by 50 percent, primarily by increasing urinary excretion of vitamin C.

There is some evidence, though controversial, that vitamin C interacts with anticoagulant medications (blood thinners) such as warfarin (coumadin). Large doses of vitamin C may block the action of warfarin, requiring an increase in dose to maintain its effectiveness. Individuals on anticoagulants should limit their vitamin C intake to 1 gram/day and have their prothrombin time monitored by the clinician following their anticoagulant therapy. Because high doses of vitamin C have also been found to interfere with the interpretation of certain laboratory tests, it is important to inform one's health care provider of any recent supplement use.

As shown in the table below, different fruits and vegetables vary in their vitamin C content, but 5 servings should average out to at least 200 milligrams (mg.) of vitamin C. One fruit serving should be considered to be one medium piece of fruit, 1/2 cup of canned or cooked fruit, or 3/4 cup of fruit juice. One vegetable serving should be considered to be one cup of raw leafy vegetables, 1/2 cup of other vegetables, cooked or raw, or 3/4 cup of vegetable juice. If you wish to check foods you eat frequently for their nutrient content, search the USDA food composition database.

Food	Serving	Vitamin C (mg.)
Orange juice	3/4 cup (6 ounces)	75
Grapefruit juice	3/4 cup (6 ounces)	60
Orange	1 medium	70
Grapefruit	1/2 medium	44
Strawberries	1 cup, whole	82
Tomato	1 medium	23
Sweet red pepper	1/2 cup, raw chopped	141
Broccoli	1/2 cup, cooked	58
Potato	1 medium, baked	26

Chapter Twenty-Three

Minerals and Memory

Although most minerals are found in very small concentrations in the body, they play a vitally important role in maintaining good health and sound memory. Here are some examples.

Boron

Boron is a trace mineral that is necessary for the proper absorption and utilization of calcium. Recent studies on boron indicate that it may help prevent postmenopausal osteoporosis, or loss of bone mass. In a study of postmenopausal women aged 48 to 82, those taking 3mg. of boron per day retained higher levels of dietary calcium, magnesium and phosphorus.

Researchers have also found that boron significantly increases production of estrogen and testosterone. Supplementation of boron has doubled the level of estrogen in some patients.

Although I have seen no definitive research linking boron with dementia prevention, these findings suggest the possibility that boron could have a preventive effect on dementia, as it is known that estrogen therapy does reduce dementia risk. Deficiencies of boron, potassium, and selenium have been found in people with Alzheimer's disease.

Five separate studies conducted by J. G. Penland at the Grand Forks Human Nutrition Research Center showed that boron deprivation resulted in decreased brain electrical activity similar to that seen in malnutrition. Assessments of cognitive function in boron deficient subjects revealed impaired performance in motor speed and dexterity, attention, and short-term memory.

Dietary sources of boron include alfalfa, cabbage, lettuce, peas, snap beans, soy beans, sweet clover and leafy vegetables. Fruits rich in boron include prunes, grapes, raisins, apples, dates, and pears. Nuts containing boron include almonds, hazel nuts, and peanuts. Stinging nettle is also rich in boron. Boron supplements are available in capsule form. The recommended dosage is 3mg. per day.

Calcium

Boron is needed to help vitamin D stimulate the absorption and utilization of calcium. Over half of all Americans don't get enough calcium. Although it's well-known that calcium helps keep bones and teeth strong, it also plays a vital role in other body functions.

For example, as discussed previously, over 50 million Americans suffer from high blood pressure. Left untreated, even mildly elevated blood pressure can reduce the life expectancy of a 35-year-old by several years.

Studies suggest that in some people, increased calcium consumption can help control blood pressure without medication. The results of a thirteen-year survey by the National Center for Health Statistics showed that people who consumed 1300mg. of calcium per day were 12 percent less likely to develop high blood pressure than those consuming 300mg. per day. Those under age 40 had a 25 percent reduction in risk. For this reason, it may be prudent for those with hypertension to increase their calcium intake.

Several studies suggest that calcium may also lower cholesterol. In a study at the Center for Human Nutrition at the University of Texas, three men with moderately high cholesterol levels were given a low calcium diet (410mg. per day) for ten days. Then, for another ten days, the men were given 2,200mg. of calcium daily.

The results showed that the high-calcium levels reduced the level of total cholesterol by 6 percent and lowered LDL cholesterol (the bad cholesterol) by 11 percent, while HDL (good cholesterol) levels stayed the same.

Chromium

Chromium is necessary for proper metabolism of sugar, and is useful to people with diabetes and hypoglycemia.

The average American eats too much refined sugar, which depletes the body of chromium. Consequently, many people today are low in both red blood cell and intercellular chromium. Lack of chromium can cause headaches, mood swings, fatigue and sweating.

Chromium is also essential in the manufacture of trypsin, a digestive enzyme which is necessary for the absorption of other nutrients. It is important too in the metabolizing of cholesterol. Proper levels of chromium prevent the accumulation of deposits on the arterial walls, thus reducing the risk of arteriosclerosis.

Studies on nutrition and the elderly show that about 70 percent of people over 70 are chromium deficient. In addition, 40 percent of people over 40 have abnormal glucose-tolerance test results, which suggest chromium deficiency. The most popular source of chromium today is chromium picolinate. This nutritional supplement has been shown to be useful in stabilizing blood sugar, increasing energy, and maintaining weight loss.

Germanium

Germanium is found in minute quantities in many medicinal herbs, including garlic, ginseng and chlorella. Technically, germanium is a trace element found in the Earth's crust. Germanium has been considered as a memory enhancer since the 1980s. It increases the body's ability to accept oxygen and therefore increases brain function.

Research suggests that germanium stimulates the immune system and has a positive effect against tumors, cancer, and several viruses.

Germanium also has the ability to capture heavy metal toxins in your body and to remove them within twenty-four hours.

Some of the most common natural sources of germanium are garlic, onions, aloe vera, watercress, barley, the herbs comfrey, ginseng, angelica, and suma, shiitake and reishi mushrooms. The recommended dosage is 30mg. daily, while some nutritionists recommend 60mg. per day.

Iron

The average healthy person contains about four grams of iron, 70 percent of which is found in the blood inside a molecule called hemoglobin. Another 5 percent is found in myoglobin, the material which makes up muscle. Still another 5 percent is located in special respiratory enzymes, and 20 percent is used in the manufacturing and storage areas of the bone marrow, the liver, and the spleen.

A tiny amount of iron (about four milligrams) is not bound to hemoglobin, but floats free in the bloodstream. This is recycled iron that the body actually salvages from old red blood cells, recirculates it in the blood as free iron salts and transports it to the bone marrow where it is used to make new blood cells.

Iron is important to the left hemisphere of the brain (in right-handed people), and affects word fluency. For some reason not yet fully understood, low iron impairs thinking and word finding in women, but not in men.

Iron deficiency is common in women. About one in ten pre-menopausal women is low in iron. Harold Hanstead at the University of Texas found that women given 30mg. of iron a day improved their scores on memory tests by 15 to 20 percent. Iron appears to improve verbal recall — the ability to repeat what you have heard.

Recently some studies have suggested that too much iron in the diet can increase the risk of heart attack in men. For this reason, iron supplements are not recommended in males unless they have a diagnosed clinical deficiency. One cause of iron deficiency is undiagnosed gastrointestinal bleeding, often caused by ulcers or the use of aspirin.

Magnesium

Magnesium is a mineral that is required for the proper growth and formation of human bones, muscle tissues, and enzymes. In the body it helps to convert carbohydrates, fats, and proteins into energy.

As we have seen, oxygen supply is vital to memory function. According to a study in England, adults taking an average of 38mg. of magnesium per day showed increased lung function. This increase was present in smokers as well as non-smokers.

Magnesium is also involved in the transmission of nerve impulses. Magnesium and calcium work together in the body. An excess of calcium or a deficiency of magnesium can cause depression, irritability, and nervousness. Magnesium also helps prevent muscle twitching, heart disorders, and high blood pressure.

The Recommended Daily Allowance for magnesium is 400 mg. per day. Foods high in magnesium include dairy products, fish, whole grains, lean meats, seeds, and vegetables.

Magnesium absorption is inhibited by consuming foods high in oxalic acid, such as cocoa, spinach, and tea. The use of alcohol, fats, diuretic drugs, large doses of zinc and vitamin D all increase the body's need for magnesium.

Manganese

Manganese is important for normal central nervous system function. Like chromium, a manganese deficiency can lower your glucose tolerance, and exacerbate a diabetic condition. Manganese is also involved in the metabolism of vitamin C and the nutrient choline, which is discussed in another chapter.

While there is no recommended daily allowance for manganese, most nutritionists recommend between 2 and 9mg. per day. Dietary sources of manganese include blueberries, seaweed, dried peas, avocados, nuts and seeds, egg yolks, legumes, whole grains, especially buckwheat and green leafy vegetables.

Potassium

Potassium plays an important role in regulating heart rhythms and in the transmission of messages though the central nervous system. It is also involved in helping nutrients to be absorbed and metabolized by the cells.

More importantly for our needs here, potassium helps to maintain the body's water balance and the regulation of blood pressure, and may also prevent strokes.

Extended use of laxatives or diuretic drugs can cause potassium deficiency. Deficiencies can also be caused by frequent vomiting, diabetic acidosis, kidney disease, and chronic diarrhea.

Low levels of potassium can lead to weakness, mental confusion, and general apathy. Extreme deficiency can cause heart failure, dehydration, and death.

The minimum daily requirement for potassium is about 500mg. The average American already consumes about 1200mg. of this mineral each day, so supplementation is rarely necessary.

Foods high in potassium include dairy products, fish, apricots, avocados, bananas, molasses, brewers yeast, brown rice, raisins, potatoes, legumes, meat, poultry, vegetables and whole grains.

Selenium

Selenium is one of the most poisonous substances known to man. It is also absolutely necessary for our survival. Selenium is a trace element, which means it is present in extremely small quantities in the body. As well as being an antioxidant, selenium increases the effectiveness of vitamin E, and has been shown to be an anti-carcinogen.

Several studies show that selenium can reduce cancer in animals. Other studies suggest that there is a relationship between low selenium levels and heart attack. Selenium also helps remove toxic metals such as mercury and lead from the body.

Foods high in selenium include garlic, liver, brewer's yeast, brown rice, and eggs. It is also available in multivitamins and in tablet form, combined with vitamin E.

Silicon

Silicon is used in the body in the formation of collagen and connective tissues, and in hair and nails. This mineral is important in that it reduces the effect of aluminum on the body, and therefore may play a role in delaying the onset of Alzheimer's disease.

There are conflicting opinions about silicon's involvement in cardiovascular disease. Although it is known that the substance is necessary for maintaining flexible arteries, many people with atherosclerosis have been found to have high serum levels.

Because silicon is found in abundance in the average American diet, deficiencies are rare. The main dietary sources are alfalfa, beets, bell peppers, beans, cereals, whole grain breads and peas.

Zinc

Many older people do not get enough zinc in their diet because they can't afford the foods (such as meat and seafood) that contain it. Low zinc causes loss of taste and smell, which lessens appetite.

Mari Golub from U.C. Davis studied the effects of dietary zinc using Rhesus monkeys. One group was given one hundred parts per million and the other group four parts per million in their daily diet. The low zinc animals took three times longer to learn the difference between a circle and a cross. Other studies also suggest that zinc improves associative memory.

In a recent government hearing, reports were given indicating that thirty-two states now have zinc-deficient soil. This makes it possible that many of us are zinc deficient.

On the other hand, too much zinc can be dangerous. Some researchers believe that zinc can increase the amount of toxic amyloid (a protein that plays an important role in causing Alzheimer's) that is deposited in the brain. Investigators at Massachusetts General Hospital found that an increase in zinc caused the amyloid molecules to clump together within only two minutes.

In addition, dietary zinc has been shown to markedly decrease mental functioning in people with Alzheimer's. Although the results are preliminary, there is enough evidence to warn against taking megadoses of zinc. This is important in light of the fact that zinc has become a popular cold remedy. A safe dose of zinc is about 15mg. a day.

Chapter Twenty-Four

Nutrients that Improve Memory

Proper nutrition is essential for a healthy mind. Vitamins and minerals are essential nutrients that have specific effects on brain function, but many nutrients that are not classified as vitamins or minerals also have substantial effects on memory.

Phenylalanine

Noradrenalin is a substance in the brain that is similar to adrenalin. It acts in the brain as a stimulant, and affects emotion, memory, and sex drive.

Noradrenalin seems to play an important role in learning and memory. In experiments with animals, learning has been prevented by administering drugs that rob the brain of noradrenalin.

Coffee is stimulating because caffeine increases the brain's sensitivity to noradrenalin. Coffee doesn't make noradrenalin, but raises its use. When the brain's supply of noradrenaline becomes depleted, coffee will no longer give you a lift, but instead will make you feel spaced out and jittery.

Like caffeine, other stimulants such as amphetamine, Ritalin, magnesium pemoline, and cocaine initially increase the amount of noradrenalin used by the brain, but these drugs interfere with the brain's ability to recycle the chemical, which results in a low level of the substance. Depression and memory problems are the result.

Noradrenalin is made from the amino acid phenylalanine. But consuming phenylalanine will not increase brain levels unless it is taken in along with a carbohydrate, which helps it pass the blood-brain barrier.

For phenylalanine to be transformed into noradrenalin, supplements of vitamin B6, folic acid, vitamin C, and copper are also required.

As the brain ages, the number of noradrenalin receptors decreases. Supplementing the brain with phenylalanine and the proper cofactors compensates for the loss. When used in this manner, phenylalanine can also act as an antidepressant.

In particular, women with low folate levels in their blood will benefit from phenylalanine supplements. It has been discovered that women who have low levels of folate, the by-products of folic acid found in the blood, appear to be at greater risk of Alzheimer's disease, according to the results of a study of Catholic nuns.

In the study of 30 nuns who participated in a long-term study of Alzheimer's disease, half had brain changes consistent with the memory-robbing illness at autopsy. The women, aged 78 to 101 when they died, had lived at the same convent for most of their lives, according to Dr. David A. Snowdon and colleagues at the University of Kentucky in Lexington.

Snowdon's team looked at data collected earlier in the study and found that those women with Alzheimer's disease were more likely to have low blood levels of folate than women without the illness. None of the other nutritional markers analyzed in the blood samples was related to brain degeneration or Alzheimer's disease, according to the report in the April Issue of the *American Journal of Clinical Nutrition.*

The authors noted that the study could not determine whether low levels of folate actually cause Alzheimer's. And the findings do not provide any evidence that taking folic acid supplements can prevent the disease or slow it down. It is possible that the women had low blood levels of folate due to problems absorbing or metabolizing the nutrient. The women all ate in the same kitchen and, presumably, had similar intakes of folic acid.

The researchers call for further research in this area, noting that there are several possible explanations for the relationship between the nutrient and this disease.

Folic acid, a nutrient found in green leafy vegetables, liver, kidney, whole grains and nuts, is important in the development of the central nervous system and in the maintenance of blood vessels. Lack of this nutrient can cause birth defects in the developing fetus.

DNA/RNA

Storing long-term memories requires significant quantities of nucleic acids. The body normally makes nucleic acids from the amino acids and nutrients found in our diet. Studies show that high levels of brain RNA improve learning and memory. When ribonuclease, a substance that destroys RNA, is injected into the brains of animals, they are unable to learn. Several companies now manufacture RNA supplements. There are many claims made that DNA/RNA supplements improve memory. Biochemically this makes sense, but there is little research available to substantiate the claims.

L-Glutamine

The brain uses this amino acid as a source of energy. It readily crosses the blood brain barrier, and has been shown to improve concentration. It has also been shown to reduce the craving for alcohol and sugar.

Zimmerman, Burgemiester, and Putnam used Glutamic acid on sixty nine mentally retarded children ages 5 to 17, whose average I.Q. was 65. For one year they were given twelve grams of glutamic acid per day in their diet. The average gain in I.Q. was 11 points, the highest gain was 17 points. Roger Williams raised I.Q.s of retarded children with l-glutamine. This is fascinating evidence that we actually may be able to raise our I.Q. through nutritional modification.

Tyrosine

Tyrosine has shown to be an antidepressant. The brain uses tyrosine to make the neurotransmitters dopamine and norepinephrine, both of which play a part in thinking, long-term memory, and alertness. When tyrosine levels rise in the brain, they stimulate it to peak levels of clarity for several hours. Tyrosine is found in meat, poultry, seafood and beans, or can be taken as a nutritional supplement.

Coenzyme Q10

This enzyme acts as an antioxidant to retard brain aging. It has also been shown to increase cardiac strength, which helps brain blood flow.

Much of the research on brain function and CoQ10 has been done by Dr. Denham Harman of Omaha, Nebraska. Harman was one of the pioneers in linking free radicals to the aging process. Harman formulated a theory linking Alzheimer's disease to free radical damage, which causes mutations in DNA.

According to Harman's theory, the DNA damage occurs early in life, possibly even during fetal development. But the effects of this damage are not seen until at least middle age.

The consequences include an accumulation of hydrogen peroxide and hydroxyl radicals, chemicals that Harman sees as having a role in the development of Alzheimer's disease. Harman believes that CoQ10 and other antioxidants can improve mental function, even in cases of Alzheimer's.

Acetylcholine

Acetylcholine is a neurotransmitter involved in transferring short-term memory to long term memory. Acetylcholine also plays a role in movement, sleep, and such primitive drives as the desire for sex, food, and acquisition.

In an experiment where young people were given scopolamine, a drug which blocks the use of acetylcholine, the subjects showed a pattern of learning deficits which resemble the pattern found in old age. Several over-the-counter sleep aids, such as Sleepeze, contain scopolamine, and could therefore interfere with memory.

The amount of acetylcholine in the brain decreases with age. Since it has been well-established that acetylcholine plays an important part in memory, scientists have looked at ways to increase brain levels of this substance. There are several ways this can be accomplished, which will be discussed in the following section.

Physostigmine

Physostigmine is a drug extracted from a poisonous plant called the Calabar bean *(Physostigma venenosum)*. This substance was actually patented in 1864, and was used to treat glaucoma. In 1979, researchers discovered that the drug could improve memory in old Rhesus monkeys. Human studies, however failed to duplicate these memory gains. Recently it was discovered that the duration of dosage was the critical factor. Yaakov Stern from Columbia University has found that humans who use the drug for at least six to eight months show some memory improvement. Proper dosage must be established to minimize side effects. The drug's memory boosting power lies in its ability to prolong the activity of acetylcholine.

In a study conducted at the National Institute on Aging, researchers used positron emission tomography (PET scans) to monitor the areas of the human brain activated during working memory to determine how activity in those regions was modified by the drug. The researchers found that the subject's ability to recognize faces improved when given physostigmine

The drug seems to reduce the effort needed to perform working memory tasks by increasing the activity of brain regions activated by the task. The authors suggest that the drug may enhance brain efficiency by focusing attention on the task, which reduces the effects of distracting stimuli.

The results of this study suggest that enhancing acetylcholine with physostigmine resulted in improved working memory performance and altered neural activity in a cortical region known to be important to this memory task.

Tacrine (discussed in chapter six), the first approved drug for treatment against Alzheimer's disease, acts on the acetylcholine system in a way similar to physostigmine. Unfortunately, the drug has a high level of side effects. Almost two thirds of people taking this drug stop because of side effects such as vomiting, nausea and abdominal cramps.

Choline

Choline was discovered by Dr. A. Strecher in 1930. It is often classified as a B vitamin, but it's technically not a vitamin. Choline is used by the body to help build cells, to keep the liver from forming fatty deposits, and to manufacture acetylcholine, a neurotransmitter necessary for memory. Taking supplements of choline appears to increase the brain's ability to take in information. It increases attention span, and facilitates transfer of information from short-term to long-term memory.

In a study done at the National Institute of Mental Health (NIMH), subjects given a single ten-gram dose of choline showed improvement in both memory retention and recall. An effective dose of choline is 3,000 to 10,000mg.

Unfortunately, Alzheimer's patients given choline show little or no improvement. Studies of the brains of Alzheimer's patients reveal that they lack the important enzyme, choline-acetyltransferase, which is needed to convert choline into acetylcholine.

Phosphatidylcholine (Lecithin)

Lecithin is found in every living cell. Thirty percent of the brain is lecithin. High levels of lecithin compounds (such as phosphatidyl-choline and phosphatidyl-ethanolamine) in the blood may have a protective effect against Alzheimer's disease.

In the blood stream, lecithin helps prevent cholesterol and fats from accumulating on the walls of the arteries. In the liver, lecithin metabolizes fat and lessens the chance of liver degeneration.

Phosphatidylcholine supplementation stimulates the production of acetylcholine, the neurotransmitter necessary for the transfer of short-term memory to long-term memory. Taking choline does this also, but lecithin contains many other ingredients, such as fatty acids, sugars, and phosphate.

Choline metabolizes rapidly — blood levels peak within a few hours of taking it, but phosphatidylcholine breaks down slowly, and provides the brain with a more constant supply of choline.

In 1993 researchers Ladd and Sommer did a double-blind experiment with college students to test the effect of phosphatidylcholine on explicit memory (the memory of events in one's life). With a 25g. dose of phosphatidylcholine there was a significant improvement in explicit memory, measured by a serial learning task. This was the first study to show a relationship between a single dose of phosphatidylcholine and explicit memory on normal human subjects. Other clinical trials with the substance show mixed results.

AL721 (Egg Lecithin)

AL721 is a type of lecithin that is extracted from egg yolk. The number 721 signifies that the compound is seven parts neutral lipids (which are oils), two parts phosphatidylcholine, and one part phosphatydylethanolamine. AL721 is used in Israel to treat viral diseases, senility, and AIDS. Research suggests that the compound enhances a cell's ability to repair cell membranes. This product is available in the United States under the brand name Eggs-ACT.

CDP Choline

This nutrient is currently approved in Europe and Japan for use in stroke, Parkinson's disease, and other neurological disorders. Studies show that CDP-choline helps make phosphatidylcholine in brain cell membranes in older individuals. It also increases acetylcholine synthesis and improves mental performance in patients with Alzheimer's disease. When given at a daily dose of 1000mg it improves memory in elderly patients by increasing activity in fronto-temporal regions in occipital areas, and increasing blood flow velocity in the brain. CDP-choline became available over the counter in the U.S. in 1998.

Acetyl-L-Carnitine

Research scientist Luciano Angellucci, M.D., who studied aging and the brain for many years, discovered a substance called acetyl-l-carnitine (ALC) which is found in muscle tissue, and converts fat into energy.

Acetyl-l-carnitine is similar to another form of the amino acid called carnitine. However, Angellucci says taking carnitine alone will not work for older people, because the enzymes needed to transform it into acetyl-l-carnitine decrease with age.

Studies show that ALC slows the loss of nerve growth factor (NGF), a group of chemicals that helps brain cells stay young. These important chemicals provide support for the healthy functioning of brain cells, especially in the hippocampus and frontal cortex of the brain.

The degenerative changes associated with brain aging seem to be caused, in part, by a decline in nerve growth factor. Several studies show that supplementing NGF reverses both physical and behavioral deficits in aged rats. Giving the rats ALC increased the NGF levels by 39 percent in the central nervous system.

ALC also increases the level of an enzyme that scavenges free radicals, and it enhances the function of an important neurotransmitter, acetylcholine, which plays an essential role in learning and memory.

Long-term treatment with ALC completely prevented the loss of choline-acetyltransferase (CHAT) activity in the brains of rats. CHAT is the enzyme that helps to transform choline into acetylcholine.

The nutrient ALC also appears to slow the progression of Alzheimer's disease. In Milan, Italy, 130 patients with Alzheimer's disease were given 2 grams a day of ALC for a year, and were compared to patients receiving placebos. The results showed a markedly slower rate of deterioration in patients receiving acetyl-l-carnitine. In another study the nutrient was successful in slowing the cognitive decline of sixty-three people diagnosed with Alzheimer's. These patients scored higher than untreated individuals in thirteen of fourteen measures of mental performance.

At Columbus University, people with Alzheimer's who were given 2,500 to 3,500mg. of acetyl-l-carnitine per day showed significantly less memory deterioration than those given a placebo. Studies in England and at Georgia State University show similar results.

New research shows that brain cell aging can indeed be slowed or prevented by treatment with acetyl-l-carnitine. In a recent study done in Rome, scientists used ALC to prevent the age-dependent loss of neurons in certain areas of the rat brain, especially the hippocampus. In another study, rats treated for eight months with ALC showed no age-related loss of ability to find their way through a maze.

ALC appears to have both curative and preventive properties when given to elderly people. ALC might be even more beneficial in slowing or preventing cognitive and behavioral deficits in normally-aging persons without overt signs of disease. The evidence suggests that long-term treatment with acetyl-l-carnitine could stop the progress of age-related neurodegenerative diseases, such as Alzheimer's disease, and could slow normal aging in humans.

New research suggests that acetyl-l-carnitine repairs this DNA damage in peripheral blood lymphocytes (white blood cells), suggesting that it can help prevent the age-related decline of the immune system. DNA is constantly under attack from environmental toxins, and radiation, and these attacks cause structural damage to the DNA molecule.

Acetyl-l-carnitine's beneficial effects seem to work in concert with coenzyme Q10, and phosphatidylcholine, and phosphatidylserine.

Sigma Tau Pharmaceuticals in Gaithsburg, MD, is the American developer of the nutrient.

NADH

Nicotinamideadeninedinucleotide (NADH) is a co-enzymatic form of vitamin B3.

A small number of short term studies done with NADH have shown that it has slight to moderate benefits in regards to depression, Parkinson's disease, and Alzheimer's disease. In one study, there was an improvement in mental function within twelve weeks, using 5mg. per day. Based on the mini-mental state examination, the minimum improvement was 6 points and the maximum improvement 14 points with a mean value of 8.35 points.

However, in 2002 a 3-month study in which 25 patients with mild to moderate Alzheimer's, vascular, and fronto-temporal dementia were given10mg. of NADH a day in addition to their current medication. In 19 patients who completed the study, there was no evidence of any cognitive improvement. Further research is needed.

An eight week double blind study done at Georgetown University Medical Center found some patients with chronic fatigue syndrome to benefit from taking NADH at a daily dose of 10mg. However, long term studies are required to determine if benefits from taking daily NADH continue with time, or whether tolerance develops.

Arginine

Arginine is an amino acid produced naturally in the human body. It can also be found in small amounts in many nuts and seeds. Recent studies show that arginine can lower blood pressure, enhance the immune system, and stimulate the release of human growth hormone. In animal studies, arginine speeds up wound healing and reduces the damage caused by heart attacks and strokes.

The body converts arginine to spermine, which is a chemical found in semen, blood tissue, and brain cells. If you are low in spermine, you may start to show early signs of memory loss and senility.

A 1990 headline in *The New York Times* declared: "Human Growth Hormone Reverses the Effects of Aging." This synthetically produced growth hormone costs $20,000 a year to take, which puts it out of reach. But two progressive nutritionists developed a much cheaper, but equally effective alternative.

Durk Pearson and Sandy Shaw, authors of the best-selling book *Life Extension,* came up with an alternative way to increase the levels of growth hormones in the brain. They recommend combining six grams of arginine, 600mg. of choline, and 500mg. vitamin B5.

Studies with human subjects show that arginine combats cancer and cardiovascular disease. A 1991 study in Germany showed that arginine supplementation increased the blood flow in the small blood vessels of the human heart by as much as 198 percent. The researchers feel that arginine does this by restoring the function of endothelial cells that line the walls of the blood vessels. Arginine is available in health food stores everywhere.

Tryptophan

The amino acid, tryptophan is used by your brain to make the neurotransmitter serotonin, a substance which induces sleep and slows down overall nerve transmission and reaction time. High levels of serotonin are needed to ward off depression. Prozac, the most popular antidepressant in history, works by raising levels of serotonin in the brain.

Tryptophan is found in milk, dairy products, bananas, sunflower seeds, and turkey. Tryptophan used to be available as a supplement, and was used to treat depression and insomnia, but a contaminant found in one batch of it caused the FDA to take all tryptophan off the market.

After a meal containing both protein and carbohydrate, if tryptophan crosses the blood-brain barrier before tyrosine can, you will become sleepy. For this reason, eat protein before you eat the carbohydrates in your meal if you wish to stay awake and alert.

Omega-3 Fatty Acids

All over the globe studies suggest that decreases in omega-3 fatty acid consumption are related to increasing rates of depression. This is consistent with a well-known positive relationship between depression, coronary artery disease, and cell loss in parts of the brain that mediate pain.

Drs. Joseph Hibbeln and Norman Salem Jr., from the National Institute of Alcohol Abuse in Rockville, Maryland, have done epidemiological studies to determine the relationship of dietary fats and depression. In an article published in *Lancet* in 1998, the doctors compared fish consumption to the prevalence of major depression in eleven countries. They found that the more fish consumed in a country, the less the risk for depression.

Omega-3 oils have the ability to block disease processes at the cellular level by maintaining cell wall integrity. These fats are also important in preventing cardiovascular disease, stroke and heart attacks.

Fish oil has also been found to increase blood circulation and reduce insulin sensitivity. Diabetics who eat fish regularly have a significantly lower risk of coronary heart disease and death than those who don't eat fish.

But more importantly, several studies show that dietary intake of omega-3 fatty acids and weekly consumption of fish may reduce the risk of Alzheimer's disease. In a study published in the July 2003 journal *Archives of Neurology,* participants who consumed fish once per week or more had 60 percent less risk of Alzheimer's disease compared with those who rarely or never ate fish!

Omega-3 fatty acids are available from either plant or marine sources. Plant sources include unrefined vegetable oils, flax seed oil, raw nuts, seeds and beans.

Nutrition researchers believe that the omega-3 fats that are most important are eicosapentaenoic acid (EPA) and docosahexaenoic acid (DHA) both found in fatty fish such as mackerel, lake trout, herring, sardines, bluefish, anchovies, Atlantic sturgeon, sablefish, albacore tuna and salmon.

Recently there has been concern that the fish oil derived omega-3s may contain mercury, which is a potent neurotoxin. For this reason several companies now market mercury free omega 3s. Actually, the element mercury cannot mix with fat, so all fish oil capsules are essentially mercury-free. Mercury can only be ingested by eating the fish.

Should you avoid eating fish? The *Harvard Heart Letter* says no. The EPA and DHA in the capsule are probably the leading factors in fish oil's health benefits, but there may be other as yet unknown helpful components in the fish as well.

Protein

The need for protein depends on many factors, including age, body weight, general health, and level of mental exertion.

Most nutritionists believe that on the whole, Americans eat too much protein. For many years, red meat consumption has been the hallmark of the American diet. But red meat has been linked to many diseases and health conditions such as arteriosclerosis, and the trend has been to reduce red meat consumption.

However, many vegetarians and many older people do not get enough protein in their diet. Vegetarians sometimes simply eliminate protein and do not replace it by eating the right combinations of beans, seeds, and nuts. As a result they are chronically protein deficient, and often fatigued, confused, and unmotivated.

Shellfish

Shellfish, such as oysters and clams, are very low in carbohydrates and fat and are very high in protein. Eating 3 or 4 ounces of shellfish as an appetizer delivers an adequate dose of tyrosine quickly to the brain. For this reason shellfish can stimulate mental activity, improve mood, and elevate brain performance. Be aware that shellfish tend to accumulate more toxins and pollutants than regular fish, because they filter their nutrients from sea water.

What about Fat and Carbohydrates?

In a study in the *American Journal of Clinical Nutrition,* in 2001 Kaplan et al. examined the effects of pure protein, fat, and carbohydrate on the cognitive performance in a group of elderly subjects.

Cognitive test scores improved after consumption of all three of the macronutrients when compared with a placebo, with a more pronounced effect on delayed recall than immediate recall. The improvements were stronger 60 minutes following ingestion than they were for 15 minutes following ingestion.

Most interesting was the finding that carbohydrates improved the subjects' composite score in all testing at all time intervals.

Protein and fat also enhanced memory. But fat was the only substance that improved attention. The authors suggest that each nutrient may improve performance by distinct mechanisms mediated by different brain regions.

It's been noted by nutritionists that many older people simply cannot afford enough protein and fats in their diet to stay healthy and are therefore perpetually malnourished. Research continues to show that proper nutrition is essential for peak mental performance.

Chapter Twenty-Five

Herbs and Memory

Millions of years before the age of medicine, humankind was using herbs to heal their woes and soothe their pains. All over the world, people have discovered the magic healing powers of plants. The modern sciences of medicine and pharmacology are in fact outgrowths of herbology. Many modern medicines actually are derived from herbs. For example, aspirin, one of the most widely used drugs in the world, is an extract of willow *(Salix)* bark.

For many centuries, various flowers, herbs, and roots have been used for the improvement of memory. Today, science has verified that many of these plants do indeed have positive effects.

In China, increasing emphasis has been placed on research of these natural products. In the last several years over 140 new drugs have been developed from Chinese medicinal plants. These drugs include Huperzine, a potent and reversible inhibitor of acetyl-cholinesterase which appears to be superior to donepezil; Clausen-amide, a potassium channel blocker with a memory enhancing effect 50–100 times more potent than that of piracetam; and Salvianolic acid B, a very strong antioxidant agent with potential anti-dementia effects.

Although herbs are natural substances and relatively safe, do not take any herb without consulting a professional herbalist. Before you take any of these herbs, tell your doctor what you intend to do, as herbs can be powerful and may interact with other medication you are taking.

Ginkgo Biloba

The first written record of the use of ginkgo appears in a Chinese medical text written in 2800 B.C. Ginkgo biloba is an extract of the leaf of the ginkgo tree. A native of China, this amazing tree lives for more than 1,000 years.

In 1754, the tree was introduced to England. Since that time, hundreds of studies have revealed that this ancient herb has the power to improve memory, clarify concentration, and aid in emotional stability.

There are over seventy-five published papers documenting the ability of ginkgo to improve and protect vascular health and to enhance mental function. Currently, ginkgo is the most frequently prescribed drug in Europe because of its numerous disease preventing properties.

Ginkgo has also been shown to have a positive effect on asthma, allergies, and blood clots. The ginkgo extract also aids brain function by acting as a free radical scavenger, and by increasing the brain's ability to use oxygen. Ginkgo extract is available in most health food stores. It is made in both oral and injectable forms.

Having said the above it is important to report that researchers from the Netherlands reported in the October 2000 issue of the _Journal of the American Geriatrics Society_ that a standardized extract of the widely hyped herb ginkgo biloba has been found ineffective for older adults with dementia and age-associated memory impairment. The results of this study contrast sharply with those of previous ginkgo biloba trials.

According to the report, the trial lasted 24 weeks and involved 214 residents of homes for the elderly. Their average age was greater than 80 years. Of these 214 patients, 63 were demented and 151 were not but had substantial cognitive decline. The trial was randomized, placebo-controlled, and double blind. This type of study design is the scientific "gold standard" for testing a hypothesis about the effectiveness of drugs or other medical interventions.

Potential trial subjects were screened to ensure that those who participated had dementia, either mild to moderate Alzheimer's dementia or vascular dementia or age-associated memory impairment.

The results of this trial led the researchers to conclude "… that treatment with ginkgo is not efficacious, irrespective of dose, in older patients with mild to moderate dementia or age-associated memory impairment."

Why did the results of this trial contrast so sharply to several recent randomized, placebo-controlled, double blind trials showing a benefit for ginkgo biloba? There are some differences between this study and those showing a positive effect for the herb, including the diagnosis of the patients, severity of disease, age, and the rating scales used to test ginkgo's efficacy.

There are other possible explanations for the results of this study. One of which is the marketing hoopla that often overrides the true benefits of an herb or medication.

As dietary and herbal supplements, such as ginkgo biloba, are subjected to more rigorous scientific scrutiny, it is becoming clearer that their success in the marketplace in many cases is a result of misleading advertising rather than any type of proven benefit to consumers.

If you are a user of ginkgo biloba and you believe it has been of benefit to you, it's probably harmless to continue its use, for personal conviction is a strong medicine in itself.

Gotu-Kola

This herb, whose botanical name is *Centella asiatica,* originates in India, where it grows along stone walls and rocky outcroppings. Ayurvedic practitioners use Gotu-kola to combat aging and senility. This herb has been used for centuries as a memory aid. Gotu-kola is also found in Asia and Australia, where it is used to heal wounds, improve skin, and reduce cellulite. It is also used there as a brain tonic to improve memory and increase intelligence.

In a recent study done with thirty developmentally disabled children, a twelve week program of Gotu-kola supplementation improved attentiveness and concentration. The active ingredients in Gotu-kola are thought to be a group of substances called triterpenes.

In India, people take Gotu-kola to increase mental stamina and memory. The recommended dosage is one cup of tea at bedtime.

Animal studies show that this herb protects against radiation exposure.

Herbalists advise that gotu kola should not be used for more than 6 weeks. People taking the herb for this period of time should take a 2-week break before taking the herb again.

Asiaticoside, a major component of gotu kola, has also been associated with tumor growth in mice. Though more studies are needed, this herb should not be taken by anyone with a history of precancerous or cancerous skin lesions — such as squamous cell, basal cell skin cancer, or melanoma.

People older than 65 years should take gotu kola at a lower than standard dose.

Kola

Kola (*Kola vera*) originates from Africa. Its main action is from caffeine, a central nervous system stimulant, which increases alertness.

Carrot Juice

Carrot juice while technically not an herb, is a long-standing natural treatment for mental illness, including schizophrenia. It contains high levels of beta-carotene. Although this is a popular tonic for nerve problems, beyond its vitamin content, there is little hard scientific evidence for its effectiveness.

Holly

For many generations, holly *(Ilex)* seeds have been said to strengthen memory. I could find no scientific studies to substantiate this, but some studies indicate that an extract of Holly has significant antioxidant properties.

Schizandra

Schizandra *(Schizandra propinqua)* is an herb that originates from China. This is also a central nervous system stimulant, and an adaptogen, a substance that helps the body maintain metabolic balance. Clinically, the liver protecting and antioxidant actions of Schizandra have proven beneficial in the treatment of chronic viral hepatitis. there has been little research done on the cognitive effects of schizandra, but one study done at the University of Tokyo, Japan, did demonstrate that an herbal prescription called S-113m, consisting of biota, ginseng and schizandra, improved memory retention in mice.

Valerian Root

Valerian root, from the family *valerianaceae*, has been used as a medicinal herb for several thousand years. It was taken by the ancient Greeks as a digestive aid, and for urinary tract problems. The herb was also used by the Chinese and in Indian Ayurvedic medicine. It is popular today throughout Europe, Canada, Mexico, and New Zealand.

The valerian plant is a perennial herb that grows up to five feet high from a short rhizome. The plant has small pink, lavender, or sometimes red flowers. Although many types of valerian have been used medicinally, the wild root is usually stronger than the plants found in the garden. The species used most often is *Valeriana officinalis*.

The name valerian comes from the Latin *valere* which means "to be in health." Most people dislike the smell of valerian, but researchers believe that the same chemicals that give the herb its odor are responsible for its medicinal properties.

Most modern herbalists recommend valerian for its sedative qualities. Valerian root is a natural tranquilizer and sleep inducer. The few scientific studies that have been done on valerian show it to be an effective sedative, and that it improves the quality of sleep. Good sleep means improved memory.

Valerian is non-toxic, nonaddictive, and has very few side effects. Valerian may cause increased urination in some people.

Ginseng

Ginseng *(Panax)* is of Chinese origin. Its beneficial effects on the human body have been known to the Chinese for at least 4,000 years. It is quite possibly the most widely used medicinal herb in the Orient. It has been used for centuries by the Russians and Chinese to increase stamina and alertness.

Ginseng is also an adaptogenic herb. This means it is an herb that helps to bring your body back to equilibrium. Sometimes ginseng is taken as a tincture, a liquid solution which combines an extract of the herb with alcohol.

The ginseng root, which is the part of the plant used to make the tincture, resembles a tiny human. This is why the ancient healers called ginseng the "root of life plant." Around 200 A.D., a Chinese emperor dubbed it panax ginseng, meaning "panacea from ginseng," and the botanical name has remained with the plant ever since.

Ginseng contains a family of chemicals called saponins (also called glycosides or ginsenosides), which influence the metabolism of certain brain chemicals involved in mental functions.

Ginseng improves mental performance, especially in conditions of stress, fatigue, and overwork by increasing the levels of the neuro-transmitter norepinephrine, which increases arousal and attention. Stress can deplete the brain's supply of norepinephrine, but ginseng levels out its release and inhibits its depletion.

In 2001 researchers David Kennedy, Andrew Scholey and Keith Wesnes at the University of Northumbria conducted the first study of single doses of ginseng and cognitive performance. After one dose of ginseng there was a significant improvement in factors called "Quality of Memory" and "Speed of Attention."

Ginseng comes in the form of tinctures, pills, extracts, capsules, tablets, powders, pastes, as dried roots, granulated teas, and even as an element in wines and liquors. But typically you will find it as an extract.

Doses of 500 to 3,000mg. of the tincture per day are recommended. It is suggested that you start with the low dose and gradually increase it. Like ginkgo, its effects are cumulative. The herb should be taken for a month before seeing major effects.

Calamus Root

This herb, (*Acorus calamus*) also called sweet flag, is sometimes used to treat epilepsy, to strengthen the memory, and to stimulate higher brain functions.

Ayurvedic practitioners feel that the herb has sattvic energy, which pertains to clarity of consciousness. Many Ayurvedic healers consider calamus to be one of the most effective herbs for mental clarity. They have praised calamus for centuries for its ability to purify and revitalize the brain, increase blood circulation, strengthen memory, and stimulate awareness. Recent studies suggest the herb may in fact have the ability to reduce blood lipids, increasing circulation.

Herbalists recommend a pinch of powdered calamus (250-500mg.) mixed with 2 to 3 teaspoons of honey, in the morning and in the evening.

Nutmeg

Nutmeg *(Muristica frangrans)* is considered to be a tonic for both the heart and brain. When taken in quantities no greater than a pinch at a time, it is also a relaxant which can help eliminate insomnia and increase restful sleep. Large amounts of this herb can be toxic.

A chemical called thujone which is related to the nutmeg family is also a powerful brain stimulant. It is found in small amounts in vermouth, and is a component of cedar leaf oil. It is also the toxic agent in absinthe, a liqueur popular in the 19th and early 20th centuries.

Basil

When taken as a powder in doses of 250mg. to 1gm. or as a tea mixed with honey, basil *(Ocimum basilicum)* is said to heighten the acuteness of the senses, strengthen nerve tissue, increase memory, and promote clarity of thought.

Bhringaraj

This Ayurvedic herb also grows in the American Southwest. It has also been called fesharaia, or Eclipta, (which literally means "ruler of the hair" because it is claimed to promote hair growth). This herb is used to calm the mind, to promote restful sleep, and to act as a general brain tonic.

Lemon Balm

Lemon balm, also called *Melissa officinalis,* has been used for centuries as a memory tonic. Seventeenth century herbalist John

Evelyn wrote, "Balm is sovereign for the brain, strengthening the memory and powerfully chasing away melancholy." The recommended dosage is several cups per day, a few hours apart.

Recent experiments suggest that this herb does improve cognition and mood, and may actually have some benefit in treating cognitive impairment and Alzheimer's disease.

A 2003 study conducted in Roozbeh Psychiatric Hospital at Tehran University showed that people with mild to moderate Alzheimer's showed less agitation and an improvement in mood when given the herb. Another study demonstrated that using *Melissa* as aroma therapy was effective in calming patients with advanced dementia.

Sage

Sage *(Salvia)* is recognized in Ayurvedic medicine and in traditional Chinese medicine for its ability to reduce the severity of emotional upsets and to promote calmness. Sage is sometimes mixed with Gotu-kola or Bhringaraj.

Chinese Sage

Chinese Sage, also known as *Salvia Miltorrhiza Bunge,* is a Chinese herb which is frequently used to treat strokes and ischemic heart disease.

An extract of this herb, Salvianolic acid B, is a very strong antioxidant agent with potential anti-dementia effects. Studies have demonstrated that Salvianolic acid can reduce the area of cerebral infarct in ischemia-reperfusion injured rats, suggesting it may be useful in the treatment of cerebral infarct in humans. This therapeutic effect may be partly due to its free radical scavenging activities.

Even more intriguing is the finding that salvianolic acid B inhibits amyloid-beta aggregation and fibril formation in the brain, which is one of the primary abnormalities seen in Alzheimer's. It also directly inhibits the cellular toxicity of Amyloid-beta.

Spanish Sage

Salvia lavandulaefolia Vahl (Spanish sage) may be an important herb in the fight against dementia. It has been shown to inhibit the enzyme acetylcholinesterase, a property shared by all drugs used to treat Alzheimer's disease.

Other activities relevant to Alzheimer's disease include antioxidant, anti-inflammatory and estrogenic effects The herb seems to play a part in all of these processes, making it a valuable substance.

Results demonstrate that Spanish Sage, its essential oil and some chemical constituents, have properties vital to the treatment of Alzheimer's disease. More research is being done currently.

Haritaki

Haritaki (also called Chebulic myrobalan and *Terminalia chebula)* is a fruit that is known as the "king of medicines" in Tibet. It is said to rejuvenate and energize the brain and nerves. Haritaki is available as a decoction, powder, or paste. Decoctions may be made by boiling the herb in water. There is some evidence that this herb may reduce cholesterol, can act as an antioxidant, and regulate blood sugar.

Kelp

Kelp *(Alaria esculenta)* is a nutritionally rich sea vegetable that also has tension-reducing properties. Kelp may achieve this effect by insulating heart and nerve tissue from stress. It is also high in iodine, which is essential for proper thyroid function.

Peppermint

Peppermint *(Mentha piperita)* is believed by many herbalists to prevent congestion in cerebral blood circulation. It is also widely used as a tonic to calm jangled nerves. Peppermint is said to increase concentration. Students using peppermint before exams have scored better on tests, because of the stimulating effect it has on olfactory memory.

Skullcap

Skullcap *(Scutellaria lateriflora)* is a commonly used nerve tonic, which is also useful in treating insomnia. It is said to have a positive effect on mental clarity which may be due to its ability to reduce nervous tension.

Wood Betony

Officially called *Betonica officinalis,* wood betony is known to reduce tension and nervousness, and is used by herbalists as a sedative.

Rosemary

Rosemary *(Rosmarinus officinalis)* has been known for centuries as the "herb of memory." It was believed by the ancient Greeks that putting a stalk of rosemary in one's hair would improve memory. It's also been used by Chinese practitioners to treat circulatory problems, and as a smooth muscle stimulant.

In 2003 the Human Cognitive Neuroscience Unit, University of Northumbria in England conducted a study to assess the olfactory impact of the essential oils of lavender *(Lavandula angustifolia)* and rosemary on cognitive performance and mood.

Lavender decreased the performance of working memory, and impaired reaction times for both memory and attention, while rosemary produced a significant enhancement of performance for overall quality of memory and secondary memory factors.

Garlic

Aged Garlic *(Allium Sativum)* is most likely the most widely recognized medicinal herb. Used for centuries for the treatment of circulatory problems, this substance reduces glucose metabolism in diabetics, prevents blood clots and protects against stroke, atherosclerosis, and heart attacks. It also appears to lower LDL and raise HDL. A study at Loma Linda University showed that taking *allium sativum* resulted in a 12 to 31 percent drop in cholesterol levels.

Of great importance today is the finding that garlic may also help the body protect itself from heavy-metal accumulation, which can result from eating fish that may be high in mercury, or from air pollution.

But the most interesting findings in garlic research come from studies performed in Japan. Researchers at Nihon University have found a chemical in garlic called *allyl-L-cysteine* which acts like a nerve growth factor in the brain. The substance seems to increase neuron branching in the hippocampus — the part of the brain that processes memory, and also reduces the damage done to neurons by beta amylod — the molecule that causes Alzheimer's.

European Bilberry

Bilberry *(Vaccinium myrtellus)* extract contains flavonoids and anthocyanin, which prevent capillary fragility by strengthening the walls of capillaries, which are tiny blood vessels. Weak capillaries are a major cause of transient ischemic attacks (TIAs) which were discussed in an earlier chapter. The extract also reduces the risk of brain hemorrhage induced by hypertension. It reduces blood clots by inhibiting platelet aggregation.

Anthocyanin, a natural antioxidant found in bilberry, also lowers blood pressure, and stimulates the release of vasodilators, which improves blood supply to the nervous system.

Bilberry also contains glucoquinine which has the ability to lower blood sugar. Regulating blood sugar is an important factor in improving cognition.

Another benefit of bilberry extract is its effect on night vision. During World War II, British pilots reported a dramatic increase in night vision after consuming bilberry jam. An Italian study recently showed that 75 percent of people improve their night vision after taking bilberry supplements.

St. John's Wort

Hypericum perforatum is a native plant of Europe, West Asia, North Africa, Madeira, and the Azores. Today it can also be found in North America and Australia.

Known in the U.S. as St. John's wort, this herb has a long medicinal history. It can be traced back to the ancient Greeks and Romans, who used the plant to treat burns, ulcers, malaria, kidney ailments, and nervous disorders. *Hypericum perforatum* has for many centuries been used as a folk remedy for depression, anxiety, mania, hysteria, and insomnia.

Today, however, Hypericum is used as a natural alternative to prescription antidepressants. Over twenty-five controlled studies on Hypericum have been published which show that it works as well as antidepressant drugs with fewer side effects. In a German study, fifteen women suffering from depression were given hypericum and reported substantial improvement in their quality of life. This was measured by a greater interest in life, improved feelings of self-worth, increased appetite, and more normal sleep patterns. In another study, 60 percent of those taking a *Hypericum* extract reported good to very good results compared with 10 percent in the placebo group.

The active ingredient in the herb is hypericin which has the ability to inhibit the activity of monoamine oxidase (MAO), the enzyme linked to depression. The most common side effect of hypericum is upset stomach, which can be avoided by taking it with food. The dosage needs to be sufficient for the desired results to be obtained. Although the effective dose may vary with each individual, up to 900mg. a day can be taken safely.

Clausenamide

Researcher Zhang Juntian at the Chinese Academy of Medical Sciences in Beijing, China is currently studying a substance called clausenamide, an alkaloid extracted from a plant called Wampi *(Clausena lansium)*. This substance is reported to increase intracellular calcium and to promote memory storage in the hippocampus. It is claimed to ameliorate amnesia, ands it's suggested that it may improve intelligence in normal adults.

Huperzine

Known in China as "Qian Ceng Ta," the club moss *Huperzia Serrata* contains a substance now known as Huperzine A which has memory-enhancing properties. The moss is found on the ground deep in damp forests and in rock crevices.

In the 1980s, scientists in China discovered that purified Huperzine A prevents the enzyme acetylcholinesterase (AchE) from breaking down acetylcholine, and therefore increases acetylcholine concentrations. It does this by occupying the active site of the enzyme acetylcholinesterase. Because of its potency as an acetylcholinesterase inhibitor, Huperzine A is now considered to be an effective agent in improving memory and learning, especially in individuals suffering form early stage or moderate forms of Alzheimer's. Recently, it has been reported that it can reduce neuronal cell death caused by glutamate. Huperzine A is available over the counter.

Despite its memory enhancing potential, Huperzine A has never been developed as a drug in America. This is in part because of the lack of intellectual property protection for this herbal material.

But Virginia Tech researcher Paul R. Carlier, working in collaboration with researchers at the Hong Kong University of Science and Technology and the Mayo Clinic, found that a fragment of the Huperzine A molecule could be easily synthesized from cheap, commercially available chemicals.

By itself this fragment is useless. However, based on a detailed analysis of acetylcholinesterase, the brain enzyme with which Huperzine A interacts, Carlier prepared a new molecule by joining two of these fragments with a molecular tether.

Remarkably, the substance created by this linkage, called 'Huperzine A Fragment Dimer' is more than twice as potent as Huperzine A itself. The enhanced potency is said to occur because of the two-point attachment of the drug to cetylcholinesterase. No human trials have been done at the time of this writing.

Bramhi

Brahmi *(Bacopa monniera)* is a succulent found throughout India. It has long been used as an ayruvedic herb that can improve mental acuity and reduce anxiety.

Studies indicate that Brahmi improves protein synthesis in brain cells, but it also has the ability to lower blood pressure (probably through its diuretic properties), and has been shown to be an effective antioxidant and anti-inflammatory.

Several studies report that the herb has cognitive enhancing effects in animals. However a 2004 study using a combination of ginkgo and brahmi in healthy subjects showed no effect.

Other studies using brahmi alone show significant memory enhancing effects by way of its antioxidant and anti-inflammatory properties. A study done at the University of Catania, Italy, showed that the herb did have significant antioxidant properties and reduced DNA damage. In a 2002 study performed at the University of Wollongong, in

Australia, 76 adults between 40 and 65 years of age took part in a double-blind randomized, placebo control study in which various memory functions were tested and levels of anxiety measured. The results show a significant effect of the Brahmi on a test for the retention of new information. The herb also has been found to protect the brain from cognitive deficits induced by phenytoin, a popular medication used for epilepsy.

For more information about herbs, contact

Herb Research Foundation
4140 15th St.
Boulder, CO 80304
800-748-2617
http://www.herbs.org

American Botanical Council
6200 Manor Rd
Austin, TX 78723
512-926-4900
http://www.herbalgram.org/

References

Chapter 1: Losing Our Minds

Noll, R., Turkington, C. (1994) *The Encyclopedia of Memory and Memory Disorders.* Facts on File, NY, p5.

Birren, J. (1977) *Handbook of the Psychology of Aging.* Van Nostrand Rhinehold, NY.

Birren, J., Cunningham, W. (1983) Psychology of Adult Development and Aging. *Annual Review of Psychology.* 34:543-575.

Buell, S. (1981) New thoughts on old neurons. *Seminars in Neurology* 1(1):31-35.

Jarvik, L. (1975) The aging nervous system. *Clinical Aspects. Aging* 1.

Gilbert, J. (1971) Patterns of declining memory. *Journal of Gerontology* 28(1).

Katzman, R., Terry, R. (1983) *The Neurology of Aging.* F.A. Davis Company, Philadelphia.

Racagni, G., Mendlewicz, J. (1992) Treatment of Age Related Cognitive Dysfunction. *Pharmacological and Clinical Evaluation.* Karger, Basil.

Wilson, B., Moffat, N. (1984) *Clinical Management of Memory Problems.* Croom Helm, London.

Poon, W. (1985) Differences in human memory with aging: nature, causes, and clinical applications. *Handbook of the Psychology of Aging,* 2nd ed., J. E. Birren and K. W. Schaie, eds. Van Nostrand Reinhold, NY. pp427 62.

Gutfeld, G., et al. (1991) The memory remains: Recall ability may not fade with age. *Prevention* 43(2):18.

Willis, S., Schaie, K. (1986) Practical Intelligence in Later Adulthood. *Practical Intelligence: Nature and Origins of Competence in the Everyday World.* R. Sternberg, R. Wagner, eds. Cambridge University Press, Cambridge, pp236 68.

McEvoy, C., Moon, J. (1988) Assessment and Treatment of Everyday Memory Problems in the Elderly. *Practical Aspects of Memory: Current Research and Issues.* M. Gruneberg, P. Morris, R. Sykes, eds. Wiley, Chichester, England

Golomb, J., de Leon, M., et al. (1993) Hippocampal atrophy in normal aging. An association with recent memory impairment. *Archives of Neurology* 50(9):967 73.

Chapter 2: Aging and Memory

Folstein, M. F., Folstein, S. E., McHugh, P. R. (1975) "Mini-Mental State": A practical method for grading the cognitive state of patients for the clinician. *J Psychiatr Res.* 12(3):189-98.

Derrer, D. S., Howieson, D. B., Mueller, E. A., Camicioli, R. M., Sexton,. G, Kaye, J. A. (2001) Memory testing in dementia: How much is enough? *J Geriatric Psychiatr Neurol.* Spring;14(1):1-6.

de Jager, C. A., Milwain, E., Badge, M. (2002) Early detection of isolated memory deficits in the elderly: The need for more sensitive neuropsychological tests. *Psychol Med.* Apr;32(3):483-91.

Braverman, E. R., Blum, K. (2003) P300 (latency) event-related potential: An accurate predictor of memory impairment. *Clin Electroencephalogr.* Jul;34(3):124-39.

Kilpelainen, R., Kostinen, A,. Kononen, M., Herrgard, E., Partanen, J., Karhu, J. (1999) P300 sequence effects differ between children and adults for auditory stimuli. *Psychophysiology.* May;36(3):343-50.

Himani, A., Tandon, O. P., Bhatia, M. S. (1999) A study of P300 event-related evoked potential in the patients of major depression. *Indian J Physiol Pharmacol.* Jul;43(3):367-72.

Kurita, A., Mochio, S., Isogai, Y. (1995) Changes in auditory P300 event-related potentials and brainstem evoked potentials in diabetes mellitus. *Acta Neurol Scand.* Oct;92(4):319-23.

Bauer, L. O., Costa, L., Hesselbrock, V. M. (2001) Effects of alcoholism, anxiety, and depression on P300 in women: A pilot study. *J Stud Alcohol.* Sep;62(5):571-9.

AAMI

Krzyminski, S. Age-associated memory impairment. *Psychiatr Pol.* (1995) May-Jun;29(3):319-31. Review. Polish.

Youngjohn, J., Crook, T., (1993) Stability of everyday memory in age associated memory impairment: A longitudinal study. *Neuropsychology* v7 (n3):406 416.

Youngjohn, J., Larrabee, G., Crook, T. (1992) Discriminating age associated memory impairment from Alzheimer's disease. *Psychological Assessment* 4 (1):54 59.

Marwick, C. (1993) What is age associated memory impairment? *JAMA, The Journal of the American Medical Association* 269 (1):356.

Crook, T., Bartus, R., Ferris, S., Whitehouse, P., Cohen, G., Gershon, S. (1986) Age associated memory impairment: Proposed diagnostic criteria and measures of clinical change. Report of a National Institute of Mental Health Workgroup. *Developmental Neuropsychology* 2(4): 261 276.

Crook, T., Larrabee, G. (1988) Age associated memory impairment: Diagnostic criteria and treatment strategies. *Psychopharmacology Bulletin* 24(4): 509 514.

MCI

Petersen, R. C., Smith, G. E., Waring, S. C., Ivnik, R. J., Tangalos, E. G., Kokmen, E. (1999) Mild cognitive impairment: Clinical characterization and outcome. *Arch Neurol.* Mar;56(3):303-8.

Rosler, A., Gonnenwein, C., Muller, N., Sterzer, P., Kleinschmidt, A., Frolich, L. (2004) The Fuzzy Frontier between Subjective Memory Complaints and Early Dementia. A Survey of Patient Management in German Memory Clinics. *Dement Geriatr Cogn Disord.* 2004;17(3):222-230. Epub Jan 20.

Grundman, M., et al. (2004) Mild cognitive impairment can be distinguished from Alzheimer's disease and normal aging for clinical trials. *Arch Neurol.* Jan;61(1):59-66.

Jungwirth, S., Fischer, P., Weissgram, S., Kirchmeyr, W., Bauer, P., Tragl, K. H. (2004) Subjective memory complaints and objective memory impairment in the Vienna-Transdanube aging community. *J Am Geriatr Soc.* Feb;52(2):263-8.

Rivas-Vazquez, R. A., Mendez, C., Rey, G. J., Carrazana, E. J. (2004) Mild cognitive impairment: New neuropsychological and pharmacological target. *Arch Clin Neuropsychol.* Jan;19(1):11-27.

Ritchie, K., Artero, S,. Touchon, J. (2004) Classification criteria for mild cognitive impairment: A population-based validation study. *Neurology.* 2001 Jan 9;56(1):37-42.

Scali, Bruce. Life Extension for the Brain. *Life extension Magazine.* March .

Chapter 3: Dementia

[No Author cited] (2000) Vascular Dementia: A diagnosis of dementia does not always mean an unavoidable decline. Memory Loss and the Brain, Summer.

Willcox, S. M., Himmelstein, D. U., Woolhandler, S. (1994) Inappropriate drug prescribing for the community-dwelling elderly. *JAMA.* Jul 27;272(4):292-6.

Brookmeyer, R., Gary, S., Kawas, C. (1998) Projections of Alzheimer's disease in the United States and the public health impact of delaying disease onset. *Am J Public Health.* Sep;88(9):1337-42.

Buell, S., Coleman, P. (1979) Dendritic growth in the aged human brain and failure of growth in senile dementia. *Science.* 206:854-856.

Petersen, R., et al. (1995) Apolipoprotein E status as a predictor of the development of Alzheimer's disease in memory impaired individuals. *JAMA, The Journal of the American Medical Association.* 273 (5):274.

Hock, C., Konietzko, U., Streffer, J. R., Tracy, J. (2003) Antibodies against beta-amyloid slow cognitive decline in Alzheimer's disease. *Neuron.* May 22;38(4):547-54.

McLaurin, J., Cecal, R., Kierstead, M. E., Tian, X., Phinney, A. L. (2002) Therapeutically effective antibodies against amyloid-beta peptide target amyloid-beta residues 4-10 and inhibit cytotoxicity and fibrillogenesis. *Nat Med.* Nov;8(11):1263-9. Epub Oct 15.

Wolf-Klein, G. P., Silverstone, F. A., Levy, A. P. (1992) Nutritional patterns and weight change in Alzheimer patients. *Int Psychogeriatrics.* Summer; 4(1):103-18.

Multi-infarct Dementia

Vascular Dementia: A diagnosis of dementia does not always mean an unavoidable decline http://www.memorylossonline.com/pastissues/ summer2000/vascu-lardementia.html

Fackelmann, K. (2003) A dose of hope vs. Alzheimer's. *USA Today.* Posted 7/27/2003. http://www.usatoday.com/news/health/2003-07-27-alzheimers-cover_x.htm

White, H., Pieper, C., Schmader, K., Fillenbaum, G. (1996) Weight change in Alzheimer's disease.*J Am Geriatr Soc.* Mar;44(3):265-72.

Causes

Chartier-Harlin, M. C., Crawford, F., Houlden, H., Warren, A., Hughes, D., Fidani, L., Goate, A., Rossor, M., Roques, P., Hardy, J. (1991) Early-onset Alzheimer's disease caused by mutations at codon 717 of the beta-amyloid precursor protein gene. *Nature.* Oct 31; 353(6347):844-6.

Lin,W. R., et.al., (1996) Neurotropic viruses and Alzheimer's disease. Interaction of herpes simplex type 1 virus and apolipoprotein E in the etiology of the disease. *Mol Chem Neuropathol.* 28:135-141.

Lin, W. W., et.al. (1995) Alzheimer's disease, herpes simple virus type 1, cold sores, and apolipoprotein E4. *Biochem Soc Trans.* 23:5945

Risk Factors

Family History

Rossor, M., Newman, S., et al. (1993) Alzheimer's disease in families with amyloid precursor protein mutations. *Annals of the New York Academy of Sciences,* 695:198 202.

Pedersen, N. L., Gatz, M., Berg, S., Johansson, B. (2004) How heritable is Alzheimer's disease late in life? Findings from Swedish twins. *Ann Neurol.* Feb;55(2):180-5.

Pedersen, N. L., Berg, S., Johansson, B., Johansson, K., Viitanen, M., Winblad, B., Gatz, M. (1998) [Genetic factors are often found inl Alzheimer disease. An extensive twin study to clarify the heredity-environment relationship] [Article in Swedish] *Lakartidningen.* May 27;95(22):2585-8

Family History of Down's syndrome

Schupf, N., Kapell, D., Lee, J. H., Ottman, R., Mayeux, R. (1994) Increased risk of Alzheimer's disease in mothers of adults with Down's syndrome. *Lancet.* Aug 6; 344(8919):353-6.

Family Size

Moceri, Ph.D.,V. M. et al. (2000) Early-life risk factors and the development of Alzheimer's disease. *Neurology,* Jan 54: 415.

Marital Status

Helmer, C., Damon, D., Letenneur, L., Fabrigoule, C., Barberger-Gateau, P., Lafont, S., Fuhrer, R., Antonucci, T., Commenges, D., Orgogozo, J. M., Dartigues, J. F. (1999) Marital status and risk of Alzheimer's disease: A French population-based cohort study. *Neurology.* Dec 10;53(9):1953-8.

History of Depression

Jorm, A. F. (2001), History of depression as a risk factor for dementia: An updated review. *Aust N Z J Psychiatry* 35(6):776-781.

Sleep Apnea

Macey, P. M., et al. (2002) Brain morphology associated with obstructive sleep apnea. *American Journal of Respiratory and Critical Care Medicine.* Nov 15;166(10):1382-7.

Svaldi, Jennifer J., Mackinger, Herbert F. (2003) Obstructive sleep apnea syndrome: Autobiographical memory predicts the course of depressive affect after nCPAP therapy. *Scandinavian Journal of Psychology* Volume 44 Issue 1 Page 31 - February

Steiner, M. C., Ward, M. J., Ali, N. J. (1999) Dementia and snoring. *Lancet.* Jan 16;353(9148):204

Gozal, D (2002) The Brain in Sleep-disordered Breathing: Is It the Chicken or Is It the Egg? *American Journal of Respiratory and Critical Care Medicine* Vol 166. pp. 1305-1306,

Schmidt, E. (2002) UCLA Scientists Link Sleep Apnea to Brain Damage; Childhood Stuttering Suggests Disorder Results From Early Brain Flaw http://newsroom. ucla.edu/page.asp?id=3693 November 20

Estrogen Deficiency

Paganini-Hill, A., Henderson, V. W. (1994) Estrogen deficiency and risk of Alzheimer's disease in women. *Am J Epidemiol.* Aug 1; 140(3):256-61

Birge, S. J. (1996) Is there a role for estrogen replacement therapy in the prevention and treatment of dementia? *J Am Geriatr Soc.* Jul; 44(7):865-70.

Head Trauma

Mehta, K. M., Ott, A., Kalmijn, S., Slooter, A. J., van Duijn, C. M., Hofman, A, Breteler, M. M. (1999) Head trauma and risk of dementia and Alzheimer's disease: The Rotterdam Study. *Neurology.* Dec 10;53(9):1959-62.

Mortimer, J. A., van Duijn, C. M., Chandra, V., Fratiglioni, L,. Graves, A. B., Heyman, A., Jorm, A. F., Kokmen, E., Kondo, K., Rocca, W. A (1991) Head trauma as a risk factor for Alzheimer's disease: A collaborative re-analysis of case-control studies. EURODEM Risk Factors Research Group. *Int J Epidemiol.* 20 Suppl 2:S28-35

Roberts, G. W., Allsop, D., Bruton, C. (1990) The occult aftermath of boxing. *J Neurol Neurosurg Psychiatry.* May;53(5):373-8.

Surgery

Raja, P. V., Blumenthal, J. A., Doraiswamy, P. M. (2004) Cognitive deficits following coronary artery bypass grafting: Prevalence, prognosis, and therapeutic strategies. *CNS Spectr.* Oct;9(10):763-72.

Johannessen, N. W., Cooper, J. B., Gravenstein, J. S., Chraemmer-Jorgensen, B., Wiberg-Jorgensen, F., Djernes, M., Heslet, L., Johansen, S. H. (1993) Randomized evaluation of pulse oximetry in 20,802 patients. I. Design, demography, pulse oximetry failure and overall complication rate. *Anesthesiology.* 78: 436-444.

Moller, J. T., Svennild, I., Johannessen, N. W., Jensen, P. F., Espersen, K., Gravenstein, J. S., Cooper, J. B., Djernes, M., Johansen, S. H. (1993) Association between intraoperative pulse oximetry monitoring and postoperative cognitive function. *Br J Anaesth.* 71: 340-347.

Silverstein, J. H., Beneken, J. E. W., Gravenstein, J. S. (1998) For the ISPOCD investigators. Long-term postoperative cognitive dysfunction in the elderly: ISPOCD 1 study. *Lancet.* 351: 857-61

Stockton, Ph.D., Patricia, Cohen-Mansfield, Ph.D., Jiska, Billig, M.D., Nathan. (2000) Mental Status Change in Older Surgical Patients Cognition, Depression, and Other Comorbidity. *Am J Geriatr Psychiatry.* 8:40-46, February

Newman, M. F., Kirchner, J. L,. Phillips-Bute, B. (2000) Longitudinal assessment of neurocognitive function after coronary-artery bypass surgery. *N Engl J Med,* vol. 344, pp. 395—402

Moller, J. T., et al. (1998) Long-term postoperative cognitive dysfunction in the elderly ISPOCD1 study. ISPOCD investigators. International Study of Post-Operative Cognitive Dysfunction. *Lancet.* Mar 21;351 (9106):857-61.

Newman, M. F., Kirchner, J. L., Phillips-Bute, B. et al. Longitudinal Assessment of Neurocognitive Function after Coronary-Artery Bypass Surgery, *NEJM,* 344 (6) http://www.nejm.org

Sabik, J., Gillinov, M., Blackstone, E., Vacha, C., et al. (2002) Do Off Pump Techniques Reduce the Morbidity and Mortality of Coronary Artery Bypass Surgery? *J Thorac Cardiovasc Surg* Oct;124(4):698-707, http://www2.us.elsevierhealth.com/scripts/om.dll/serve?retrieve=/pii/S0022522302001411

Fogoros, Richard N. (2004) Preventing Pump Head http://heartdisease. about.com /cs/bypasssurgery/a /prevpumphead.htm

Other risk factors

Monro, C. A., Saxton, J., Butters, M. A. (2001). Alcohol dementia: 'cortical' or 'subcortical dementia. *Archives of Clinical Neuropsychology.*16, 523-533.

Smith, D. M. Atkinson, R. M. (1995) Alcoholism and Dementia. *International Journal of the Addictions,* 30(13-14), 1843-1869.

Lopez, O. L., Becker, J. T., Klunk, W., et al. (2000). Research evaluation and diagnosis of possible Alzheimer's disease over the last two decades: II. *Neurology,* 55 (12),1863-1869.

Thomas, V.S . Rockwood, K .J. (2001). Alcohol abuse, cognitive impairment, and mortality among older people. *American Geriatrics Society,* 49 (4), 415-20.

Kivipelto, M., Helkala, E. L., Laakso, M. P., Hanninen, T., Hallikainen, M., Alhainen, K., Soininen, H., Tuomilehto, J., Nissinen, A. (2001) Midlife vascular risk factors and Alzheimer's disease in later life: Longitudinal, population based study. *BMJ.* Jun 16;322(7300):1447-51.

Moceri, V. M., Kukull, W. A., Emanuel, I., van Belle, G., Larson, E. B. (2000) Early-life risk factors and the development of Alzheimer's disease. *Neurology.* Jan 25;54(2):415-20.

Hofman, A., Schulte, W., Tanja, T. A., van Duijn ,C. M., Haaxma, R., Lameris. A, J., Otten, V. M., Saan, R. J. (1989) History of dementia and Parkinson's disease in 1st-degree relatives of patients with Alzheimer's disease. *Neurology.* Dec;39(12):1589-92. Related Articles, Links

Davis, J. D., Stern, R. A., Flashman, L. A. (2003) Cognitive and neuropsychiatric aspects of subclinical hypothyroidism: Significance in the elderly. *Curr Psychiatry Rep.* Oct;5(5):384-90. Related Articles, Links

Poor Education

Karp, A., Kareholt, I., Qiu, C., Bellander, T., Winblad, B., Fratiglioni, L. (2004) Relation of education and occupation-based socioeconomic status to incident Alzheimer's disease. *Am J Epidemiol.* Jan 15;159(2):175-83

Intelligence

Scarmeas, N., Stern, Y. (2003) Cognitive reserve and lifestyle. *J Clin Exp Neuropsychol.* Aug;25(5):625-33. *N Engl J Med.* 2003 Jun 19;348(25):2508-16. 0-2.

Verghese, J., Lipton, R. B., Katz, M. J., Hall, C. B., Derby, C. A., Kuslansky, G., Ambrose, A. F,. Sliwinski, M., Buschke, H. (2003) Leisure activities and the risk of dementia in the elderly. *N Engl J Med.* Sep 25;349(13):1290-2; author reply 1290-2.

Snowdon, D. A., Greiner, L. H., Markesbery, W. R (2000) Linguistic ability in early life and the neuropathology of Alzheimer's disease and cerebrovascular disease. Findings from the Nun Study. *Ann N Y Acad Sci.* Apr;903:34-8

Snowdon, D. A., Kemper, S. J., Mortimer, J. A., Greiner, L. H., Wekstein, D. R., Markesbery, W. R. (1996) Linguistic ability in early life and cognitive function and Alzheimer's disease in late life. Findings from the Nun Study. *JAMA.* Feb 21;275(7):528-32

Diagnosing Dementia

Kier, F. J., Molinari, V. (2003) "Do-it-yourself" dementia testing: Issues regarding an Alzheimer's home screening test. *Gerontologist.* Jun;43(3):295-301.

Lange, R., Donathan, C. L., Hughes, L. F. (2002) Assessing olfactory abilities with the University of Pennsylvania smell identification test: A Rasch scaling approach. *J Alzheimers Dis.* Apr;4(2):77-91

McMahon, C., Scadding, G. K. (1996) Le Nez du Vin—a quick test of olfaction. *Clin Otolaryngol.* Jun;21(3):278-80.

Gray, A. J., Staples, V., Murren, K., Dhariwal, A., Bentham, P. (2001) Olfactory identification is impaired in clinic-based patients with vascular dementia and senile dementia of Alzheimer's type. *Int J Geriatr Psychiatry.* May;16(5):513-7.

Felber, S. R. (2002) Magnetic resonance in the differential diagnosis of dementia. *J Neural Transm.* Jul;109(7-8):1045-51.

Treatment

S12024

Allain, H., et al. (1997) Bridging study of S 12024 in 53 inpatients with Alzheimer's disease. *Journal of the American Geriatrics Society* (45): 125-6

Tacrine

Laine, K., Palovaara, S., Tapanainen, P., Manninen, P. (1999) Plasma tacrine concentrations are significantly increased by concomitant hormone replacement therapy. *Clin Pharmacol Ther.* Dec;66(6):602-8.

Aricept

Schneider, L. S. (2004) AD2000: Donepezil in Alzheimer's disease. *Lancet.* Jun 26;363(9427):2100-1.

Reminyl

Cummings, J. L., Schneider, L., Tariot, P. N., Kershaw, P. R., Yuan, W. (2004) Reduction of behavioral disturbances and caregiver distress by galantamine in patients with Alzheimer's disease. *Am J Psychiatry.* Mar;161(3):532-8

Allgaier, C., Arendt, T. (2004) [Galantamine, An acetylcholinesterase inhibitor with various actions] *Med Monatsschr Pharm.* Jul;27(7):223-7. [Article in German]

Exelon

Ballard, C. G. (2002) Advances in the treatment of Alzheimer's disease: Benefits of dual cholinesterase inhibition. *Eur Neurol,* vol. 47, pp. 64–70

Gilatide

Greig, N. H., De Micheli, E., Holloway, H. W., Yu, Q. S., Utsuki, T., Perry, T. A., Brossi, A., Ingram, D.K., Deutsch, J., Lahiri, D. K., Soncrant, T. T. (2000) The experimental Alzheimer's drug phenserine: Preclinical pharmacokinetics and pharmacodynamics. *Acta Neurol Scand Suppl.* 176:74-84.

Namenda

Reisberg, B., Doody, R., Stoffler, A., Schmitt, F., Ferris, S., Mobius, H. J. (2003) Memantine Study Group. Memantine in moderate-to-severe Alzheimer's disease. *N Engl J Med.* Apr 3;348(14):1333-41.

Clioquinol

Melov, S. (2002) 'And C is for Clioquinol' — the AbetaCs of Alzheimer's disease. *Trends Neurosci.* Mar;25(3):121-3;

Cole, G. M. (2003) Ironic fate: Can a banned drug control metal heavies in neurodegenerative diseases? *Neuron.* Mar 27;37(6):889-90.

Finefrock, A. E,. Bush, A. I., Doraiswamy, P. M. (2003) Current status of metals as therapeutic targets in Alzheimer's disease. *Journal of the American Geriatrics Society.* Aug;51(8):1143-8. .

Bush, A. I. (2003) The metallobiology of Alzheimer's disease. *Trends Neurosci.* Apr;26(4):207-14.

Gouras, G. K., Beal, M. F. (2001) Metal chelator decreases Alzheimer's beta-amyloid plaques. *Neuron.* Jun;30(3):641-2.

Cherny, R. A., et al. (2001) Treatment with a copper-zinc chelator markedly and rapidly inhibits beta-amyloid accumulation in Alzheimer's disease transgenic mice. *Neuron.* Jun;30(3):665-76

Sparks, D. L., Schreurs, B. G. (2003) Trace amounts of copper in water induce beta-amyloid plaques and learning deficits in a rabbit model of Alzheimer's disease. *Proc Natl Acad Sci U S A.* Sep 16;100(19):11065-9. Epub 2003 Aug 14

Sparks, D. L., Lochhead, J., Horstman, D., Wagoner, T., Martin, T. (2002) Water quality has a pronounced effect on cholesterol-induced accumulation of Alzheimer's amyloid beta (Abeta) in rabbit brain. *J Alzheimers Dis.* Dec;4(6):523-9

Cuajungco, M. P., Faget, K.Y. (2003) Zinc takes the center stage: Its paradoxical role in Alzheimer's disease. *Brain Res Rev.* Jan;41(1):44-56

Ampakines

Danysz W. (2002) CX-516 Cortex pharmaceuticals. *Curr Opin Investig Drugs.* Jul;3(7):1081-8.

Other medications

Coull, J. T., Sahakian, B. J., Hodges, J. R. (1996) The alpha-sub-2 antagonist idazoxan remediates certain attentional and executive dysfunction in patients with dementia of frontal type. *Psychopharmacology.* 123(3):239-49.

Hsu, R. S., DiLeo, E. M., Chesson, S. M., Klein, J. T., Effland, R. C. (1991) Determination of HP 749, a potential therapeutic agent for Alzheimer's disease, in plasma by high-performance liquid chromatography. *Chromatogr.* Dec 6;572(1-2):352-9.

Yankner, B. A., Caceres, A., Duffy, L. K. (1990) Nerve growth factor potentiates the neurotoxicity of beta amyloid. *Proc Natl Acad Sci U S A.* Nov;87(22):9020-3.

Kowall, N. W., Beal, M. F., Busciglio, J., Duffy, L. K., Yankner, B. A. (1991) An in vivo model for the neurodegenerative effects of ≤ amyloid and protection by substance P. *Proc Natl Acad Sci USA* 88:7247-7251.

Chapter 4: The Many Types of Memory

Strobel, G. (1993) Different memories go different places. *Science News* Nov 27. 44(1):367.

Olfactory Memory

Herz, R. S., Engen, T. (1996) Odor memory: review and analysis. *Psychonomic Bulletin and Review* 3: n3 300-313

Herz, R. S. (1997) The effects of cue distinctiveness on odor-based context dependent memory. *Memory and Cognition,* 25, 375-380.

Wippich, W. (1990) Recall of odors: Naming and autobiographical memories illustrate odor aftereffects. *Zeitschrift fur Experimentelle und Angewandte Psychologie* 37(4):679 95.

Engen, T. (1980) Why the aroma lingers on. *Psychology Today,* May.

Schab, F., Crowder, R. eds. (1995) *Memory for Odors.* Lawrence Erlbaum Associates, Inc, Mahwah, NJ.

Visceral Memory

Miranda, M. I., Ferreira, G., Ramirez-Lugo, L., Bermudez-Rattoni, F. (2002) Glutamatergic activity in the amygdala signals visceral input during taste memory formation. *Proc Natl Acad Sci U S A.* Aug 20;99(17):11417-22.

Price, J. L. (1999) Prefrontal cortical networks related to visceral function and mood. *Ann N Y Acad Sci.* Jun 29;877:383-96.

Skinner, J. D., Carruth, B. R., Bounds, B., Ziegler, P., Reidy, K. (2002) Do food-related experiences in the first 2 years of life predict dietary variety in school-aged children? *J Nutr Educ Behav* ; 34: 310-315.

Auditory Memory

Levitin, Daniel J., Cook, Perry R. (1996) Memory for musical tempo: Additional evidence that auditory memory is absolute. *Perception & Psychophysics* 58:pp. 927-935.

Noll, R., Turkington, C. (1994) *Encyclopedia of Memory and Memory Disorders,* p147. Facts on File

Winograd, E. (1980) Face Saving Memory. *Psychology Today,* Feb.

Baddely, A. (1986) *Working Memory.* Oxford University Press, London.

Huyge, P. (1985) Voices, glances, flashbacks: Our first memories: Considering the novelty and richness of the first few years of life, why are our early memories so fragmented? *Psychology Today* Sept. p48(5).

Skill Memory

LaBarge, E., Smith, D. S., Dick, L., Storandt, M. (1992) Agraphia in dementia of the Alzheimer's type. *Arch Neurol.* Nov;49(11):1151-6

Chapter 5: The Memory Process

Benderly, B. (1981) Flashbulb memory. *Psychology Today,* June

Mood and Memory

Bower, G. (1961) *Mood & Memory.* June

Lisman, J. E., Idiart, M. A. (1995) Storage of 7 +/- 2 short-term memories in oscillatory subcycles. *Science.* Mar 10;267(5203):1512-5.

Chapter 6: Why and What We Forget

Receptor Problems

Colsher, P., Wallace, R. (1990) Are hearing and visual dysfunction associated with cognitive impairment? A population based approach. *Journal of Applied Gerontology* 9 (1):91 105.

Baddeley, A. (1982) *Your Memory: A User's Guide.* Macmillan Publishing, NY.

Intentional Forgetting

Bjork, E. L., Bjork, R. A. (2003) Intentional forgetting can increase, not decrease, residual influences of to-be-forgotten information. *J Exp Psychol Learn Mem Cogn.* Jul;29(4):524-31.

Kimball, D. R., Bjork, R. A. (2002) Influences of intentional and unintentional forgetting on false memories. *J Exp Psychol Gen.* Mar;131(1):116-30.

Lehman, E. B., Morath, R., Franklin, K., Elbaz, V. (1998) Knowing what to remember and forget: A developmental study of cue memory in intentional forgetting. *Mem Cognit.* Sep;26(5):860-8.

Motivated Forgetting

Anderson, M. C., Ochsner, K. N., Kuhl, B., Cooper, J., Robertson, E., Gabrieli, S. W., Glover, G. H., Gabrieli, J. D. (2004) Neural systems underlying the suppression of unwanted memories. *Science.* Jan 9;303(5655):232-5.

Blum, G. S., Barbour, J. S. (1979) Selective inattention to anxiety-linked stimuli. *J Exp Psychol Gen.* Jun;108(2):182-224.

Weiner, B. (1968) Motivated forgetting and the study of repression. *J Pers.* Jun;36(2):213-34.

Glucksberg, S., King, L. J. (1967) Motivated forgetting mediated by implicit verbal chaining: A laboratory analog of repression. *Science.* Oct 27;158(800):517-9.

Anderson, M. C., Ochsner, K. N., Kuhl, B., Cooper, J., Robertson, E., Gabrieli, S. W., Glover, G. H., Gabrieli, J. D. (2004) Neural systems underlying the suppression of unwanted memories. *Science.* Jan 9;303(5655):232-5.

Rappoport, D. (1961) *Emotions and Memory.* Science Editions Inc., NY.

Retrieval Failure

Maril, A., Simons, J. S., Mitchell, J. P., Schwartz, B. L., Schacter, D. L. (2003) Feeling-of-knowing in episodic memory: An event-related fMRI study. *Neuroimage.* Apr;18(4):827-36.

Maril, A., Wagner, A. D., Schacter, D. L. (2001) On the tip of the tongue: an event-related fMRI study of semantic retrieval failure and cognitive conflict. *Neuron.* Aug 30;31(4):653-60.

Spencer, W. D,. Raz, N. (1995) Differential effects of aging on memory for content and context: A meta-analysis. *Psychol Aging.* Dec;10(4):527-39

Dobson, M., Markham, R. (1992) Individual differences in anxiety level and eyewitness memory. *J Gen Psychol.* Oct;119(4):343-50.

Chiarello, C., Hoyer, W. J. (1988) Adult age differences in implicit and explicit memory: Time course and encoding effects. *Psychol Aging.* Dec;3(4):358-66.

Kato, T., Krinsky, R., Nelson, T. O. (1985) The feeling of knowing for different types of retrieval failure. *Acta Psychol* (Amst). Feb;58(2):141-58.

Smith, A. D., Park, D. C., Cherry, K., Berkovsky, K. (1990) Age differences in memory for concrete and abstract pictures. *J Gerontol.* Sep;45(5):P205-9.

State Dependence

Forgas, J. P., Bower, G. H. (1987) Mood effects on person-perception judgments. *J Pers Soc Psychol.* Jul;53(1):53-60.

Bower, G. H. Commentary on mood and memory. *Behav Res Ther.* 987;25(6):443-55. Review.

Mayer, J. D., Bower, G. H. (1985) Mood-dependent retrieval: Commentary on Wetzler. *Psychol Rep.* Dec;57(3 Pt 1):1000-2.

Bower, G. H. Mood and memory. *Am Psychologist* 1981 Feb;36(2):129-48.

Stress

Bornstein, A. (1983) Stress: A good memory's worst enemy, *Executive Fitness Newsletter,* vol 14(18).

Repression

Pressman, M. (1969) The cognitive function of the ego in psychoanalysis, II. Repression, incognizance and insight formation. *International Journal of Psychoanalysis* 50(3):343 51.

Chapter 7: How to Learn New Information

Monk, T. H., Folkard, S. (1978) Concealed inefficiency of late-night study. *Nature.* May 25;273 (5660):296-7.

Hill, R., Storandt, M., Simeone, C. (1990) The Effect of Memory Skills Training and Incentives on Free Recall in Older Learners. *Gerontology* 45(6):227-232.

Maddox, H. (1964) *How to Study.* Crest Books, London.

Lorayne, H. (1976) *Good Memory, Successful Student.* Stein and Day, NY.

Chapter 8: How to Stop Losing and Forgetting Things

Cassedy, E. (1990) It isn't lost; I just can't find it: 6 easy ways to stop losing things. *Woman's Day* Oct 2, 53(3):40.

Schreiner, S. Jr. (1988) How not to lose things. *Reader's Digest,* Sept 133(4):55.

Chapter 9: Factors for Maximizing Memory

Roth, D. (1948) *The Roth Memory Course.* Ralston Publishing, Cleveland, OH.

Roberts, P. (1983) Memory strategy instruction with the elderly: What should memory training be the training of? *Cognitive Strategy Research: Psychological Foundations,* M. Pressley, J. Levin, eds. Springer Verlag, NY pp75 100.

Chapter 10: Memory Systems

Yovel, G., Paller, K. A. (2004) The neural basis of the butcher-on-the-bus phenomenon: When a face seems familiar but is not remembered. *Neuroimage.* Feb;21(2):789-800.

Poon, L., Walsh Sweeney, L., Fozard, L. (1980) Memory Skill Training for the Elderly: Salient Issues on the Use of Imagery Mnemonics," *New Directions in Memory and Aging,* Poon, L., Fozard, J., Cermak, L., Arenberg, D., Thompson, L. Erlbaum, eds. Hillsdale NJ. Pp461 84;

Grady, C., et al. (1995) Age related reductions in human recognition memory due to impaired encoding. *Science* 269(4):218.

Giordano, G. (1982) Mnemonic techniques that improve reading comprehension, *Clearing House* 56(1):164.

Yesavage, J. (1988) Techniques for cognitive training of memory in Age Associated Memory Impairment. Symposium: Memory and aging. *Archives of Gerontology & Geriatrics,* Suppl, v1:185 190.

Chapter 11: Sleep, Biological Rhythms And Memory

Monk, T. H., Knauth, P., Folkard, S., Rutenfranz, J. (1978) Memory based performance measures in studies of shiftwork. *Ergonomics.* Oct;21(10):819-26.

Monk, T. H., Folkard, S. (1976) Adjusting to the changes to and from Daylight Saving Time. *Nature.* Jun 24;261(5562):688-9.

Folkard, S., Knauth, P., Monk, T. H. (1976) The effect of memory load on the circadian variation in performance efficiency under a rapidly rotating shift system. *Ergonomics.* Jul;19(4):479-88.

Rubin, Z. (1979) *Seasonal Rhythms in Behavior.* Dec.

Folkard, S. (1982) Circadian rhythms and human memory. *Rhythmic Aspects of Human Behavior.* F. Brown, R. Graeber, eds. Erlbaum Associates, Hillsdale, NJ, p313 344

Kripke (1982) Ultradian Rhythms in behavior and physiology. *Rhythmic Aspects of Human Behavior,* F. Brown, R. Graeber, eds, Erlbaum Associates, Hillsdale, NJ.

Rasmunsen (1986) Physiological interactions of the basic rest-activity cycle of the brain: Pulsatile luteinizing hormone secretion as a model. *Psychoneuroendocrinology.* 11(4) 389 405.

Chase, M. (1979) Every 90 Minutes a Brainstorm. *Psychology Today* Nov.

Palombo, S. (1978) *Dreaming and Memory.* Basic Books, NY.

Roffwarg, H., et al. (1978) The effects of sustained alterations of waking visual input on dream content. *The Mind in Sleep: Psychology and Psychophysiology.* Arkin, Antrobus, Ellman, eds. Lawrence Erlbaum. Hillsdale, NJ. p295.

Lichstein, M. (1990) Low sleep need causes confusion. *Brain/Mind Bulletin* 15(7). Originally in *Behavior Therapy* 19: 625 632

Hoddes, E. (1977) Does Sleep Help You Study? *Psychology Today,* April.

Plasma melatonin rhythm in normal aging and Alzheimer's Disease (1986). *J. Neural Transm.* Suppl.21:494

Alterations in nocturnal serum melatonin levels in humans with growth and aging (1988). *J. Clin. Endocrinol. Metab.* 66:648 652

Daily variation in the concentration of melatonin and 5 methoxy-tryptophol in the human pineal gland: Effect of age and Alzheimer's Disease (1990) *Brain Res.* 628:170 174

Insomnia and Immune Function

Irwin, M., Clark, C., Kennedy, B., Christian Gillin, J., Ziegler, M. (2003) Nocturnal catecholamines and immune function in insomniacs, depressed patients, and control subjects. *Brain Behav Immun.* Oct;17(5):365-72.

Savard, J., Laroche, L., Simard, S., Ivers, H., Morin, C. M. (2003) Chronic insomnia and immune functioning. *Psychosom Med.* Mar-Apr;65(2):211-21.

Irwin M. (2002) Effects of sleep and sleep loss on immunity and cytokines. Brain Behav Immun. Oct;16(5):503-12. Review.

Prolo, P., Chiappelli, F., Fiorucci, A., Dovio, A., Sartori, M. L., Angeli, A. (2002) Psychoneuroimmunology: New avenues of research for the twenty-first century. *Ann N Y Acad Sci.* Jun;966:400-8. Review.

Chapter 12: Brain Function and Blood Flow

Jennett, B. et al. (1976) Effect of Carotid Artery Surgery on Cerebral Blood Flow. *Excerpta Medica,* Amsterdam.

Sangiorgio, M., et al. (1992) Aerobic memory. (exercise and memory) *Prevention* 44(2):4

American Heart Association's Conference on Cardiovascular Disease Epidemiology and Prevention, March, 1996.

Folkins, C. H., Sime, W. E. (1981) Physical fitness training and mental health. *Am Psychol.* Apr;36(4):373-89.

Runte, T. (1980) The bright stuff. *Wholemind Newsletter* 1(12)

Coffee

Lindsay, J., Laurin, D., Verreault, R., Hebert, R., Helliwell, B., Hill, G. B., McDowell, I. (2002) Risk factors for Alzheimer's disease: A prospective analysis from the Canadian Study of Health and Aging. *American Journal of Epidemiology* Sep 1;156(5):445-53

Jee, S. H., He, J., Appel, L. J. et al. (2001) Coffee consumption and serum lipids: Meta-analysis of randomized controlled clinical trials. *American Journal of Epidemiology,* vol. 153, pp. 353--362

Haffner, S. et al. (1985) Coffee Consumption, Diet and Lipids. *American Journal of Epidemiology* 122:1 12.

Curb, J., et al. (1986) Coffee, caffeine and serum cholesterol in Japanese men in Hawaii. *American Journal of Epidemiology* 123:648-655.

Mathias, S., et al. (1985) Coffee, plasma cholesterol, and lipoproteins: A population study in an adult community. *American Journal of Epidemiology* 121:890-905.

Klatsky, A., et al. (1985) Coffee, tea and cholesterol. *Am. J. of Cardiology* 55:577-578.

Thelle, D., et al. (1983) The Tromso Heart Study: "Does coffee raise serum cholesterol?" *NEJMedicine* 308:1454 1457.

Williams, P., et al. (1985) Coffee intake and elevated cholesterol and apolipoprotein B levels in men. *JAMA* 253:1407 1411.

Coffee Consumption Linked with Rising Serum Cholesterol. *Medial. World News* 26(15):2324, Aug. 12, 1985.

Forde, O., et al. (1985) The Tromso Heart Study: Coffee consumption and serum lipid concentrations in men with hypercholesterolaemia: A Randomised Intervention Study. *British Med J.* 290: 893- 895.

Naismith, D., et al. (1970) The effect in volunteers of coffee and decaffeinated coffee on blood glucose, insulin, plasma lipids, and some factors involved in blood clotting. *Nutr. Metab.* 12:144 151.

Little, J., et al. (1966) Coffee and Serum Lipids in Coronary Heart Disease. *Lancet* 1:732 734.

Kark, J., et al. (1985) Coffee, tea, and plasma cholesterol: The Jerusalem Lipid Research Clinic. *Br. Med J.* 292:699 704.

Haffner, S., et al. (1985) Coffee consumption, diet, and lipids. *Am. J. Epidemiol.* 122:1 12.

C-reactive Protein

Ridker, P., Nader, R., et al. (1999) Long-term effects of pravastatin on plasma concentration of C-reactive protein. *Circulation.* 100:230-235

Mendall, M. A., Patel, P., Ballam, L., et al. (1996) C-reactive protein and its relation to cardiovascular risk factor: A population based cross sectional study. *BMJ.* 312:1061-1065.

Riker, P., Haughie, P. (1998) Prospective studies of C-reactive protein as a risk factor for cardiovascular disease. *J Investig Med.* 46:391-395.

Carnosine

Zieba, R., Wagrowska-Danilewicz, M. (2003) Influence of carnosine on the cardiotoxicity of doxorubicin in rabbits. *Pol J Pharmacol.* Nov-Dec;55(6): 1079-87. PMID: 14730104

Gariballa, S. E., Sinclair, A. J. (2000) Carnosine: Physiological properties and therapeutic potential. *Age and Aging,* 29: 207-210.

Boldyrev, A. A., Gallant, S. C., Suhkich, G. T. Carnosine, the protective, anti-aging peptide. *Biosci Rep,* 1999, 19 (6).

Statins

Wolozin, B., Kellman, W., Ruosseau, P., et al. (2000) Decreased prevalence of Alzheimer's disease associated with 3-hydroxy-3-methyglutaryl coenzyme A reductase inhibitors. *Arch Neurol.* 57:1439-1443.

Jick, H., Zornberg, G. L., Jick, S. S., et al. (2000) Statins and the risk of dementia. *Lancet.* 356:1627-1631.

Haley, R. W., Dietschy, J. M. (2000) Is there a connection between the concentration of cholesterol circulating in plasma and the rate of neuritic plaque formation in Alzheimer's disease? [editorial] *Arch Neurol.* 57:1410-1412.

ALLHAT Officers and Coordinators for the ALLHAT Collaborative Research Group Major outcomes in moderately hypercholesterolemic, hypertensive patients randomized to pravastatin vs usual care: The Antihypertensive and Lipid-Lowering Treatment to Prevent Heart Attack Trial (ALLHAT-LLT). *JAMA.* 2002 Dec 18;288(23):2998-3007.

Hecht, H. S., Harman, S. M. (2003) Relation of aggressiveness of lipid-lowering treatment to changes in calcified plaque burden by electron beam tomography. *Am J Cardiol.* Aug 1;92(3):334-6.

Sjogren, M., Gustafsson, K., Syversen, S., Olsson, A., Edman, A., Davidsson, P., Wallin, A., Blennow, K. (2003) Treatment with simvastatin in patients with Alzheimer's disease lowers both alpha- and beta-cleaved amyloid precursor protein. *Dement Geriatr Cogn Disord.* 16(1):25-30.

Red Yeast Rice

Thompson Coon, J. S., Ernst, E. (2003) Herbs for serum cholesterol reduction: A systematic view. *J Fam Pract.* Jun;52(6):468-78.

Man, R. Y., Lynn, E. G., Cheung, F., Tsang, P. S., O K. (2002) Cholestin inhibits cholesterol synthesis and secretion in hepatic cells (HepG2). *Mol Cell Biochem.* Apr;233(1-2):153-8.

Heber, D., Yip, I., Ashley, J. M., Elashoff, D. A., Elashoff, R. M., Go, V. L. (1999) Cholesterol-lowering effects of a proprietary Chinese red-yeast-rice dietary supplement. *Am J Clin Nutr.* Feb;69(2):231-6.

Varady, K. A., Wang, Y., Jones, P. J. (2003) Role of policosanols in the prevention and treatment of cardiovascular disease. *Nutr Rev.* Nov;61(11):376-83.

Pepping, J. (2003) Policosanol. *Am J Health Syst Pharm.* Jun 1;60(11):1112-5.

Gugul

Firenzuoli, F., Gori, L. (2003) Guggulipid and cholesterol levels. *JAMA.* Dec 3;290(21):2800; author reply 2801.

Szapary, P. O., Wolfe, M. L., Bloedon, L. T., Cucchiara, A. J., DerMarderosian, A. H., Cirigliano, M. D., Rader, D. J. (2003) Guggulipid for the treatment of hypercholesterolemia: A randomized controlled trial. *JAMA.* Aug 13;290(6):765-72.

Urizar, N. L., Moore, D. D. (2003) Guggulipid: a natural cholesterol-lowering agent. *Annu Rev Nutr.* 2003;23:303-13. Epub Feb 26.

Das Gupta, R. (1990) A new hypolipidaemic agent (gugulipid). *Assoc Physicians India.* Feb;38(2):186.

Alfalfa

Chu, S., Qu, W., Pang, X., Sun, B., Huang, X. (2003) [Effect of saponin from Tribulus terrestris on hyperlipidemia] *Zhong Yao Cai.* May;26(5):341-4. [Article in Chinese]

Story, J. A., LePage, S. L., Petro, M. S., West, L. G., Cassidy, M. M., Lightfoot, F. G., Vahouny, G. V. (1984) Interactions of alfalfa plant and sprout saponins with cholesterol in vitro and in cholesterol-fed rats. *Am J Clin Nutr.* Jun;39(6):917-29.

Malinow, M. R., Connor, W. E., McLaughlin, P., Stafford, C., Lin, D. S., Livingston, A. L., Kohler, G. O., McNulty, W. P. (1981) Cholesterol and bile acid balance in Macaca fascicularis. Effects of alfalfa saponins. *Clin Invest.* Jan;67(1):156-62.

Malinow, M. R., McLaughlin, P., Stafford, C., Livingston, A. L., Kohler, G. O. (1980) Alfalfa saponins and alfalfa seeds. Dietary effects in cholesterol-fed rabbits. *Atherosclerosis.* Nov;37(3):433-8.

Molgaard, J., von Schenck, H., Olsson, A. G. (1987) Alfalfa seeds lower low density lipoprotein cholesterol and apolipoprotein B concentrations in patients with type II hyperlipoproteinemia. *Atherosclerosis.* May;65(1-2):173-9.

Malinow, M. R., McLaughlin, P., Stafford, C. (1980) Alfalfa seeds: Effects on cholesterol metabolism. *Experientia.* May 15;36(5):562-4.

Stroke

John Sharkey, Ph.D.; Jane H. Crawford, B.Sc.; Steven P. Butcher, Ph.D.; Hugh M. Marston, Ph.D. (1996) Tacrolimus (FK506) Ameliorates Skilled Motor Deficits Produced by Middle Cerebral Artery Occlusion in Rats. *Stroke.* 27:2282-2286.)

Hiroyuki Takamatsu, Hideo Tsukada, Akihiro Noda, Takeharu Kakiuchi, Shingo Nishiyama, Shintaro Nishimura, Kazuo Umemura. FK506 Attenuates Early Ischemic Neuronal Death in a Monkey Model of Stroke. *Journal of Nuclear Medicine* Vol. 42 No. 12 1833-1840

Bochelen, D., Rudin, M., Sauter., A. (1999) Calcineurin Inhibitors FK506 and SDZ ASM 981 Alleviate the Outcome of Focal Cerebral Ischemic/Reperfusion Injury. *Pharmacology* Vol. 288, Issue 2, 653-659, February.

Chapter 13: Blood Pressure

Low Blood Pressure

Verghese, J., Lipton, R. B., Hall, C. B., Kuslansky, G., Katz, M. J. (2003) Low blood pressure and the risk of dementia in very old individuals. *Neurology*. Dec 23;61(12):1667-1672.

Qiu, C., von Strauss, E., Fastbom, J., Winblad, B., Fratiglioni, L. (2003) Low blood pressure and risk of dementia in the Kungsholmen project: A 6-year follow-up study. *Archives of Neurolology* Feb;60(2):223-8

Diabetes

Akyol, A., Kiylioglu, N., Bolukbasi, O., Guney, E., Yurekli, Y. (2003) Repeated hypoglycemia and cognitive decline. A case report. *Neuroendocrinol Lett.* Feb-Apr;24(1-2):54-6.

Blass, J. P., Gibson, G. E., Hoyer, S. (2002) The role of the metabolic lesion in Alzheimer's disease. *J Alzheimer's Dis.* Jun;4(3):225-32.

Resveratrol

Sun, A. Y., Draczynska-Lusiak, B., Sun, G. Y. (2001) Oxidized lipoproteins, beta amyloid peptides and Alzheimer's disease. *Neurotox Res.* Apr;3(2):167-78.

Draczynska-Lusiak, B., Doung, A., Sun, A. Y. (1998) Oxidized lipoproteins may play a role in neuronal cell death in Alzheimer's disease. *Mol Chem Neuropathol.* Feb;33(2):139-48.

Sharma, M., Gupta, Y. K. (2002) Chronic treatment with trans resveratrol prevents intracerebroventricular streptozotocin induced cognitive impairment and oxidative stress in rats. *Life Sci.* Oct 11;71(21):2489-98.

Tredici, G., Miloso, M., Nicolini, G., Galbiati, S., Cavaletti, G., Bertelli, A. (1999) Resveratrol, map kinases and neuronal cells: Might wine be a neuroprotectant? 25(2-3):99-103.

Lu, R., Serrero, G. (1999) Resveratrol, a natural product derived from grape, exhibits antiestrogenic activity and inhibits the growth of human breast cancer cells. *Cell Journal of Physiology* Jun;179(3):297-304

Chervil

Zwaving, J. H., Smith, D., Bos, R. (1971) The essential oil of chervil, *Anthriscus cerefolium* (L.) Hoffm. Isolation of 1-allyl-2,4-dimethoxybenzene. *Pharm Weekbl.* Mar 19;106(12):182-9.

Fejes, S., Blazovics, A., Lemberkovics, E., Petri, G., Szoke, E., Kery, A., Nymex, A., Hill, W. (2000) Free radical scavenging and membrane protective effects of methanol extracts from *Anthriscus cerefolium* L. (Hoffm.) and Petroselinum crispum(Mill.). *Phytother Res.* Aug;14(5):362-5.

Fejes, S., Blazovics, A., Lugasi, A., Lemberkovics, E., Petri, G., Kery, A. (2000) In vitro antioxidant activity of *Anthriscus cerefolium* L. (Hoffm.) extracts. *J Ethnopharmacol.* Mar;69(3):259-65.

Cohosh

Castelman, M. (1991) *The Healing Herbs.* Emmaus, PA., Rodale Press, pp. 75-78

Schoenberger, C. (1998) Materia Medica. *Carolina J. Pharm.,* 78(May-June), 14-15

Foster, S., Tyler, V. E. (1999) *Tyler's Honest Herbal. A Sensible Guide to the use of Herbs and Related Remedies,* 4th edition, Binghamton, NY, The Haworth Press, pp. 51-53

Celery

Tsi, D., Das, N. P., Tan, B. K. (1995) Effects of aqueous celery *(Apium graveolens)* extract on lipid parameters of rats fed a high fat diet. *Planta Med.* Feb;61(1):18-21.

Bromelain

Gutfreund, A. E., Taussig, S. J., Morris, A. K. (1978) Effect of oral bromelain on blood pressure and heart rate of hypertensive patients. *Hawaii Med J* 37:143–46

Kelly, G. S. (1996) Bromelain: A literature review and discussion of its therapeutic applications. *Alt Med Rev* 1:243–57

Heinicke, R. M., VanderWal, M., Yokoyama, M. M. (1972) Effect of Bromelain on Human Platelet Aggregation. *Experientia.* 28:844-45.

Somomen, S., et al. (1983) Impairment of memory function by hypertensive medication. *Archives of General Psychiatry* 40:1109-1112.

Ghosh, S. (1976) Methyldopa and Forgetfulness, *Lancet* 1:202-203.

Cahn, J., Borzeix, M. (1983) Aging and hypertension as risk factors for the brain related to free radical damages to membranes. *Aging* 23:413-425.

Douglas, M., et al. (1985) Effects of a raw food diet on hypertension and obesity. *Southern Medical Journal* 78(8):841.

Fioravanti, M., Agazzani, D. et al. (1991) Relationship between hypertension and early indicators of cognitive decline. *Dementia* 2(1):51 56.

Elias, M., Wolf, P., D'Agostino, R., Cobb, J., White, L. (1993) Untreated blood pressure level is inversely related to cognitive functioning: The Framingham Study. *American Journal of Epidemiology* 138(6):353 64.

Farmer, M., Kittner, S. et al. (1990) Longitudinally measured blood pressure, antihypertensive medication use, and cognitive performance: The Framingham Study. *Journal of Clinical Epidemiology* 43(5): 475 80.

Steunberg, G. (1991) Cough Syrup and Stroke *Longevity*. May

Madden, D. J. Blumenthal, J. A. (1989) Slowing of memory-search performance in men with mild hypertension. *Health Psychol* 8:131-142.

Douglas, J., et al. (1985) The effects of a raw food diet on hypertension and obesity. *Southern Medical Journal* 78(7):841.

Chapter 14: A Whack on the Head

Kra, S. (1986) Subdural hematomas. *Aging Myths*. p202.

Robinson, R. (1984) Chronic subdural hematoma: Surgical management in 133 patients. *Journal of Neurosurgery* 61(2):263 8.

Tsuboi, K., Maki, Y., Nose, T., Matsuki, T. (1984) Psychiatric symptoms of patients with chronic subdural hematoma. *Neurological Surgery* 12(3 Suppl):275 9.

Rimel, R., Giordani, B., Barth, J., Jane, J. (1982) Moderate head injury: Completing the clinical spectrum of brain trauma. *Neurosurgery* 11(3):344 51.

Chapter 15: Depression and Memory

Kra, S. (1986) *Aging Myths: Reversible Causes of Mind and Memory Loss,* McGraw-Hill, NY, p51.

Sabelli, H (1996) J. Neuropsychiatry. *Clin. Neuroscience* 8:168-171.

Croog, S., et al. (1986) The Effects of Antihypertensive Therapy on the Quality of Life, *New England Journal of Medicine* 314:165-1664, 1986.

Hibbeln, J. R., Salem, N. Jr. (1995) Dietary polyunsaturated fatty acids and depression: When cholesterol does not satisfy. *Am J Clin Nutr.* Jul;62(1):1-9

Biopterin

Morar, C., Whitburn, S. B., Blair, J. A., Leeming, R. J., Wilcock, G. K. (1983) Tetrahydrobiopterin metabolism in senile dementia of Alzheimer's type. *J Neurol Neurosurg Psychiatry.* Jun;46(6):582. Related

Blair, J. A., et al. (1984) Tetrahydrobiopterin metabolism in depression. *Lancet.* Jul 21;2(8395):163.

Hull, M., Pasinetti, G. M., Aisen, P. S. (2000) Elevated plasma neopterin levels in Alzheimer's disease. *Alzheimer Dis Assoc Disord.* Oct-Dec; 14(4):228-30.

Cattell, R. J., Hamon, C. G., Corbett, J. A., Lejeune, J., Blair, J. A. (1989) Neopterin: biopterin ratios in Down's syndrome. *J Neurol Neurosurg Psychiatry.* Aug; 52(8):1015-6

Hamon, C. G., Cattell, R. J., Wright, C. E., Wychrij, O., Blair, J. A., Harding, G. F. (1988) Visual evoked potentials and neopterin: biopterin ratios in urine show a high correlation in Alzheimer's disease. *J Neurol Neurosurg Psychiatry.* Feb; 51(2):314-5.

Hamon, C. G., Blair, J. A. (1987) Pathogenesis of Alzheimer's disease. *J R Soc Med.* Feb;80(2):127-9.

Hamon, C. G., Blair, J. A., Barford, P. A. (1986) The effect of tetrahydrofolate on tetrahydrobiopterin metabolism. *J Ment Defic Res.* Jun;30 (Pt 2):179-83.

Aziz, A. A., Leeming, R. J., Blair, J. A. (1983) Tetrahydrobiopterin metabolism in senile dementia of Alzheimer's type. *J Neurol Neurosurg Psychiatry.* May; 46(5):410-3

Kay, A. D., Milstien, S., Kaufman, S., Creasey, H., Haxby, J. V., Cutler, N. R., Rapoport, S. I. (1986) Cerebrospinal fluid biopterin is decreased in Alzheimer's disease. *Arch Neurol.* Oct; 43(10):996-9.

Barford, P. A., Blair, J. A., Eggar, C., Hamon, C., Morar, C., Whitburn, S. B. (1984) Tetrahydrobiopterin metabolism in the temporal lobe of patients dying with senile dementia of Alzheimer's type. *J Neurol Neurosurg Psychiatry.* Jul;47(7):736-8.

Leeming, R. J. (1981) The role of tetrahydrobiopterin in neurological disease: A review. *J Ment Defic Res.* Dec;25 Pt 4:231-41.

SAMe

Delle Chiaie, R., Pancheri, P., Scapicchio, P. (2002) Efficacy and tolerability of oral and intramuscular S-adenosyl-L-methionine 1,4-butanedisulfonate (SAMe) in the treatment of major depression: Comparison with imipramine in 2 multi-center studies. *Am J Clin Nutr.* Nov;76(5):1172S-6S

EPA

Puri, B. K., Counsell, S. J., Hamilton, G., Richardson, A. J., Horrobin, D. F. (2001) Ecosapentaenoic acid in treatment-resistant depression associated with symptom remission, structural brain changes and reduced neuronal phospholipid turnover. *Int J Clin Pract* Oct;55(8):560-3

St John's Wort

Cott, J. M., Rosenthal, N., Blumenthal, M. (2001) St John's Wort and major depression. *JAMA.* Jul 4;286(1):42; author reply 44-5.

Tatum, P., Lindbloom, E. J. (2001) Is St. John's Wort an effective treatment for major depression? *J Fam Pract.* Jul;50(7):624.

Hoffmann, J., Kuhl, E. (1979). Therapie von depressiven Zust-anden mit Hypericin (Treatment of depressive conditions with Hypericin). *Z. Allgemeinmed* 12:776 782.

Morauoni, P., Bombardellie, F. (1994). Hypericum perforatum. *Indona*. Milan, Italy.

Hobbs, C. (1988). St. John's Wort: A Review. *HerbalGram* No. 18 19.

Harrer, G., Sommel, H. (1994).Treatment of mild/moderate depressions with Hypericum. *Phytomedicine;* 1:3 8.

Depression

Wood, Debbie. (1996) Professor's research finds link with memory and depression. *Kansas State Collegian* Wednesday, October 23.

Svaldi, Jennifer J., Mackinger, Herbert F. (2003) Obstructive sleep apnea syndrome: Autobiographical memory predicts the course of depressive affect after nCPAP therapy. *Scandinavian Journal of Psychology* Vol. 44 Issue 1 Page 31 February

Depression and Amygdala

Siegle, G. J., et al. (2002) Can't shake that feeling: Event-related fMRI assessment of sustained amygdala activity in response to emotional information in depressed individuals. *Biological Psychiatry.* May 1;51(9):693-707.

Siegle, G. J. (1999) A neural network model of attention biases in depression. *Prog Brain Res.* 121:407-32.

Abercrombie, H. C., Schaefer, S. M., Larson, C. L., Oakes, T. R., Lindgren, K. A., Holden, J. E., Perlman, S. B., Turski, P. A., Krahn, D. D., Benca, R. M., Davidson, R. J. (1998) Metabolic rate in the right amygdala predicts negative affect in depressed patients. *Neuroreport*, 9:3301-3307.

Baker, S. C., Frith, C. D., Dolan, R. J. (1997): The interaction between mood and cognitive function studied with PET. *Psychological Medicine,* 27:565-578.

Baxter, L. R,. Schwartz, J. M., Phelps, M. E., Mazziotta, J. C., Guze, B. H., Selin, C. E., Gerner, R. H., Sumida, R. M. (1989) Reduction of prefrontal glucose metabolism common to three types of depression. *Archives of General Psychiatry* 46:243-250.

Melton, L. (2004) Aching atrophy. More than unpleasant, chronic pain shrinks the brain. *Sci Am.* Jan; 290(1):22-4

Grachev, I. D., Fredrickson, B. E., Apkarian, A. V. (2000) Abnormal brain chemistry in chronic back pain: An in vivo proton magnetic resonance spectroscopy study. Dec 15;89(1):7-18.

Liao, Y. C., Liu, R. S., Lee, Y. C., Sun, C. M., Liu, C. Y., Wang, P. S., Wang, P. N., Liu, H. C. (2003) Selective hypoperfusion of anterior cingulate gyrus in depressed AD patients: A brain SPECT finding by statistical parametric mapping. *Dement Geriatr Cogn Disord.* 16(4): 238-44

STX

Qiu, J., Bosch, M, A., Tobias, S. C., Grandy, D. K., Scanlan, T. S., Ronnekleiv, O. K., Kelly, M. J. (2003) Rapid signaling of estrogen in hypothalamic neurons involves a novel G-protein-coupled estrogen receptor that activates protein kinase C. *J Neurosci.* Oct 22;23(29):9529-40.

Chapter 16: Hormones and Memory

McGaugh, J. (1983) Preserving the presence of the past: Hormonal influences on memory storage. *American Psychologist* 38(2) 161 173.

McGaugh, J. (1983) Hormonal influences on memory. *Annual review of Psychology* 34: 297-324.

Vasopressin

Diaz, Brinton R. (1998) Vasopressin in the mammalian brain: The neurobiology of a mnemonic peptide, *Prog Brain Res* 119:177-99

Diaz, Brinton R. (1998) Vasopressin metabolites: a link between vasopressin and memory? *Prog Brain Res* 119:523-35

Legros (1978) Influence of vasopressin on memory and learning. *Lancet* 7 Jan:41.

Minninger, Joan (1984) *Total Recall,* Ballantine p91.

Oliveros et al. (1978) Vasopressin and Amnesia. *Lancet,* 7 Jan:42.

DHEA

Flood, J., et al. (1988) Dehydroepiandrosterone and its sulfate enhance memory retention in mice. *Brain Research* 447:269 278.

Rudman. D., et al. (1990) Plasma dehydroepiandrosterone sulfate in nursing home men. *J. American Geriatric Soc.* 35: 421 427.

Bologa, L., et al. (1987) Dehydroepiandrosterone and its sulfated derivative reduce neuronal death and enhance astrocytic differentiation in brain cell cultures. *J. Neuroscoience Research* 17:225 234.

Roberts, E., et al. (1987) Effects of dehydroepiandrosterone and its sulfate on brain tissue in culture and on memory in mice. *Brain Research* 406:357 362.

Flood, J. F., Roberts, E. (1988) Dehydroepiandrosterone sulfate improves memory in aging mice. *Brain Res* 448(1):178-181.

Nasman, B., Olsson, T., Backstron, T., Eriksson, S., Grankvist, K., Viitanen, M., Bucht, G. (1991) Serum dehydroepiandrosterone sulfate in Alzheimer's disease and in multi-infarct dementia. *Biol Psychiatry* 30(7):684-690.

Melatonin

Sharma, M., Gupta, Y. K. (2001) Effect of chronic treatment of melatonin on learning, memory and oxidative deficiencies induced by intracerebroventricular streptozotocin in rats. *Pharmacol Biochem Behav* Oct;70(2-3):325-31

Magri, F., Locatelli, M., Balza, G., Molla, G., Cuzzoni, G., Fioravanti, M., et. al. (1997) Changes in endocrine circadian rhythms as markers of physiological and pathological brain aging. *Chronobiol Int* 14(4):385-396.

Maurizi, C. P. (1995) The mystery of Alzheimer's disease and its prevention by melatonin. *Med Hypotheses* 45(4): 339-340.

Maurizi, C. P. (1997) Loss of intraventricular fluid melatonin can explain the neuropathology of Alzheimer's disease. *Med Hypotheses* 49(2):153-158.

Pappolla, M., Bozner, P., Soto, C., Shao, H., Robakis, N. K., Zagorski, M., Frangione, B., Ghiso, J. (1998) Inhibition of Alzheimer's beta-Fibrillogenesis by Melatonin. *J Biol Chem* Mar 27;273(13):7185-7188

Poeggeler, B., Reiter, R. J., Tan, D. X., Chen, L. D., Manchester, L. C. (1993) Melatonin, hydroxyl radical-mediated oxidative damage, and aging: A hypothesis. *J Pineal Res.* May;14(4):151-68.

Maurizi, C. P. (2001) Alzheimer's disease: Roles for mitochondrial damage, the hydroxyl radical, and cerebrospinal fluid deficiency of melatonin. *Med Hypotheses.* Aug;57(2):156-60.

Brown, G. M., Young, S. N., Gauthier, S., Tsui, H., Grota, L. J. (1979) Melatonin in human cerebrospinal fluid in daytime; Its origin and variation with age. *Life Sci.* Sep 11;25(11):929-36.

Pierpaoli, W., Regelson, W. (1994) Pineal control of aging: Effect of melatonin and pineal grafting on aging mice. *Proc Natl Acad Sci U S A.* Jan 18;91(2):787-91.

Pierpaoli, W., Dall'Ara, A., Pedrinis, E., Regelson, W. (1991) The pineal control of aging. The effects of melatonin and pineal grafting on the survival of older mice. *Ann N Y Acad Sci.* 621:291-313. No abstract available.

Trentini, G. P., De Gaetani, C., Criscuolo, M. (1991) Pineal gland and aging. *Aging* (Milano). Jun;3(2):103-16.

Armstrong, S. M., Redman, J. R. (1991) Melatonin: A chronobiotic with anti-aging properties? *Med Hypotheses.* Apr;34(4):300-9.

Reiter, R. J. (1992) The ageing pineal gland and its physiological consequences. *Bioessays.* Mar;14(3):169-75.

Tohgi, H., Abe, T., Takahashi, S., Takahashi, J., Hamato, H. (1992) Concentrations of serotonin and its related substances in the cerebro-spinal fluid in patients with Alzheimer's type dementia. *Neurosci. Lett.* 141:9 12

Scaccianoce, S., Alema, S., Cigliana, G., Navarra, D., Ramacci, M. T., Angelucci, L. (1991) Pituitary adrenocortical and pineal activities in the aged rat. *Ann. N.Y. Acad. Sci.* 621:256 261

Guerrero J. M. (1993) Antioxidant capacity of melatonin: A novel action not requiring a receptor. *Neuroendocrinol.* Lett. 15:103 116

Dawson, D., Encel, N., (1993) Melatonin and sleep in humans *J Pineal Res* 15:1 12

Thyroid

McGaugh, J. L. (1983) Preserving the presence of the past. Hormonal influences on memory storage. *Am Psychol.* Feb;38(2):161-74.

Gould, E., Wooley, C. S., McEwen, B. S. (1991) The hippocampal formation: Morphological changes induced by thryoid, gonadal and adrenal hormones. *Psychoneuroendocrinol* 16(1-3):67-84.

Boillet, D., Szoke, A. (1998) Psychiatric manifestations as the only clinical sign of hypothyroidism. Apropos of a case. [French] *Encephale* 24(1):65-8.

Prinz, P. N., Scanlan, J. M., Vialiano, P. P., Moe, K. E., Borson, S., Toivola, B., Merriuam, G. R., Larsen, L. H., Reed, H. L. (1999) Thyroid hormones: Positive relationships with cognition in healthy, euthyroid older men. *J Gerontol A Biol Sci Med Sci* 54(3):M111-6.

Wahlin, A., Wahlin, T. B., Small, B. J., Backman, L. (1998) Influences of thyroid stimulating hormone on cognitive functioning in very old age. *J Gerontol B Psychol Sci Soc Sci* 53(4):P234-9.

Baldinia, I. M., Vita, A., Mauri, M. C., Amodei, V., Carrisi, M., Bravin, S., Cantalamessa, L. (1997) Psychopathological and cognitive features in subclinical hypothyroidism. *Prog Neuropsychopharmacol Biol Psychiatry* 21(6):925-35.

Cortisol

Kirschbaum, C., Wolf, O. T., May, M., Wippich, W., Hellhammer, D. H. (1996) Stress- and treatment-induced elevations of cortisol levels associated with impaired declarative memory in healthy adults. *Life Sci* 58(17):1475-1483

Lupien, S. J., Gaudreau, S., Tchiteya, B. M., Maheu, F., Sharma, S., Naier, N. P., et. al. (1997) Stress-induced declarative memory impairment in healthy elderly subjects: Relationship to cortisol reactivity. *J Clin Endocrinol Metab* 82(7):2070-5.

Testosterone

Moffat, S. D., et al. (2002) Longitudinal Assessment of Serum Free Testosterone Concentration Predicts Memory Performance and Cognitive Status in Elderly Men. *The Journal of Clinical Endocrinology & Metabolism,* 87 (11): 5001-5007.

Pregnenolone

Darnaudery, M., Koehl, M., Piazza, P. V., Le Moal, M., Mayo, W. (2000) Pregnenolone sulfate increases hippocampal acetylcholine release and spatial recognition. *Brain Research* Jan 3;852(1):173-9.

Mayo, W., et al. Individual differences in cognitive aging: Implication of pregnenolone sulfate. *Prog Neurobiol.* 2003 Sep;71(1):43-8.

ACTH

Smolnik, R., Perras, B., Molle, M., Fehm, H. L., Born, J. Event-related brain potentials and working memory function in healthy humans after single-dose and prolonged intranasal administration of adrenocorticotropin 4-10 and desacetyl-alpha-melanocyte stimulating hormone. *J Clin Psychopharmacol.* 2000 Aug;20(4):445-54.

de Wied, D., van Ree, J. M. Neuropeptides: Animal behaviour and human psychopathology. *Eur Arch Psychiatry Neurol Sci.* 1989;238(5-6):323-31.

Isoflavonesi

Kritz-Silverstein, D., Von Muhlen, D., Barrett-Connor, E., Bressel, M. A. Isoflavones and cognitive function in older women: the Soy and Postmenopausal Health In Aging (SOPHIA) Study. *Menopause.* 2003 May-Jun;10(3):196-202.

Cushing's

Starkman, M. N., Giordani, B., Gebarski, S. S., Schteingart, D. E. (2003) Improvement in learning associated with increase in hippocampal formation volume. *Biological Psychiatry.* Feb 1;53(3):233-8

Chapter 17: Medications and Memory

Greenblatt, D., et al. (1982) Drug Disposition in Old Age. *New England Journal of. Medicine* 306:1081 1088,

Williams, P., and Rush, D. (1986) Geriatric Polypharmacy. *Hospital Practice* Feb. 15.

Mangini, Richard J., ed. (1986) *Drug Interaction Facts,* Lippincott, St. Louis.

Pearson, M. (1985) Prescribing for the elderly Can. audit. *The Practitioner* 229:85 86, 1985.

Williamson, J., Chopin, J. (1980) Adverse Reactions to Prescribed Drugs in the Elderly: A multi-centre investigation. *Age and Ageing* 9:7380.

Farley, Dixie. Protecting the elderly from medication misuse. *FDA Consumer* 20(8):2831, 1986.

Morris, H. H. 3rd, Estes, M. L. (198) Traveler's amnesia. Transient global amnesia secondary to triazolam. *JAMA.* 7 Aug 21;258(7):945-6.

Kiyingi, K. (1993) How much do outpatients know about drugs prescribed to them? A pilot study. *PNG Med Journal* 36(1):29 32.

Kra, S. (1986) *Aging Myths: Reversible Causes of Mind and Memory Loss,* McGraw-Hill, NY, p169.

Goodwin, F. (1991) Diazepam and memory loss. *JAMA, Journal of the American Medical Association* August 28 266(1):1056

[No authors listed] Cimetidine (Tagamet): (1978) Update on Adverse Effects. *Med Let.* 20:77 78.

Schentag, J., et al. (1979) Pharmacokinetic and clinical studies in patients with cimetidine associated mental confusion. *Lancet* 1:177 181.

Basavaraju, N. (1980) Cimetidine induced mental confusion in the elderly. *New York State J. Med.,* July 1287 1288.

Van Sweden, B., Kamphusen, H. (1984) Cimetidine neurotoxicity. *Neurol.* 23:300-305.

Cerra, Frank B., et al. (1982) Mental Status, the intensive care unit, and cimetidine. *Annals of Surgery* 196:565-570.

Mani, R. (1984) H2 Receptor blockers and mental confusion. *Lancet* 2:98.

Fisher, C. (1992) Amnestic syndrome associated with propranolol toxicity: A case report. *Clinical Neuropharmacology,* 15 (5): 397 403.

Ghosh, S. (1976) Methyldopa and forgetfulness. *Lancet* 1:202 203.

Aminoguanidine

Munch, G., et al. (1997) Influence of advanced glycation end-products and AGE-inhibitors on nucleation-dependent polymerization of beta-amyloid peptide. *Biochim Biophys Acta.* Feb 27;1360(1):17-29.

Munch, G., Taneli, Y., Schraven, E., Schindler, U., Schinzel, R., Palm, D., Riederer, P. (1994) The cognition-enhancing drug tenilsetam is an inhibitor of protein crosslinking by advanced glycosylation. *J Neural Transm Park Dis Dement Sect.* 8(3):193-208.

Propentofylline

Frampton, M., Harvey, R. J., Kirchner, V. (2004) Propentofylline for Dementia. *Cochrane Review: The Cochrane Library,* Issue 1, Chichester, UK: John Wiley & Sons, Ltd.

Chapter 18: Neurotoxins and Memory

Commitee on Science & Technology. (1989) *Neurotoxins at Home and the Workplace.* U.S Government Printing Office, Washington, DC

Warren, T.(1991) *Beating Alzheimer's,* Avery Publishing Group, Garden City Park, NY

Aspartame

Davoli, E., et al. (1986) Serum Methanol Concentrations in Rats and in Men After a Single Dose of Aspartame. *Food and Chemical Toxicology,* Volume 24, No. 3, page 187-189.

Lawrence, J. F., Iyengar, J. R. (1987). Liquid Chromatographic Determination of Beta-Aspartame in Diet Soft Drinks, Beverage Powders and Pudding Mixes, *Journal of Chromatography,* Volume 404, page 261-266.

Monte, Woodrow C. (1984). Aspartame: Methanol and the Public Health. *Journal of Applied Nutrition,* Volume 36, NO. 1, page 42-54.

Stamp, Jeffrey A., Labuza, Theodore P. (1989a). An Ion-Pair High Performance Liquid Chromatographic Method for the Determination of Aspartame and its Decomposition Products. *Journal of Food Science,* volume 54, NO. 4, pg. 1043-1046.

Stegink, Lewis D., et al. (1987a) Plasma Amino Acid Concentrations in Normal Adults Administered Aspartame in Capsules or Solution: Lack of Bioequivalence. *Metabolism,* Volume 36, NO. 5, page 507-512.

Stegink, Lewis D., et al. (1987b) Plasma Amino Acid Concentrations in Normal Adults Ingesting Aspartame and Monosodium L-Glutamate as Part of a Soup/Beverage Meal. *Metabolism,* Volume 36, No. 11, page 1073-1079.

Tsang, Wing-Sum, et al. (1985) Determination of Aspartame and Its Breakdown Products in Soft Drinks by Reverse-Phase Chromatography with UV Detection. *Journal Agriculture and Food Chemistry,* Vol 33, No. 4, page 734-738

Alcohol

Bleich, S., Bandelow, B., Javaheripour, K., Muller, A., Degner, D., Wilhelm, J., Havemann-Reinecke, U., Sperling, W., Ruther, E., Kornhuber, J. (2003) Hyperhomocystinemia as a new risk factor for brain shrinkage in patients with alcoholism. *Neurosci Lett.* Jan 2;335(3):179-82

Harper, C., Kril, J. (1985) Brain atrophy in chronic alcoholic patients: a quantitative pathological study. *Neurol Neurosurg Psychiatry.* Mar; 48(3):211-7.

Jingzhong, Ding, et al. (2004) Alcohol Intake and Cerebral Abnormalities on Magnetic Resonance Imaging in a Community-Based Population of Middle-Aged Adults The Atherosclerosis Risk in Communities (ARIC) Study. *Stroke.* 35:16.

Horrobin, D. (1980) A biochemical basis for alcoholism and alcohol induced damage including the fetal alcohol syndrome and cirrhosis: Interference with essential fatty acids and prostaglandin metabolism. *Medical Hypothesis* 6:929:942.

Forander (1958) *Quarterly Journal of Studies on Alcohol* 19:379.

Kanazawa, S., Herbert, V. (1985) Total corinoid cobalamin (vitamin B12) and cobalamin analogue levels may be normal in serum despite cobalamin in liver depletion in patients with alcoholism. *Lab Investigation* 53(1):108-110.

Leo, M., Lieber, C. (1983) Interaction of ethanol with vitamin A.

Garrett-Laster, M. (1984) Impairment of taste and olfaction in patients with cirrhosis: The role of vitamin A. *Human Nutrition: Clinical Nutrition* 38C:203-214.

Lieber, C. (1983) Alcohol Nutrition Interaction. *Contemporary Nutrition.* Dec.

Lowe. (1987) Combined effects of nicotine and caffeine on state dependent learning. *Medical Science Research* 15: 25 26

Majumdar, S. (1981) Vitamin utilization status in chronic alcoholics. *International Journal of Vitamin and Nutrition Research* 51(1):54-58.

Thompson, A., Majumdar, S. (1981) The influence of ethanol on intestinal absorption and utilization of nutrients.

Majundar, S. (1983) Vitamin A Utilization Status in Chronic Alcoholic Patients. *International Journal of Vitamin and Nutrition Research* 53(3):273-279.

Sherlock, S. (1984) Nutrition and the Alcoholic. *Lancet* 1:436-438.

Mercury

Queen, H. (1988) *Chronic Mercury Toxicity.* Queen & Co.

Lead

Heffley, James. (2003) To Your Health, *Austin Chronicle* Oct 10th. http://www.austinchronicle. com/issues/dispatch /2003-10-10/cols_health.html

McCafferty, Peter et al, (1995) Lead contamination in Perth drinking water. *Chemistry in Australia,* August

Hodge, M. (1991) Getting the lead out. *Longevity,* May p14.(1989)

Farmanfarmanaian, R. (1990) Lead's new hideout: Fast food brews. *Longevity* Jun. p15.

Mold

Anyanwu, E., Campbell, A. W., Jones, J., Ehiri, J. E., Akpan, A. I. (2003) The neurological significance of abnormal natural killer cell activity in chronic toxigenic mold exposures. *Scientific World Journal.* Nov 13;3(11):1128-37

Tin

Corrigan, F. M., Van Rhijn, A. G., Ijomah, G., McIntyre, F., Skinner, E. R., Horrobin, D. F., Ward, N. I. (1991) Tin and fatty acids in dementia. *Prostaglandins Leukot Essent Fatty Acids.* Aug;43(4):229-38.

Corrigan, F. M., Crichton, J. S., Ward, N. I., Horrobin, D. F. (1992) Blood tin concentrations in Alzheimer's disease. *Biol Psychiatry.* Apr 1;31(7):749-50.

Aluminum

Bolla, K. (1993) Neurocognitive effects of aluminum. *Archives of Neurology* 49:1021 1026

Bjorkstein, J., Yaeger, L. L., Wallace, T. (1988) Control of aluminum ingestion and its relation to longevity. *Int J Vitam Nutr Res.* 58(4):462-5

Markesbery, W., Ehmann, W. (1993) Brain trace elements in Alzheimer's disease. *Alzheimer's Disease.* pp. 353-367. New York, NY: Raven Press, Green-Field Library Call number: WM 220 A4745 1993

Yumoto, S., Kakimi, S., Matsushima, H., et al. (1998) Demonstration of aluminum in the brain of patients with Alzheimer's disease. pp. 293-300. *Advances in Behavioral Biology,* volume 49.

Polizzi, S., Pira, E., Ferrara, M., Bugiani, M., Papaleo, A., Albera, R., Palmi, S. (2002) Neurotoxic effects of aluminium among foundry workers and Alzheimer's disease. *Neurotoxicology.* Dec;23(6):761-74

Domingo, J. et al. (1988) Citric, Malic and Succinic acid as possible alternatives to deferoxamine in aluminum toxicity. *Journal of Toxicology* 26(1-2):67-79

Cowburn, J. D., Blair, J. A. (1989) Aluminium chelator (transferrin) reverses biochemical deficiency in Alzheimer's brain preparations. *Lancet.* Jan 14;1(8629):99. Related Articles, Links

Storey, E., Masters, C. L. (1995) Amyloid, aluminium and the aetiology of Alzheimer's disease. *Med J Aust.* Sep 4;163(5):256-9

Atwood, C. S., Huang, X., Moir, R. D., Tanzi, R. E., Bush, A. I. (1999) Role of free radicals and metal ions in the pathogenesis of Alzheimer's disease. *Met Ions Biol Syst.* 36:309-64

Armstrong, R. A., Winsper, S. J., Blair, J. A. (1996) Aluminium and Alzheimer's disease: review of possible pathogenic mechanisms. *Dementia.* Jan-Feb;7(1):1-9.

Chang, L. (1985) Neuropathological effects of toxic metal ions, in Metal Ions. *Neurology and Psychiatry* Liss, A., ed. p207.

Marijuana

Marijuana mangles memory. v136 *Science News* Nov 18 136(1):332.

Loftis, Elizabeth (1980) Alcohol, Marijuana, and Memory. *Psychology Today,* March, pp42 56.

Diana, G., Malloni, M., Pieri, M. (2003) Effects of the synthetic cannabinoid nabilone on spatial learning and hippocampal neurotransmission. *Pharmacol Biochem Behav.* Jun;75(3):585-91.

Kishi, H., et al. (1975) Bioenergetics in clinical medicine. III. Inhibition of coenzyme Q10-enzymes by clinically used anti-hypertensive drugs. *Res Commun Chem Pathol Pharmacol* 12(3): 533-540,

Leirer, V., Yesavage, J., Morrow, D. (1991) Marijuana carry over effects on aircraft pilot performance. *Aviation Space and Environmental Medicine* 62(3):221 7.

Chapter 19: Free Radicals and Antioxidants

Keli, S. O., Hertog, M. G., Feskens, E. J., Kromhout, D. (1996) Dietary flavonoids, antioxidant vitamins, and incidence of stroke: the Zutphen study., Archives of Internal Medicine. Mar 25;156(6):637-42

Reuben, C. (1995) *Antioxidants: Your Complete Guide.* Prima Publishing

Free radicals in brain metabolism and pathology (1993) *British Medical Bulletin* 49:3;577 587

deJesus Greenberg, D. (1981) Hyperbaric Oxygen Therapy Critical Care Update 8(2) 8 20.

Hyperbaric Oxygen Therapy: A Committee Report, Feb. 1981. Under-sea medical Society, Inc. 9650 Rockville Pike, Bethesda Maryland 20014 (UMS Publication #30 CR(HBO)2 23 81).

Bjorksten, J. (1980) Possibilities and limitations of chelation as a means for life extension. *Rejuvenation* 8 67-72.

Chapter 20: Drugs That Improve Memory.

Bartus, R., Dean, R. (1981) Age related memory loss and drug therapy: Possible directions based on animal models. *Aging* 17:209-223.

Bylinski, G. (1986) Medicine's next marvel: The memory pill. *Fortune* Jan 20 p68-72.

Diamond, S., Bowers, E. (1976) Increase in the power of human memory in normal man through the use of drugs. *Psychopharmacology* 49:307 9.

Donaldson, T. (1984) Therapies to Improve Memory. *Anti Aging News* 4 no: 13 21.

Giurgia, C. (1973) The Nootropic Approach to the Pharmacology of the Integrative Activity of the Brain. *Conditioned Reflex* vol 8, no 2 p108-115.

Giurgia, C. (1980) A drug for the mind. *Chemtech* Jun p360-365.

Giurgia, C., Salama, M. (1977) Nootropic drugs. *Progress in Neuropsychopharmacology* (1):235-237.

Modafinil and Adrafinil

Jouvet, M., Albarede, J. L., Lubin, S., Meyrignac, C. (1991) Noradrenaline and cerebral aging. *Encephale.* May-Jun; 17(3):187-95

Centrophenoxine

Sharma, D., Singh, R. (1995) Centrophenoxine activates acetylcholinesterase activity in hippocampus of aged rats. *Indian J Exp Biol* May;33(5):365-8

Nandy, K. (1978) Centrophenoxine: Effects on aging mammalian brain. *J Am Ger Soc* 26, 74-81.

Zs-Nagy, I., Semsei, I. (1984) Centrophenoxine increases the rates of total and mRNA synthesis in the brain cortex of old rats: An explanation of its action in terms of the membrane hypothesis of aging. *Exp Gerontal* 19, 171-78.

Roy, D., Singh, R. (1988) Age-related change in the multiple unit activity of the rat brain parietal cortex and the effect of centrophenoxine. *Exp Gerontal* 23, 161-74.

Riga, S., Riga, D. (1974) Effects of centrophenoxine on the lipofuscin pigments in the nervous system of old rats. *Brain Res* 72, 265-75.

Fulop, T. Jr. et al. (1990) Effects of centrophenoxine on body composition and some biochemical parameters of demented elderly people. *Arch Gerontal Geriatr* 10, 239-51.

DMAE

Casey, D., Denny, D. (1979) Mood alterations During Deanol Therapy. *Psychopharmacology* 62: 187 91.

Ceder, G. (1978) Effects of 2-Dimethylamonoethanol (Deanol) on the metabolism of choline in Plasma. *Neurochemistry* 30::1293-1296.

Casey, D,. Denny, D. (1974) Dimethyl amino ethanol in tardive dyskinesia. *New England Journal of Medicine* 291:797.

Ansell, G. (1962) The Effects of 2-Dimehtylamono-ethanol on brain phospholipid metabolism. *Journal of Neurochemistry* 9:253-263.

Hydergine

Olin, J., Schneider, L., Novit, A., Luczak, S. (2003) Hydergine for dementia. *Cochrane Review. The Cochrane Library,* Issue 4. Chichester, UK: John Wiley & Sons, Ltd.

Copeland, R. (1981) Behavioral and neurochemical effects of Hydergine in rats. *Archives of International Pharmacodynamics* 252:113-123.

Emmenegger, H., Meier Ruge, W. (1968) The Actions of Hydergine on the Brain. *Pharmacology* 1 :65 78.

Exton-Smith, A. (1983) Clinical experience with ergot alkaloids. *Aging* 23:323.

Fanchamps, A. (1983) Dihidroergotoxin in senile Cerebral insufficiency. *Aging* 23:311322

Goldstien, et al, eds. (1980) *Ergot Compounds and Brain Function,* Raven Press.

Hindmarch, I. (1979) The effects of ergot alkaloid derivative (Hyder-gine) on aspects of psychomotor performance, arousal, and cognitive processing ability. *Journal of Clinical Pharmacology* Nov :726-731.

Sandoz (no date) Age related Mental Decline and Dementias: The Place for Hydergine Products. Literature Booklet.

Piracetam

Bartus, R. et al (1981) Profound effects of combining choline and piracetam on memory enhancement and cholinergic function in aged rats. *Neurobiology of Aging* 2:105-111.

Friedman, E. (1981) Clinical response to choline plus piracetam in senile dementia: Relation to red cell choline levels. *New England Journal of Medicine* 304 no 24, p1490-1491.

Ferris, S. (1982) Combination of Choline/Piracetam in the treatment of senile dementia. *Psychopharmacology Bulletin* vol 18 p94-98.

Buresova, O., Bures, J. (1976) Piracetam-induced facilitation of interhemispheric transfer of visual information in rats. *Psychopharmacologica* 46:93-102.

Chase, C. (1984) A new chemotherapeutic investigation: Piracetam effects on dyslexia. *Annals of Dyslexia* 34:667-673.

Dilanni, M. (1985) The Effects of Piracetam on Children with Dyslexia. *Journal of Clinical Pharmacology* vol 5, p272-278.

Dimov, S. et. al. (1982) Neurophysiological Analysis of Piracetam Effect on Memory Processes. *Behavioral Brain Research* 5, no.1:98 99.

LO59

Isoherranen, N., Yagen, B., Soback, S., Roeder, M., Schurig, V., Bialer, M. (2001) Pharmacokinetics of levetiracetam and its enantiomer(R)-alpha-ethyl-2-oxo-pyrrolidine acetamide in dogs. *Epilepsia*. Jul;42(7):825-30.

Birnstiel, S., Wulfert, E., Beck, S. G. (1997) Levetiracetam (ucb LO59) affects in vitro models of epilepsy in CA3 pyramidalneurons without altering normal synaptic transmission. *Naunyn Schmiedebergs Arch Pharmacol.* Nov;356(5):611-8.

Margineanu, D. G., Wulfert, E. (1997) Inhibition by levetiracetam of a non-GABAA receptor-associated epileptiform effect of bicuculline in rat hippocampus. *Br J Pharmacol.* Nov;122(6):1146-50.

L Dopa

Marini, P., Ramat, S., Ginestroni, A., Paganini, M.. (2003) Deficit of short-term memory in newly diagnosed untreated Parkinsonian patients: Reversal after L-dopa therapy. *Neurol Sci.* Oct;24(3):184-5.

Cools, R., Barker, R. A., Sahakian, B. J., Robbins, T. W. (2003) L-Dopa medication remediates cognitive inflexibility, but increases impulsivity in patients with Parkinson's disease. *Neuropsychologia.* 41(11):1431-41.

Kulisevsky, J. (2000) Role of dopamine in learning and memory: Implications for the treatment of cognitive dysfunction in patients with Parkinson's disease. *Drugs Aging.* May;16(5):365-79.

Cools, R., Barker, R. A., Sahakian, B. J., Robbins, T. W. (2001) Enhanced or impaired cognitive function in Parkinson's disease as a function of dopaminergic medication and task demands. *Cereb Cortex.* Dec;11(12):1136-43.

Oishi, M., Mochizuki, Y., Hara, M., Du, C. M., Takasu, T. (1996) Effects of intra-venous L-dopa on P300 and regional cerebral blood flow in Parkinsonism. *Int J Neurosci.* Mar;85(1-2):147-54.

Hietanen, M., Teravainen, H. (1988) Dementia and treatment with L-dopa in Parkinson's disease. *Mov Disord.* 3(3):263-70 .

Vinpocetine

Horvath, S. (2001) [The use of vinpocetine in chronic disorders caused by cerebral hypoperfusion] *Orv Hetil.* Feb 25;142(8):383-9. [Article in Hungarian]

Pepeu, G., Spignoli, G. (1989) Nootropic drugs and brain cholinergic mechanisms. *Prog Neuropsychopharmacol Biol Psychiatry.* 13 Suppl:S77-88.

Bhatti, J. Z., Hindmarch, I. (1987)Vinpocetine effects on cognitive impairments produced by flunitrazepam. *Int Clin Psychopharmacol.* Oct;2(4):325-31.

DeNoble, V. J. (1987) Vinpocetine enhances retrieval of a step-through passive avoidance response in rats. *Pharmacol Biochem Behav.* Jan;26(1):183-6.

Subhan, Z., Hindmarch, I. (1985) Psychopharmacological effects of vinpocetine in normal healthy volunteers. *Eur J Clin Pharmacol.* 28(5):567-71.

Clonidine

Denolle, T., Sassano, P., Allain, H., Bentue-Ferrer, D., Breton, S., Cimarosti, I., Ouatara, B., Merienne, M., Gandon, J. M. (2002) Effects of nicardipine and clonidine on cognitive functions and electroencephalography in hypertensive patients. *Fundam Clin Pharmacol.* Dec;16(6):527-35.

Bernstein, A. L., Werlin, A. (2003) Pseudodementia associated with use of ibuprofen. *Ann Pharmacother.* Jan;37(1):80-2.

Hall, J. E., Uhrich, T. D., Ebert, T. J.(2001) Sedative, analgesic and cognitive effects of clonidine infusions in humans. *Br J Anaesth.* Jan;86(1):5-11.

Riekkinen, M., Laakso, M. P., Jakala, P. (1999) Clonidine impairs sustained attention and memory in Alzheimer's disease. *Neuroscience.* 92(3):975-82.

Coull, J. T., Middleton, H. C., Robbins, T. W., Sahakian, B. J. (1995) Contrasting effects of clonidine and diazepam on tests of working memory and planning. *Psychopharmacology* (Berl). Aug;120(3):311-21.

O'Carroll, R. E., Moffoot, A., Ebmeier, K. P., Murray, C., Goodwin, G. M. (1993) Korsakoff's syndrome, cognition and clonidine. *Psychol Med.* May;23(2):341-7.

Fields, R. B., Van Kammen, D. P., Peters, J. L., Rosen, J., Van Kammen, W. B., Nugent, A., Stipetic, M., Linnoila, M. (1988) Clonidine improves memory function in schizophrenia independently from change in psychosis. Preliminary findings. *Schizophr Res.* Nov-Dec;1(6):417-23.

Bartus, R. T., Dean, R. L. (1988) Lack of efficacy of clonidine on memory in aged cebus monkeys. *Neurobiol Aging.* Jul-Aug;9(4):409-11.

Fein, G., Merrin, E. L., Davenport, L., Buffum, J. C. (1987) Memory deficits associated with clonidine. *Gen Hosp Psychiatry.* Mar;9(2):154-5. No abstract available.

Mair, R. G., McEntee, W. J. (1986) Cognitive enhancement in Korsakoff's psychosis by clonidine: A comparison with L-dopa and ephedrine. *Psychopharmacology* (Berl). 88(3):374-80.

Deprynyl

Gelowitz, D. L., Richardson, J. S., Wishart, T. B., et al. (1994) Chronic L-deprenyl or L-Amphetamine: Equal Cognitive Enhancement, Unequal MAO Inhibition, *Pharmacology Biochemistry and Behavior,* 47:41-45,

Tipton, K. (1994) What is it that l deprenyl (selegiline) might do? *Clin Pharmacol Ther* 56(6 Pt 2):781 96

Head, E., Hartley, J., Kameka, A. M., et al. (1996) The effects of L-deprenyl on spatial, short term memory in memory in young and aged dogs. *Progress in Neuropsychopharmacology & Biological Psychiatry,* 20 : 3:515-530, April

Phosphatidylserine

McDaniel, M. A., Maier, S. F., Einstein, G. O. (2003) "Brain-specific" nutrients: a memory cure? *Nutrition.* Nov-Dec;19(11-12):957-75.

Jorissen, B. L., Brouns, F., Van Boxtel, M. P., Ponds, R. W., Verhey, F. R., Jolles, J., Riedel, W. J. (2001) The influence of soy-derived phosphatidylserine on cognition in age-associated memory impairment. *Nutr Neurosci.* 4(2):121-34.

Suzuki, S., Yamatoya, H., Sakai, M., Kataoka, A., Furushiro, M., Kudo, S. (2001) Oral administration of soybean lecithin transphosphatidylated phosphatidylserine improves memory impairment in aged rats. *J Nutr.* Nov;131(11):2951-6.

Schreiber, S., Kampf-Sherf, O., Gorfine, M., Kelly, D., Oppenheim, Y., Lerer, B. (2000) An open trial of plant-source derived phosphatydilserine for treatment of age-related cognitive decline. *Isr J Psychiatry Relat Sci.* 37(4):302-7.

Alves, C. S., Andreatini, R., da Cunha, C., Tufik, S., Vital, M. A. (2000) Phosphatidylserine reverses reserpine-induced amnesia. *Eur J Pharmacol.* Sep 15;404(1-2):161-7.

Kidd, P. M. (1999) A review of nutrients and botanicals in the integrative management of cognitive dysfunction. *Altern Med Rev.* Jun;4(3):144-61. Review.

Khalsa, D. S. (1998) Integrated medicine and the prevention and reversal of memory loss. Nov;4(6):38-43. Review.

Nunzi, M. G., Guidolin, D., Petrelli, L., Polato, P., Zanotti, A. (1992) Behavioral and morpho-functional correlates of brain aging: A preclinical study with phosphatidylserine. *Adv Exp Med Biol.* 318:393-8.

Crook, T. H., Tinklenberg, J., Yesavage, J., Petrie, W., Nunzi, M. G., Massari, D. C. (1991) Effects of phosphatidylserine in age-associated memory impairment. *Neurology.* May;41(5):644-9.

Fagioli, S., Castellano, C., Oliverio, A., Pavone, F., Populin, R., Toffano, G. (1989) Phosphatidylserine administration during postnatal development improves memory in adult mice. *Neurosci Lett.* Jun 19;101(2):229-33.

Amaducci, L., Crook, T. H., Lippi, A., Bracco, L., Baldereschi, M., Latorraca, S., Piersanti, P., Tesco, G., Sorbi, S. (1991) Use of phosphatidylserine in Alzheimer's disease. *Ann N Y Acad Sci.* 640:245-9.

Gutfeld, G.(1991) Memory pills finally! Exciting new research promises the chance of regenerating failing memory banks. (phosphatidylserine may improve memory) *Prevention* August v43 p40(4)

Quinones

Yamada, K., Tanaka, T., Han, D., Senzaki, K., Kameyama, T., Nabeshima, T. (1999) Protective effects of idebenone and alpha-tocopherol on beta-amyloid-(1-42)-induced learning and memory deficits in rats: Implication of oxidative stress in beta-amyloid-induced neurotoxicity in vivo. *Eur J Neurosci.* Jan;11(1):83-90.

Gillis, J. C., Benefield, P., McTavish, D. (1994) Idebenone. A review of its pharmacodynamic and pharmacokinetic properties, and therapeutic use in age-related cognitive disorders. *Drugs Aging.* Aug;5(2):133-52.

Bergamasco, B., Scarzella, L., La Commare, P. (1994) Idebenone, a new drug in the treatment of cognitive impairment in patients with dementia of the Alzheimer type. *Funct Neurol.* May-Jun;9(3):161-8.

Nitta, A., Murakami, Y., Furukawa, Y., Kawatsura, W., Hayashi, K., Yamada, K., Hasegawa, T., Nabeshima, T. (1994) Oral administration of idebenone induces nerve growth factor in the brain and improves learning and memory in basal forebrain-lesioned rats. *Naunyn Schmiedebergs Arch Pharmacol.* Apr;349(4):401-7.

Karaev, A. L., Smirnova, T. N., Avakumov, V. M. (1993) The effect of ubiquinone Q10 and biotin on the growth and development of premature animals. *Eksp Klin Farmakol.* Sep-Oct;56(5):55-7. Russian.

Yamazaki, N., Nomura, M., Nagaoka, A., Nagawa, Y. (1989) Idebenone improves learning and memory impairment induced by cholinergic or serotonergic dysfunction in rats. *Arch Gerontol Geriatr.* May;8(3):225-39.

Yamazaki, N., Nagaoka, A., Nagawa, Y. (1985) [Effect of idebenone on scopolamine-induced impairment of short-term memory in rats.] *Yakubutsu Seishin Kodo.* Dec;5(4):321-8. Japanese.

Semax

De Wied, D. et al. (1975) Behaviorally active ACTH analogues. *Biochem. Pharmacol.* 24: 1463-1468.

De Wied, D., Jolles, J. (1982) Neuropeptides derived from proopicortin: Behavioral, physiological and neurochemical effects. *Psysiol. Rev.;* 62: 976-1059; .

Kaplan, A., et al. (1992) Increased resistance to hypoxia affected by the neuropeptide preparation Semax. *Fiziol Cheloveka.* 18:104-7

Koroleva, M., et al. (1996) Effect of the heptapeptide Semax on the human electron-cephalogram. *Bull. Exp. Biol. Med.* 121: 116-7.

Cypin

Akum, B. F., Chen, M., Gunderson, S. I., Riefler, G. M., Scerri-Hansen, M. M., Firestein, B. L. (2004) Cypin regulates dendrite patterning in hippocampal neurons by promoting microtubule assembly. *Nature Neuroscience,* 7:145-152.

Cerebrolysin

Rockenstein, E., Adame, A., Mante, M., Moessler, H., Windisch, M., Masliah, E. (2003) The neuroprotective effects of Cerebrolysin in a transgenic model of Alzheimer's disease are associated with improved behavioral performance. *J Neural Transm.* Nov;110(11):1313-27.

Ruther, E., Ritter, R., Apecechea, M. et al. (1994) Efficacy of the peptidergic nootropic drug Cerebrolysin in patients with senile dementia of the Alzheimer's disease type. *Pharmacopsychiatry.* 27: 32-40

Bae, C. H., Cho, C. Y., Cho, K., Oh, B. H. et al. (2001) A Double Blind, Placebo-Controlled, Multicentered Study of Cerebrolysin for Alzheimer's Disease. *JAGS.* 48:1566-1571.

Hartbauer, M., Hutter-Paier, B., Skofitsch, G., Windisch, M. (2001) Antiapoptotic effects of the peptidergic drug cerebrolysin on primary cultures of embryonic chick cortical neurons. *J Neural Transm.* 108(4):459-73

Chapter 21: Vitamins and Memory

Vitamin E

Fattoretti, P., Bertoni-Freddari, C., Casoli, T., Di Stefano, G., Solazzi, M., Corvi, E. (2002) Morphometry of age pigment (lipofuscin) and of ceroid pigment deposits associated with vitamin E deficiency. *Arch Gerontol Geriatr.* May-Jun;34(3):263-8.

Katz, M. L., Robison, W. G. Jr., Herrmann, R. K., Groome, A. B., Bieri, J. G. (1984) Lipofuscin accumulation resulting from senescence and vitamin E deficiency: Spectral properties and tissue distribution. *Mech Ageing Dev.* Apr-May;25(1-2):149-59.

Porta, E. A. (2002) Dietary factors in lipofuscinogenesis and ceroidogenesis. *Arch Gerontol Geriatr.* May-Jun;34(3):319-27.

Engelhart, M., Geerlings, M., Ruitenberg, A. ,et al.(200)2 Dietary intake of antioxidants and risk of Alzheimer's disease. *JAMA*, vol. 287, pp. 3223-3229

Morris, M., Evans, D., Bienias, J., et al.(2002) Dietary intake of antioxidant nutrients and risk of incident Alzheimer's disease in a biracial community study. *JAMA*, vol. 287, pp. 3230--3237

Riboflavin

Ogunleye, A. J., Odutuga, A. A. (1989) The effect of riboflavin deficiency on cerebrum and cerebellum of developing rat brain. (Tokyo). Jun;35(3):193-7

Rieder, H. P., Berger, W., Fridrich, R. (1980) [Vitamin status in diabetic neuropathy (thiamine, riboflavin, pyridoxin, cobalamin and tocopherol)] *Z Ernahrungswiss.* Mar;19(1):1-13.[Article in German]

Homocystine

Bleich, S., Kornhuber, J. (2003) Relationship between plasma homocystine levels and brain atrophy in healthy elderly individuals. *Neurology.* Apr 8;60(7):1220

Schnyder, G., Roffi, M., Flammer, Y., Pin, R., Hess, O. M. (2002) Effect of homocystine-lowering therapy with folic acid, vitamin B12, and vitamin B6 on clinical outcome after percutaneous coronary intervention: The Swiss Heart Study. *JAMA.* 288:973-979.

Stein, J. H., McBride, P. E. (1998) Hyperhomocystinemia and atherosclerotic vascular disease: Pathophysiology, screening, and treatment. *Arch Intern Med.* 158:1301-1306.

Total plasma homocystine, age, systolic blood pressure, and cognitive performance in older people. *J Am Geriatr Soc* 2002 Dec;50(12):2014-8

White, A. R., et al. (2001) Homocystine potentiates copper- and amyloid beta peptide-mediated toxicity in primary neuronal cultures: possible risk factors in the Alzheimer's-type neurodegenerative pathways. *J Neurochem.* Mar;76(5):1509-20.

Niacin

Loriaux, S. M., Deijen, J. B., Orlebeke, J. F., De Swart, J. H. (1985) The effects of nicotinic acid and xanthinol nicotinate on human memory in different categories of age. A double blind study. *Psychopharmacology* (Berl). 87(4):390-5

Rader, J. I., Calvert, R. J., Hathcock, J. N. (1992) Hepatic toxicity of unmodified and time-release preparations of niacin. *Am J Med.* Jan;92(1):77-81

Henkin, Y., Johnson, K. C., Segrest, J. P. (1990) Rechallenge with crystalline niacin after drug-induced hepatitis from sustained-release niacin. *JAMA.* Jul 11;264(2):241-3

Pantothenic Acid

Noda, S., Umezaki, H,. Yamamoto, K., Araki, T., Murakami, T., Ishii, N. (1988) Reye-like syndrome following treatment with the pantothenic acid antagonist, calcium hopantenate. *J Neurol Neurosurg Psychiatry.* Apr;51(4):582-5.

Kimura, A., et al. (1986) Acute encephalopathy with hyperammonemia and dicarboxylic aciduria during calcium hopantenate therapy: A patient report. *Brain Dev.* 8(6):601-5

Pyridoxine

Stewart, T. W., Harrison, M. W., Quitkin, F., et al. (1984) Low B6 levels in depressed outpatients. *Bio Psychiatry* 19 (4): 613-16

Russ, C. S., et al. (1983) Vitamin B6 status of depressed and obsessive-compulsive patients. *Nutr Rep Int* 27 (4): 867-73

Barnes, M. (1975) The function of Ascorbic Acid in Collagen Metabolism. *Annals of the New York Academy of Science.* 258:264.

Bell, I. (1991) B12 folate balance improves mental state of elderly patients. *Biological Psychiatry* 27:125-137.

Holmes (1956) Cerebral Manifestations of Vitamin B12 Deficiency. *British Medical Journal.*

Cone, W. (1983) Effects of megadoses of Vitamin B12 on extinction in the rat. Unpublished masters thesis California State University, Long Beach, CA.

Cole, M. (1984) Low serum B12 in Alzheimer type dementia. *Age & Ageing* 13:101-105.

Keatinge, A. (1983) Vitamin B1, B2, B6 and C status in the elderly. *Irish Medical Journal* 76:488-490.

Elsborg, L., Hansen, T., Rafaelsen, O. J. (1979) Vitamin B12 concentrations in psychiatric patients. *Acta Psychiatr Scand.* Feb;59(2):145-52.

Lesser, M. (1980) *Nutrition and Vitamin Therapy,* Bantam Books, New York.

Bieri, J. (1983) Medical Uses of Vitamin E. *New England Journal of Medicine* 308:1063.

Bober, M. (1984) Senile Dementia and Nutrition. *British Medical Journal* 288:1234.

Enk, C. (1980) Reversible dementia and neuropathy associated with folate deficiency 16 years after partial gastrectomy. *Scandanavian Journal of Haematology* 25:63.

Melamed, E. (1975) Reversable central nervous system dysfunction in folate deficiency. *Journal of Neurolgical Science* 25:93-98.

Strachan, R., Henderson, J. (1967) Dementia and Folate Defiency. *Quarterly Journal of Medicine* 36:189-204.

Sneath, P. (1973) Folate status in a geriatric population and its relation to dementia. *Age & Ageing* 2:177-182.

Shaw, D. (1984) Senile Dementia and Nutrition. *British Medical Journal* 288:792-793.

Chapter 22: Two Vitamins Essential to Memory

B12

Ikeda, T., Yamamoto, K., Takahashi, K., Kaku, Y., Uchiyama, M., Sugiyama, K., Yamada, M. (1992) Treatment Of Alzheimer's-Type Dementia With Intravenous Mecobalamin. *Clinical Therapeutics.* 14(3):426-37.

Fine, E. J., Soria, E. D. (1991) Myths about vitamin B12 deficiency. *South Med J.* Dec;84(12):1475-81

Roach, E. S., McLean, W. T. (1982) Neurologic disorders of vitamin B12 deficiency. *Am. Fam. Physician.* Jan;25(1):111-5

Vitamin C

Agus, David B., Gambhir, Sanjiv Sam, Pardridge, William M., Spielhol, Charles, Baselga, José, Vera, Juan Carlos, Golde, David W. (1997) Vitamin C Crosses the Blood-Brain Barrier in the Oxidized Form Through the Glucose Transporters. *Clin. Invest.* Volume 100, Number 11, December , 2842-2848

Masaki, K. H., Losonczy, K. G., Izmirlian, G., Foley, D. J., Ross, G. W., Petrovitch, H., Havlik, R., White, L. R. (2000) Association of vitamin E and C supplement use with cognitive function and dementia in elderly men. *Neurology.* Mar 28;54(6):1265-72.

Laurin, D., Foley, D. J., Masaki, K. H., White, L. R., Launer, L. J. (2002) Vitamin E and C supplements and risk of dementia. *JAMA.* Nov 13;288(18):2266-8

Carr, A. C., Frei, B. (1999) Toward a new recommended dietary allowance for vitamin C based on antioxidant and health effects in humans. *American Journal of Clinical Nutrition.* volume 69: pages 1086-1107.

Levine, M. et al. (1999) Criteria and recommendations for vitamin C intake. *Journal of the American Medical Association (JAMA)* ; volume 281: pages 1415-1423. (PubMed)

Gokce, N. et al. (1999) Long-term ascorbic acid administration reverses endothelial cell dysfunction in patients with coronary artery disease. *Circulation.* volume 99: pages 3234-3240. (PubMed)

Duffy, S.J. et al. (1999) Treatment of hypertension with ascorbic acid. *Lancet.* volume 354:pages 2048-2049.

Will, J. C. et al. (1999) Serum vitamin C concentrations and diabetes: Findings from the Third National Health and Nutrition Examination Survey, 1988-1994. *American Journal of Clinical Nutrition.* volume 70: pages 49-52. (PubMed)

Will, J. C., Byers, T. (1996) Does diabetes mellitus increase the requirement for vitamin C? *Nutrition Reviews.* volume 54: pages 193-202. (PubMed)

Russel, R. M., Suter, P. M. (1993) Vitamin requirements of elderly people: An update. *American Journal of Clinical Nutrition.* volume 58: pages 4-14.

Yokoyama, T., et al. (2000) Serum vitamin C concentration was inversely associated with subsequent 20-year incidence of stroke in a Japanese rural community: The Shibata Study. *Stroke.* volume 10: pages 2287-2294.

Picamilon

Voznesenskii, A. G., Kovalev, G. V., Sazhin, V. A. (1989) [Comparative study of the effect of picamilone and piracetam on learning in rats in a radial maze] *Farmakol Toksikol.* Jul-Aug;52(4):14-7.

Mirzoian, R. S., Gan'shina, T. S., Kosoi, M. I., Aleksandrin, V. V., Aleksandrin, P. N. (1989) [Effect of pikamilon on the cortical blood supply and microcirculation in the pial arteriole system] [Article in Russian] *Biull Eksp Biol Med.* May;107(5):581-2.

Karaev, A. L., Kovler, M. A., Avakumov, V. M., Kopelevich, V. M., Bulanova, L. N. (1989) [Antihypoxic properties of GABA-containing vitamin derivatives] [Article in Russian] *Farmakol Toksikol.* Jan-Feb;52(1):56-8.

Chapter 23: Minerals that Improve Memory

Boron

Penland, J. G. (1998) The importance of boron nutrition for brain and psychological function. *Biol Trace Elem Res.* Winter;66(1-3):299-317. Related Articles, Links

Iron

Addy, D. P. (1986) Happiness is:Iron. *Brit Med J* 292, 6526 (April 12): 969-70,

Pollitt, E., Soemantri, A. G., Yunis, F., et al. Cognitive effects of iron-deficiency anemia. *Lancet* i: 158, 198

Pollitt, E., Leibel, R. L., eds. (1982) *Iron Deficiency: Brain Biochemistry and Behavior.* NewYork,:Raven Press.

Chromium

Mahdi, G. S. (1996) Chromium deficiency might contribute to insulin resistance, type 2 diabetes mellitus, dyslipidaemia, and atherosclerosis. *Diabet Med.* Apr;13(4):389-90. No abstract available.

Mossop, R. T. (1991) Trivalent chromium, in atherosclerosis and diabetes. *Cent Afr J Med.* Nov;37(11):369-74.

Dubois, F., Belleville, F. (1991) [Chromium: physiologic role and implications in human pathology] *Pathol Biol* (Paris). Oct;39(8):801-8. Review. French.

Canonaco, F., Bertolani, P., Cucchi, C. (1986) [Chromium and atherosclerosis] *Pediatr Med Chir.* May-Jun;8(3):415-6. Italian.

Anke, M. (1986) [Role of trace elements in the dynamics of arteriosclerosis] *Z Gesamte Inn Med.* Feb 15;41(4):105-11. German.

Simonoff, M. (1984) Chromium deficiency and cardiovascular risk. *Cardiovasc Res.* Oct;18(10):591-6.

Schroeder, H. A., Nason, A. P., Tipton, I. H. (1970) Chromium deficiency as a factor in atherosclerosis. *J Chronic Dis.* Aug;23(2):123-42.

Hambridge, E. (1974) Chromium Nutrition in Man. *American Journal of Clinical Nutrition* 27(5):505-514.

Boyle, E., et al. (1977) Chromium Depletion in the Pathogenesis of Diabetes and Arteriosclerosis. *Southern Medical Journal* 70(2):1449-1453.

Press, R., et al. (1990) The effect of chromium picolinate on serum cholesterol and apolipoprotein in human subjects. *Western Journal of Medicine* 152(1):41-45.

Mayer, J. (1971) Chromium in medicine. *Postgrad Med.* Jan;49(1):235-6.

Mertz, W. (1992) Chromium in human nutrition: A Review. *Journal of Nutrition* 123:626-633.

Pfeiffer, C. (1975) *Mental and Elemental Nutrients,* Keats Publishing, New Canaan, CT.

Erdmann, R., Jones, M. (1988) *Minerals: Metabolic Miracle Workers,* Century, London.

Passwater, R. (no date) *Selenium as Food and Medicine,* Keats, NY.

Everson, G., Schrader, R. (1968) Manganese. *Journal of Nutrition* 94:89.

Clark, L. (1985) The Epidemiology of Selenium in Cancer. *Federal Proceedings* 44(9):2584-9.

Lerch, Sharon (1992) Memory boosters. (iron and zinc). *American Health* 11(2):129.

Emanuel, Linda (1991) Memory boosting minerals. (iron and zinc). *Health* 23(1):22.

Hullin, R. (1983) Zinc levels in psychiatric patients. *Progress in Clinical and Biological Research* 129:197-206.

Chapter 24: Nutrients that Improve Memory

Brody (1975) RNA and memory. *Aging* 1:153 155.

Odens, M. (1969) RNA effects on memory. *Vitalstoffe* 14: 144.

Odens, M. (1970) RNA effects on memory (continues). *Vitalstoffe* 15: 172.

Solyon, L., Enesco, H. E., Beaulieu, M. A. (1967) The effects of RNA on learning and activity in old and young rats. *J Gerontol* 22: 1.

Harmon, D. (1993) Free radical Theory of Aging: A hypotheses on pathogenesis of senile dementia of the Alzheimer's type. *Age.* 16:20-30.

Choline

Bland, J. (1982) Choline, Lecithin, Inositol and other 'Accessory' Nutrients. *Good Health Guide.* 1:1 25.

Hoffer, A., Walker, M. (1978) *Orthomolecular Nutrition.* Keats Publishing, New Canaan, Conn.

Sitaram, Weingartner, and Gillin (1978) Human serial learning: Enhancement with arecoline and choline and impairment with scopolamine correlate with performance on placebo. *Science* 210: 274 76.

Sitaram, et al. (1978) Choline: Selective enhancement of low imagery words in man. *Life Science,* 22:1555 1560.

CDP Choline

Laerum, O. D., Iversen, O. H. (1972) Reticuloses and epidermal tumors in hairless mice after topical skin applications of cantharidin and asiaticoside. *Cancer Research.* Jul; 32(7):1463-9.

Secades, J. J., Frontera, G. (1995) CDP-choline: Pharmacological and clinical review. *Methods Find Exp Clin Pharmacol.* Oct;17 Suppl B:1-54.

Babb, S. M., Appelmans, K. E., Renshaw, P. F., Wurtman, R. J., Cohen, B. (1996) Differential effect of CDP-choline on brain cytosolic choline levels in younger and older subjects as measured by proton magnetic resonance spectroscopy. *Psychopharmacology* (Berl). Sep;127(2):88-94.

Cacabelos, R., et al. (1996) Therapeutic effects of CDP-choline in Alzheimer's disease. Cognition, brain mapping, cerebrovascular hemodynamics, and immune factors. *Ann N Y Acad Sci.* Jan 17;777:399-403.

Alvarez, X. A., et al (1997) Citicoline improves memory performance in elderly subjects. *Methods Find Exp Clin Pharmacol.* Apr;19(3):201-10.

Caprioli, Antonio, Ghirardi, Orlando, Ramacci, Maria T., Angelucci, Luciano. (1990) Age-dependent deficits in radial maze performance in the rat: Effect of chronic treatment with acetyl-carnitine. *Progress in Neuro Psychopharmacology & Biological Psychiatry* 1(4) :359 369

Lärkfors, Lena, Ebendal, Ted, Whittemore, Scott R., Persson, Håkan, Hoffer, Barry, Olson, Lars. (1987) Decreased level of nerve growth factor (NGF) and its messenger RNA in the aged rat brain. *Molecular Brain Research.* (3):55 60.

Fischer, W., Wictorin, K., Björklund, A., Williams, L. R., Varon, S., Gage, F. H. (1987) Amelioration of cholinergic neuron atrophy and spatial memory impairment in aged rats by nerve growth factor. *Nature.* 329, 65-68

Taglialatela, G., Navarra, D., Cruciani, R., Ramacci, M. T., Alema, G. S., Angelucci (1994) Acetyl-L-carnitine treatment increases nerve growth factor levels and choline acetyltransferase activity in the central nervous system of aged rats. *Experimental Gerontology* .29:55-66

Tucker, D., Penland, J., Sandstead, H. (1990) Nutrition Status and Brain Function in Aging. *American Journal of Clinical Nutrition.* 52:93-102.

Lecithin (Phosphatidylcholine)

Sorgatz, H. (1988) Effect of lecithin on health status and concentration. Placebo-controlled double-blind study in healthy probands. *Fortschr Med.* Apr 10;106(11):233-6. [Article in German]

Sorgatz, H. (1986) Effect of lecithin on memory performance. Evaluating the validity of a learning and memory test (LGT-3) in 45 to 55-year-old patients. *Fortschr Med.* Sep 11;104(34):643-6. [Article in German]

Ladd, S. L., Sommer, S. A., LaBerge, S., Toscano, W. (1993) Effect of phosphatidylcholine on explicit memory. *Clin Neuropharmacol.* Dec;16(6):540-9.

Harris, C. M., Dysken, M. W., Fovall, P., Davis, J. M. (1983) Effect of lecithin on memory in normal adults. *Am J Psychiatry.* Aug;140(8):1010-2.

Moriyama, T., et al. (1996) Effects of dietary phosphatidylcholine on memory in memory deficient mice with low brain acetylcholine concentration. *Life Sci.* 58(6):PL111-8.

Kaye, W. H., Sitaram, N., Weingartner, H., Ebert, M. H., Smallberg, S., Gillin, J. C. (1982) Modest facilitation on memory in dementia with combined lecithin and anticholinerestase treatment. *Biological Psychiatry.* Feb;17(2):275-80

Physostigmine

Furey, M. L., et al. (1997) Cholinergic stimulation alters performance and task-specific regional cerebral blood flow during working memory. *Proc Natl Acad Sci U S A.* June 10; 94 (12): 6512-6516

Coelho Filho, J. M., Birks, J. (2003) Physostigmine for Alzheimer's disease. *Cochrane Review. The Cochrane Library,* Issue 4, Chichester, UK: John Wiley & Sons, Ltd.

Omega-3 Fatty Acids

Logan, A. C. (2003) Neurobehavioral aspects of omega-3 fatty acids: Possible mechanisms and therapeutic value in major depression. *Altern Med Rev.* Nov;8(4):410-25.

Morris, M. C. (2003) Consumption of fish and n-3 fatty acids and risk of incident Alzheimer disease. *Arch Neurol.* Jul;60(7):940-6

Corrigan, F. M., Van Rhihn, A., Horrobin, D. F. (1991) Essential fatty acids in Alzheimer's diease. *Ann N Y Acad Sci.* 640:250-252.

Yehuda, S., Rabinovtz, S., Carasso, R. L., Mostofsky, D. I. (1996) Essential fatty acids preparation (SR-3) improves Alzheimer's patients quality of life. *Int J Neurosci.* 87(3-4):141-149.

Blueberries

Joseph, J. A., et al. (2003) Blueberry supplementation enhances signaling and prevents behavioral deficits in an Alzheimer disease model. *Nutr Neurosci.* Jun; 6(3):153-62.

Bickford, P. C. (2000) Antioxidant-rich diets improve cerebellar physiology and motor learning in aged rats. *Brain Res.* Jun 2; 866(1-2):211-7.

Carbohyrates

Kaplan, Randall J. et al. (2001) Dietary protein, carbohydrate, and fat enhance memory performance in the healthy elderly. *Am J Clin Nut.* 74: 687-93.

Morley, John E. (2001) Food for thought. *Am J Clin Nutr.* 74:567-8.

Acetyl-l-carnitine

McDaniel, M. A., Maier, S. F., Einstein, G. O. (2003) "Brain-specific" nutrients: a memory cure? *Nutrition.* Nov-Dec; 19(11-12):957-75

NADH

Birkmayer, J. G. (1996) Coenzyme nicotinamide adenine dinucleotide: new therapeutic approach for improving dementia of the Alzheimer type. *Ann Clin Lab Sci.* Jan-Feb;26(1):1-9.

Forsyth, L. M., et al. (1999) Therapeutic effects of oral NADH on the symptoms of patients with chronic fatigue syndrome. *Ann Allergy Asthma Immunol.* Feb;82(2):185-91.

Rainer, M., Kraxberger, E., Haushofer, M., Mucke, H. A., Jellinger, K. A. (2000) No evidence for cognitive improvement from oral nicotinamide adenine dinucleotide (NADH) in dementia. *J Neural Transm.* 107(12):1475-81

Chapter 25: Herbs and Memory

Mowrey, D. (1986) *The Scientific Validation of Herbal Medicine,* Cormorant Books, Lehi, UT.

Lad, V. (1984) *Ayurveda: The Science of Self Healing — A Practical Guide*

Sharma, R. (2003) *Medicinal Plants of India — An Encyclopaedia,* Delhi, Daya Publishing.

Jackson, M., Teague, T. (1987) *Handbook of Alternatives to Chemical Medicine,* Bookpeople, Berkely, Ca.

Bensky, D., Gamble, A. (1986) *Chinese Herbal Medicine: Materia Medica,* Eastland Press, Seattle WA.

Duke, J. (1987) *CRC Handbook of Medicinal Herbs,* CRC Press, Boca Raton, FL.

Haritak

Thakur, C. P., Thakur, B., Singh, S., Sinha, P. K., Sinha, S. K. (1988) The Ayurvedic medicines Haritaki, Amala and Bahira reduce cholesterol-induced atherosclerosis in rabbits. *Int J Cardiol.* Nov; 21(2): 167-75.

Cheng, H. Y., Lin, T. C., Yu, K. H., Yang, C. M., Lin, C. C. (2003) Antioxidant and free radical scavenging activities of Terminalia chebula. *Biol Pharm Bull.* Sep; 26(9): 1331-5

Sabu, M. C., Kuttan, R. (2002) Anti-diabetic activity of medicinal plants and its relationship with their antioxidant property. *J Ethnopharmacol.* Jul; 81(2): 155-60

Holly

Schinella, G. R., Troiani, G., Davila, V., de Buschiazzo, P. M., Tournier, H. A. (2000) Antioxidant effects of an aqueous extract of *Ilex paraguariensis. Biochem Biophys Res Commun.* Mar 16; 269(2): 357-60.

Lemon Balm

Kennedy, D. O., Wake, G., Savelev, S., Tildesley, N. T., Perry, E. K., Wesnes, K. A., Scholey, A. B. (2003) Modulation of mood and cognitive performance following acute administration of single doses of *Melissa officinalis* (Lemon balm) with human CNS nicotinic and muscarinic receptor-binding properties. *Neuropsychopharmacology.* Oct; 28(10): 1871-81.

Akhondzadeh, S., Noroozian, M., Mohammadi, M., Ohadinia, S., Jamshidi, A. H., Khani. (2003) *Melissa officinalis* extract in the treatment of patients with mild to moderate Alzheimer's disease: A double blind, randomised, placebo controlled trial. *J Neurol Neurosurg Psychiatry.* Jul; 74(7): 863-6.

Ballard, C. G., O'Brien, J. T., Reichelt, K., Perry, E. K. (2002) Aromatherapy as a safe and effective treatment for the management of agitation in severe dementia: The results of a double-blind, placebo-controlled trial with Melissa. *Clin Psychiatry.* Jul; 63(7): 553-8.

Kennedy, D. O., Scholey, A. B., Tildesley, N. T., Perry, E. K., Wesnes, K. A. (2002) Modulation of mood and cognitive performance following acute administration of *Melissa officinalis* (lemon balm). *Pharmacol Biochem Behav.* Jul;72(4):953-64

Ginseng

Kennedy, D. O., Scholey, A. B., Wesnes, K. A. (2001) Dose dependent changes in cognitive performance and mood following acute administration of Ginseng to healthy young volunteers. *Nutr Neurosci.* 4(4):295-310

Halstead, B., Hood, L. (1985) Eleutherococcus Senticosus Siberian Ginseng: An Introduction to the concept of Adaptogenic Medicine. *Clinical Trials Journal* 22.

Schizandra

Nishiyama, N., Chu, P. J., Saito, H. (1996) An herbal prescription, S-113m, consisting of biota, ginseng and schizandra, improves learning performance in senescence accelerated mouse. *Biol Pharm Bull.* Mar;19(3):388-93

Spanish Sage

Perry, N. S., et al. (2001) In-vitro activity of *Salvia lavandulaefolia* (Spanish sage) relevant to treatment of Alzheimer's disease, *J Pharm Pharmacol.* Oct;53(10):1347-56.

Rosemary

Moss, M., Cook, J., Wesnes, K., Duckett, P. (2003) Aromas of rosemary and lavender essential oils differentially affect cognition and mood in healthy adults. *Int J Neurosci.* Jan;113(1):15-38

Thujone

Hold, K. M., Sirisoma, N. S., Ikeda, T., Narahashi, T. (2000) Casida Alpha-thujone (the active component of absinthe): gamma-aminobutyric acid type A receptor modulation and metabolic detoxification. *Proc Natl Acad Sci U S A.* Apr 11;97(8):3826-31

Calamus

Parab, R. S., Mengi, S. A. (2002) Hypolipidemic activity of *Acorus calamus L.* in rats. *Fitoterapia.* Oct;73(6):451-5.

Salvianolic Acid B

Chih-Jui Lao, et al. (2003) Effect of *Salvia Miltiorrhiza Bunge* on cerebral infarct in ischemia-reperfusion injured rats. *American Journal of Chinese Medicine,* Spring.

Yih-Jer Wu; Chuang-Ye Hong; Shing-Jong Lin; Paulin Wu; Ming-Shi Shiao. (1998) Increase of Vitamin E Content in LDL and Reduction of Atherosclerosis in Cholesterol-Fed Rabbits by a Water-Soluble Antioxidant-Rich Fraction of *Salvia miltiorrhiza. Arteriosclerosis, Thrombosis, and Vascular Biology.* 18:481-486.)

Tang, M. K., Zhang, J. T. (2001) Salvianolic acid B inhibits fibril formation and neurotoxicity of amyloid beta-protein in vitro. *Acta Pharmacol Sin.* Apr;22(4):380-4.

Hendler, S. (1991). *The Doctors' Vitamin and Mineral Encyclopedia.* New York, NY: Simon and Schuster.

Gingko

Allard, M. (1986) Treatment of old age disorders with ginkgo biloba extract. *La Presse Medicale.* 15(31):1540.

Auguet, M., et al. (1986) Bases Pharmacologiques de l'Impact Vasculaire de l'Extract de Ginkgo Biloba, *La Presse Medicale.* 15(31):1524.

Funfgeld, E. (1989) A Natural and Broad Spectrum Nootropic Substance for Treatment of SDAT the Ginkgo Biloba Extract. *Progress in Clinical and Biological Research.* 317:1247 60

Gebner, A., et al. Study of the long term action of a ginkgo biloba extract on vigilance and mental performance as determined by means of quantitative pharmaco EEG and psychometric measurements. *Arzneimittelforschung.* 35(9):1459.

Hindmarch, I. (1986) Activity of ginkgo biloba extract on short term memory. *La Presse Medicale.* 15(31): 1562-1592.

Schaffer, K., Reeh, P. (1985) Long term drug administration effects of ginkgo biloba on the performance of healthy subjects exposed to hypoxia. Agnoli, J. ed. *Effects of Ginkgo Biloba Extracts on Organic Cerebral Impairment.* Eurotext Ltd. pp77 84.

Warburton, D. (1986) Clinical psychopharmacology of ginkgo biloba extract. *La Presse Medicale.* 15(31):1595.

Gotu Kola

Sharma, J., Sharma, R. (2002) Radioprotection of Swiss albino mouse by *Centella asiatica* extract. *Phytother Res.* Dec; 16(8):785-6.

Huperzine A

Zangara. A. (2003) The psychopharmacology of huperzine A: An alkaloid with cognitive enhancing and neuroprotective properties of interest in the treatment of Alzheimer's disease. *Pharmacol Biochem Behav.* Jun;75(3):675-86

Bai, D. L., Tang, X. C., He, X. C. (2000) Huperzine A, a potential therapeutic agent for treatment of Alzheimer's disease. *Curr Med Chem.* Mar;7(3):355-74.

Ye, J. W., Cai, J. X., Wang, L. M., Tang, X. C. (1999) Improving effects of huperzine A on spatial working memory in aged monkeys and young adult monkeys with experimental cognitive impairment. *J Pharmacol Exp Ther.* Feb; 288(2):814-9.

Carlier, P. R., Du, D. M., Han, Y., Liu, J., Pang, Y. P. (1999) Potent, easily synthesized huperzine A-tacrine hybrid acetylcholinesterase inhibitors. *Bioorg Med Chem Lett.* Aug 16;9(16):2335-8.

Carlier, P. R. et al. (2000) Dimerization of an Inactive Fragment of Huperzine A Produces a Drug with Twice the Potency of the Natural Product. *Angew Chem Int Ed Engl.* May 15;39(10):1775-1777.

Wong, D. M., Greenblatt, H. M., Dvir, H., Carlier, P. R., Han, Y. F., Pang, Y. P., Silman, I., Sussman, J. L. (2003) Acetylcholinesterase complexed with bivalent ligands related to huperzine a: experimental evidence for species-dependent protein-ligand complementarity. *J Am Chem Soc.* Jan 15;125(2):363-73.

Brahmi

Nathan, P. J., Tanner, S., Lloyd, J., Harrison, B., Curran, L., Oliver, C., Stough, C. (2004) Effects of a combined extract of *Ginkgo biloba* and *Bacopa monniera* on cognitive function in healthy humans. *Hum Psychopharmacol.* Mar;19(2):91-6.

Russo, A., Izzo, A. A., Borrelli, F., Renis, M., Vanella, A. (2003) Free radical scavenging capacity and protective effect of *Bacopa monniera L.* on DNA damage. *Phytother Res.* Sep;17(8):870-5.

Roodenrys, S., Booth, D., Bulzomi, S., Phipps, A., Micallef, C., Smoker, J. (2002) Chronic effects of Brahmi *(Bacopa monnieri)* on human memory. *Neuropsychopharmacology.* Aug;27(2):279-81.

Stough, C., Lloyd, J., Clarke, J., Downey, L. A., Hutchison, C. W., Rodgers, T., Nathan, P. J. (2001) The chronic effects of an extract of *Bacopa monniera* (Brahmi) on cognitive function in healthy human subjects. *Psychopharmacology (Berl).* Aug;156(4):481-4. Related Articles, Links.

Vohora, D., Pal, S. N., Pillai, K. K. (2000) Protection from phenytoin-induced cognitive deficit by *Bacopa monniera,* a reputed Indian nootropic plant. *J Ethnopharmacol.* Aug;71(3):383-90.

Kidd, P. M. (1999) A review of nutrients and botanicals in the integrative management of cognitive dysfunction. *Altern Med Rev.* Jun;4(3):144-61.

Nathan. P. J., Clarke, J., Lloyd, J., Hutchison, C. W., Downey, L., Stough, C. (2001) The acute effects of an extract of *Bacopa monniera* (Brahmi) on cognitive function in healthy normal subjects. *Hum Psychopharmacol.* Jun;16(4):345-351.

Tripathi, Y. B., Chaurasia, S., Tripathi, E., Upadhyay, A., Dubey, G. P. (1996) *Bacopa monniera Linn.* as an antioxidant: mechanism of action. *Indian J. Exp Biol.* Jun;34(6):523-6.

Index

About the Author

Dr. Cone is Licensed Psychologist and accomplished speaker, specializing in mental health and aging, He is the author of three books, *Stop Memory Loss,* a book about preventing dementia, *Caregivers Bible,* a book for professional caregivers of the aged, and *The Abduction Enigma,* a book about how therapist unwittingly induce false memories.

Dr. Cone is currently a consultant and lecturer in the field of geriatrics. He develops and implements training programs for geropsychiatric hospitals, nursing homes, and board and care facilities throughout the nation.

Because of his expertise he has been featured on many television programs and has been a featured speaker on dozens of radio programs nationwide.

If you are interested in having Dr. Cone speak at your facility, association, or convention he can be reached at

SoundMinds
16707 Sunset Boulevard
Pacific Palisades, CA 90272
www.soundminds.net
drcone@earthlink.net
888-261-0576